Hatha Yoga Book 6
MUDRA AND BANDHA

WORLD YOGA CONVENTION 2013
GANGA DARSHAN, MUNGER, BIHAR, INDIA
23rd–27th October 2013

BIHAR SCHOOL OF YOGA

50 years

1963–2013
GOLDEN JUBILEE

CONVERSATIONS ON THE SCIENCE OF YOGA

Hatha Yoga Book 6
MUDRA AND BANDHA

From the teachings of
two great luminaries of the 20th century

Sri Swami Sivananda Saraswati
Sri Swami Satyananda Saraswati

Including answers from the satsangs of
Swami Niranjanananda Saraswati

Yoga Publications Trust, Munger, Bihar, India

Published by Yoga Publications Trust
    First edition 2013

ISBN: 978-93-81620-77-9

Publisher and distributor: Yoga Publications Trust, Ganga Darshan, Munger, Bihar, India.

Website: www.biharyoga.net
        www.rikhiapeeth.net

Printed at Aegean Offset Printers, Greater Noida

Dedication

*In humility we offer this dedication to
Swami Sivananda Saraswati, who initiated
Swami Satyananda Saraswati into the secrets of yoga
and to our guru Sri Swami Satyananda Saraswati
who continues to inspire and guide us
on our spiritual journey.*

Swami Niranjan

Contents

Contents

Preface

CONVERSATIONS ON THE SCIENCE OF YOGA

Conversations on the Science of Yoga is an encyclopaedic series which brings together the collected teachings of two generations of masters – Swami Sivananda Saraswati of Rishikesh and Swami Satyananda Saraswati of Munger. Satsangs given by Swami Niranjanananda Saraswati on his numerous national and international tours also provide the answers to many questions on this vast subject. These luminaries represent a living tradition in which the eternal knowledge and wisdom of yoga has been passed from guru to disciple in a dynamic continuum from the early twentieth century to the first decades of the twenty-first century.

The series consists of sets of books which present the timeless culture of yoga topic by topic, in question and answer format. In this way, complex and profound subjects such as karma yoga, hatha yoga and bhakti yoga, are presented in clear, simple language. These conversations on yoga reflect an ancient and enduring approach to the transmission of wisdom, in which spiritual aspirants seek answers to their questions at the feet of the guru.

Many of the answers also include verses from the various relevant scriptures, connecting the modern experience with the classical tradition. It is through the lives and teachings of the masters that the scriptures are correctly and intuitively interpreted for each generation, ensuring that the light of these revelations continues to illumine and inspire the hearts and minds of all who aspire for spiritual upliftment.

Conversations on the Science of Yoga has been compiled from the rich archive of satsangs and writings, both published and unpublished, which is held at the Bihar School of Yoga, Munger. The organization of this material into the major branches of yoga and related topics creates a unique interpretation of the classical yogic sciences for the benefit of humanity in the modern era. Deeply founded in tradition, the teachings are both systematic and practical, addressing the needs of individuals and society at a time when adjustment to constant change is placing unprecedented pressure on people all over the world.

The Bihar Yoga tradition

The Bihar School of Yoga is ideally placed to produce this major contribution to yogic literature. Founded in 1963 by Swami Satyananda Saraswati, the system known in India as Bihar Yoga and internationally as Satyananda Yoga, seamlessly integrates all facets of the yogic tradition, including the various branches of yoga, the philosophies which are fundamental to the yogic culture and the

dynamism of self-realized preceptors which ensures that the teachings remain fresh and relevant in any age. This all-inclusive approach means that yogic practices are available as tools for holistic life management, while other *vidyas*, spiritual sciences, such as Tantra, Vedanta and Samkhya provide a broad philosophical base. Emerging from this living tradition, *Conversations on the Science of Yoga* is a unique and precious offering to humanity.

Swami Sivananda Saraswati (1887–1963)

Swami Sivananda was a towering spiritual force in the yogic renaissance which developed in India in the first half of the twentieth century. After serving as a doctor in Malaya, he returned to India to pursue his spiritual aspirations, and in 1924 was initiated into Dashnami sannyasa in Rishikesh. He founded the Divine Life Society, toured India extensively, wrote hundreds of books and inspired thousands around the world to practise yoga and lead a divine life. Swami Sivananda's eightfold path of yoga – serve, love, give, purify, do good, be good, meditate, realize – expresses his philosophy of service to humanity and continues to guide the work of the Bihar School of Yoga.

Swami Satyananda Saraswati (1923–2009)

Swami Satyananda was initiated into Dashnami sannyasa by his guru Swami Sivananda, in 1947. After serving his guru's mission in Rishikesh for twelve years, he founded the International Yoga Fellowship in 1956 and the Bihar School of Yoga in 1963. From that base he took the teachings to the rest of the world, fulfilling the mandate of his guru to 'spread yoga from door to door and shore to shore.'

Through his genius and compassion, many ancient, complex and esoteric practices were systematized, simplified and made available to people of all ages, cultures and creeds. Swami Satyananda's blend of charisma and pragmatism attracted multitudes of devotees wherever he went, giving rise to a global movement and creating a far-reaching network of ashrams, yoga centres and teachers. Meanwhile, the headquarters in Bihar continued to expand its many programs, including the publishing division, producing numerous books that both preserve and disseminate the incredibly rich seam of practical wisdom which flows through this lineage.

In 1988 Swami Satyananda renounced his mission in order to live as a paramahamsa sannyasin, performing higher spiritual and vedic sadhanas in an isolated location. During this chapter of his life, he also realized his guru's teaching of 'serve, love, give', by establishing Sivananda Math, an organization dedicated to raising the living standards of the weaker and underprivileged sectors of society.

At midnight on 5 December 2009, Sri Swami Satyananda Saraswati attained mahasamadhi.

Swami Niranjanananda Saraswati (1960)

A yogi from earliest childhood, Swami Niranjanananda joined the Bihar School of Yoga in 1964 and was initiated into Dashnami sannyasa in 1971. At the age of eleven he was sent to live abroad by his guru Swami Satyananda, giving him direct experience and understanding of people from a vast array of cultures and walks of life. These years instilled in him a rare, cross-cultural insight into human nature, enabling him to communicate and interact with the international community with familiarity, ease and humour.

Combined with his depth of spiritual and yogic know-ledge, this background equipped Swami Niranjanananda to guide the Bihar School of Yoga and the international yoga movement from 1983 until 2008, when he began handing over the administration to the next generation. During this time he also authored many classic books on yoga, tantra and the upanishads and founded Bihar Yoga Bharati, the world's first yoga university, while continuing extensive national and international touring.

Following retirement from his role at the Bihar School of Yoga, Swami Niranjanananda established Sannyasa Peeth for the development and training of sannyasins, and for his own pursuit of the higher sadhanas of sannyasa.

As the spiritual successor to Swami Satyananda, Swami Niranjanananda continues to inspire aspirants around the world.

Yoga is not a philosophy, it is a practical science. Philosophy gives you knowledge, yoga gives you experience. This is the beauty of yoga. That experience is a manifestation of your inner being.

—*Swami Satyananda Saraswati*

Introduction

Yogis have experienced mudras as attitudes of energy
flow intended to link the individual pranic force with the
universal or cosmic force.

—Swami Satyananda Saraswati

With the exception of slokas in the hatha yoga scriptures,
little has been written on mudra and bandha. While
aspects of hatha yoga such as asana, and to a lesser extent
pranayama, have been widely popularized, *mudra*, the subtle
gestures and *bandha*, the energy locks, have remained the
domain of specialized or advanced practitioners. In view
of this, *Hatha Yoga Book 6: Mudra and Bandha* is a landmark
publication, systematically presenting a fund of knowledge
on this subtle category of yoga practice. As with other groups
of lesser known practices such as the shatkarmas, Satyananda
Yoga has included mudra and bandha in its general training,
presenting them in a way which is appropriate for sincere
practitioners of yoga. Bihar School of Yoga is therefore
ideally placed to compile these unique teachings which shine
a light on mudra and bandha in the twenty-first century.

Infinity of form

In spite of the dearth of teachings on the subject, the field
of mudra is vast, infinite even, and not only the province of
hatha yoga. Swami Niranjanananda Saraswati says, "There

1

are many kinds of mudras, innumerable types of mudras; they cannot be counted. The various traditions, schools of philosophy and schools of sadhana use different groups of mudras to attain whatever goal they have set for themselves." By contrast, the bandhas are only four in number, and of these, the fourth is a combination of the first three. The bandhas may be few, but they are extensively combined with other practices, such as pranayama, meditation and kriya yoga. The importance of mudra and bandha is reflected in the attention given to them in the classical texts of hatha yoga, which focus on their role in the attainment of higher states of consciousness, including samadhi.

The infinite forms of mudra are also indicated by the spontaneous occurrence of mudras that is sometimes experienced when pranic awakening generates the attitude in the body that is inherent in the altered state of consciousness. The mudra becomes an expression of the union of body, mind and prana in the manifest dimension.

The concept of mudra can also be applied at the most mundane level, where it occurs unconsciously, in what is known as body language: the way the body is held, and the expression on one's face, are gestures, attitudes, that not only express a feeling, but reinforce and generate that feeling in oneself, and even in others.

Channelling prana

The theory of mudra is based on an understanding of the *pranamaya kosha*, pranic body. In yoga, the use of this theory is based on the direct experience of the masters and seers whose intricate understanding of this kosha and its relationship with the mind led to the development of the yogic sciences. *Mudra* means gesture, or attitude, indicating that the physical position has a subtle effect involving mind and feeling. While a mudra is held, a specific energetic process occurs within, as the body, prana and mind are simultaneously focused on a certain nadi or chakra. The attitude of the body intensifies the pranic flow to that zone, assisting the mind in its role of bringing consciousness to that place. As the mudra is held, these three dimensions of being – the body, energy and mind – merge in their purpose and experience, so that the sadhaka enters the state of the mudra, becoming a reflection of its nature as the separate fields of experience become one.

Swami Satyananda Saraswati gives a simple description of the effect of the yoga mudras on prana: "Mudras manipulate prana in much the same way that energy in the form of light or sound waves is diverted by a mirror or a cliff face. The nadis and chakras constantly radiate prana which normally escapes from the body and dissipates into the external world. By creating barriers within the body through the practice of mudra, the energy is redirected within." These barriers essentially reverse the direction of pranic flow. The prana is both preserved and given a specific, purposeful direction.

Reversal of certain pranic flows is an aim of hatha yoga. This is done to intensify the flow to a specific energy centre or region for its stimulation or awakening, or to induce a particular state. Another effect of channelling the prana is to help the body heal by directing energy to strengthen the organ or area which is weak.

Categories of mudra

The yoga mudras are divided into five categories: hand mudras, head mudras, postural mudras, lock mudras and perineal mudras. With the addition of chapters on the bandhas and pancha dharanas, the discussions in *Mudra and Bandha* are based around these categories, giving a straightforward structure to this complex subject.

Significantly, the majority of mudras involve the head and hands, areas of the body which are relatively complex in their role within the total organism. Science has provided an explanation for this. Many nerves connect the head and hands with the brain, meaning that when mudras are adopted by the hands, eyes and tongue in particular, the stimulation to the brain is significant. The perineal mudras

3

are also associated with major nerve plexuses in the lower body. As the positions adopted in the mudras are unusual, new neuronal pathways are developed by their regular practise, a concept more fully understood in the light of scientific recognition of neuroplasticity – the astounding ability of the brain to restructure itself according to how it is used.

There is also an abundance of nadis in these regions. Many nadis terminate in the hands, and prana is readily lost through them. The hand mudras prevent that loss: in effect, the prana is recycled. The nadis influenced by the head mudras connect directly with important chakras, redirecting strong currents of prana to them, which in turn has a powerful effect on the mind. Hence, their extensive use in hatha yoga as a pathway into raja yoga.

Khechari mudra, commonly known as the tongue lock, is one of the most important of the yoga mudras, and is described in detail in the hatha yoga scriptures. The true hatha yoga version is extremely complex and is not taught in mainstream yoga. The simpler form, used in raja yoga and kriya yoga, is sometimes known as *nabho mudra*. This is the form taught in Satyananda Yoga, where it is referred to as khechari mudra.

The perineal mudras direct prana along powerful nadis to chakras in the lower body. Both the head and perineal mudras are used in kriya yoga along with asanas, pranayamas, bandhas and visualizations: a potent blend used to guide the awakening of kundalini. The lock mudras, which incorporate bandha, are used in hatha and kriya yoga.

The postural mudras are based around an asana and may include directing the awareness along a certain nadi, as in the hatha yoga practices of yoga mudra and vipareeta karani mudra. Another version of vipareeta karani mudra is used in kriya yoga.

The perineal mudras include vajroli and sahajoli. They are presented here both in their simple and complete forms. While the basic forms can be practised by one and all, the

4

complete forms are extremely advanced techniques which are seldom described and rarely taught. They include yogic *maithuna*, sexual intercourse with retention of both male and female reproductive fluids. The purpose is the fusion and upward flow of the energies associated with male and female union, rather than sensual pleasure. In this way the energy fundamental to creation is transformed into a great spiritual force which explodes the boundaries of the conditioned state. Both physically and mentally this is a demanding and specialized practice. It cannot be accomplished without immense mental control, intensity of focus and total restraint at the level of passion and instinct. Indeed, the power of the practice is in the combination of a complex physical technique and uncompromised focusing of the mind, both of which are only attainable by the most accomplished yogis.

Bandha

In texts such as *Hatha Yoga Pradipika* and *Gheranda Samhita* the bandhas are described along with mudras. They are, however, distinct in their action and purpose and are now regarded as a category of practice in their own right. While mudras redirect pranic flow, bandhas block the flow so that it accumulates and builds up, resulting in a powerful redirection for the awakening of sushumna nadi. Describing this, Swami Sivananda simply says, "Bandhas pertain to the prana: that which binds prana is bandha."

In classical hatha yoga pranayama is considered incomplete without bandhas, which are practised during breath retention. Bandhas are combined in various ways with asanas, mudras and visualizations in the advanced practices of hatha and kundalini yoga to specifically influence the *granthis*, psychic knots which block the rising of kundalini.

Satyananda Yoga has developed the use of bandhas for release of internal tensions held in the muscle groups associated with each bandha. Such tension can be understood as a physiological aspect of the granthis, representing a freezing or stagnation of energy in the body. This energy may be sexual, emotional or mental. Hence, the bandhas must be used with care, as their unguided practice can result in the release of disturbing samskaras and feelings requiring maturity and wisdom to recognize and manage.

The pancha dharanas

Mudra and Bandha concludes with a chapter on the *pancha dharanas*, concentrations on the elements, a sequence of meditations given in *Gheranda Samhita* within the chapter on mudra. It may be wondered why such practices are presented as mudras in a text on hatha yoga. A beautiful effect of their inclusion is expansion of the concept of mudra and therefore of the aspirant's mind. One must move beyond the notion of mudra as a fundamentally physical position. In relation to this, Swami Niranjan says, "The five dharanas focus and lock the prana and awareness on a specific point or quality using psychic rather than physical tools." The pancha dharanas do include hatha yoga techniques, such as pranayama, but their primary energetic effect is through the direction of mental energy for the awakening of the shakti inherent in each tattwa.

Diversity of tradition

As with vipareeta karani, mudras known by the same name may vary in technique depending on the branch of yoga, or the text giving the instruction. Such variations are found within the classical hatha yoga texts, and are noted where relevant in *Mudra and Bandha*, as a range of source texts are referred to in the answers. The issue of non-standard names and techniques can lead to confusion; it is better to simply accept the technique and name as they are presented in various contexts and not worry about the idea of standardizing practices.

It must be remembered that the diversity of the yogic tradition has grown from the experiences of many masters over the millennia. Such luminaries experiment, developing practices themselves; this is how yoga has evolved and remained a living science rather than being a body of static knowledge limited by rigidity of practice and understanding. The true masters build on the work of their predecessors, including adapting the system to the needs of their own times. This can be seen in the contribution of the Bihar School of Yoga lineage, most notably in the legacy of Swami Satyananda whose presentation of the practices of hatha, raja, kundalini, mantra and other branches of yoga has made it possible for people everywhere to reap the benefits of yoga while living a householder life.

Being

The journey into mudra is one of depth, subtlety and beauty. The diversity and versatility of practices reflects the nature of the medium that mudras work with – prana, in its direct connection with mind and feeling. Of all the hatha yoga practices, perhaps mudras most fully engage the link between the body, energy, mind and spirit; the position of the body is used to direct the prana in such a way that it has a sattwic effect on the mind, enabling awakening of the spiritual nature which is waiting to emerge from within. Swami Niranjan says that with the practice of mudras one moves from the 'doing' techniques to the 'being' techniques, and in this state of being, one can simply "flow with the energy that has been created."

Note

Hatha Yoga Book 6: Mudra and Bandha is not an instruction book. Yogic practices should always be learned from a qualified teacher with understanding of contra-indications and precautions.

1

Understanding Mudra

WHAT IS MUDRA?

Why are mudras important in yoga?

Swami Sivananda: Mudras concern the mind. They represent seals – mudra means 'seal' They seal the mind with the soul or *atman*. They do not allow the mind to wander outside towards objects. They direct the externalizing mind towards atman in the chambers of the heart and fix it there. The mudras and bandhas bestow all that one wants. There is nothing in this world like the mudras and bandhas for giving success.

What is the meaning of the word 'mudra'?

Swami Satyananda: The Sanskrit word *mudra* is translated as 'gesture' or 'attitude'. Mudras can be described as psychic, emotional, devotional and aesthetic gestures or attitudes. Yogis have experienced mudras as attitudes of energy flow, intended to link the individual pranic force with the universal or cosmic force. The *Kularnava Tantra* traces the word mudra to the root *mud*, meaning 'delight' or 'pleasure', and *dravay*, the causal form of *dru*, which means 'to draw forth'. Mudra is also defined as a 'seal', 'short-cut' or 'circuit bypass'.

What are mudras?

Swami Satyananda: Mudras are a combination of subtle physical movements which alter mood, attitude and perception, and which deepen awareness and concentration. A mudra may involve the whole body in a combination of asana, pranayama, bandha and visualization techniques, or it may be a simple hand position.

The *Hatha Yoga Pradipika* and other yogic texts consider mudra to be a *yoganga*, an independent branch of yoga, requiring a deeply subtle awareness. Mudras are introduced after some proficiency has been attained in asana, pranayama and bandha, and gross blockages have been removed.

What is the origin and significance of mudras and bandhas?

Swami Niranjanananda: The knowledge of mudras and bandhas was first imparted by Lord Shiva to Mother Parvati. In *Gheranda Samhita* (3:4–5) it is written:

Mudraanaam patalam devi kathitam tava sannidhau;
Yena vijnaatamaatrena sarva siddhih prajaayate.

Gopaneeyam prayatnena na deyam yasyakasyachit;
Preetidam yoginaam chaiva durlabhammarutaamapi.

Oh Goddess! I have imparted the knowledge of mudras. Mere knowledge of these provides siddhis, mastery. (4)

Their knowledge provides bliss to yogis. Their knowledge is not easily accessible even to the gods. Always keep this knowledge secret. (5)

The declaration that this knowledge is not easily accessible even to gods clearly reflects the significance of mudras. These practices should not be undertaken aimlessly. Only competent and deserving practitioners and disciples should try to master them. Knowledge of mudras and their techniques is known to very few *sadhakas*, practitioners.

How has the tradition of mudras been preserved?

Swami Satyananda: Mudras have been described in various texts from antiquity to the present day in order to preserve them for posterity. However, such references were never detailed or clearly delineated as these techniques were not intended to be learned from a book. Practical instruction from a guru was always considered to be a necessary requisite before attempting them. Mudras are higher practices which lead to awakening of the pranas, chakras and kundalini, and which can bestow major *siddhis*, psychic powers, on the advanced practitioner.

How important are mudras in hatha yoga?

Swami Niranjanananda: In yoga, the significance of mudras and bandhas is even greater than that of asana and pranayama, because mudras influence pranamaya and manomaya koshas. In the body, many sensations originate within the nervous system and many changes take place on the mental plane. In the pranic field, the production of energy in the body also fluctuates. For these reasons, both activity and dissipation are experienced in the inner mental state and also in the pranic state. In *Gheranda Samhita*, the knowledge of mudra and bandha is imparted to Sage Gheranda's disciple, King Chandakapali, to bring about mental stability

Why are mudras referred to as 'attitudes'?

Swami Niranjanananda: From the gross point of view, *mudra* is a term meaning a gesture or a particular mood or feeling of consciousness. Mudras are various attitudes or subtle postures adopted by the body to induce a change in the pranic circulatory system. The actual meaning of mudra is 'psychophysiological attitude'. The psyche is being reached by a physiological posture which creates an attitudinal feeling. A mudra always involves a peculiar influence on the human psyche.

Little has been written about mudras. The mudras described in the yogic scriptures are manifestations of special moods or feelings of consciousness, *chitta*, and states of energy, *prana*. This is a subject for scientific research: how does the effect happen, what is the meaning, what is the logic when one says that mudras are a practice of psycho-physiological attitude?

What is the relationship between mudras and the koshas?

Swami Satyananda: The attitudes and postures adopted during mudra practices establish a direct link between *annamaya kosha*, the physical body, *manomaya kosha*, the mental body and *pranamaya kosha*, the energy body. Initially, this enables the practitioner to develop awareness of the flow of prana in the body. Ultimately, it establishes pranic balance within the koshas and enables the redirection of subtle energy to the upper chakras, inducing higher states of consciousness.

What is the effect of mudras on the different forms of prana?

Swami Niranjanananda: Through mudras steadiness is experienced. That steadiness can be understood to mean the stability of pranamaya kosha and manomaya kosha. The mind is restless at first, and it is the same with prana. The purpose of the mudras is to stop this pranic restlessness and to bring one-pointedness, controlling mental restlessness. The prana shakti must be made calm and quiet, but how and where?

To know this, the different forms of prana need to be understood. One form of prana is in the *pancha pranas*, the five pranas: prana, apana, samana, udana and vyana. Another form is in the *chakras*, the psychic centres. Within the chakra system, one form of prana is in mooladhara, a second in swadhisthana, a third in manipura, a fourth in anahata and a fifth in vishuddhi. The prana existing in the chakras and pancha pranas are two different states of prana. The experience of the pancha pranas is a gross state relative to the experience of prana shakti in the chakras, which is a much subtler state.

11

The process and experience of the gross and subtle pranas can be brought under the control of consciousness through the practices of mudra and bandha. As long as there is no conscious control over the prana, the energy cannot be consciously awakened or produced. Therefore, for the smooth and controlled flow of prana, the practice of mudras to focus the mind, stop its external restlessness and achieve one-pointedness is recommended in hatha yoga.

What do mudras symbolize?

Swami Satyananda: There are many mudras and they have come to mean different things according to usage and people's different levels of understanding. *Mudra* means 'insignia' or 'symbol'. What is insignia and what is symbol? When one is crying, it means unhappiness; so is crying the symbol of unhappiness? A crying person doesn't have to say, "I'm unhappy"; the tears tell of the unhappiness. When someone dances or sings or laughs, it means they are happy. These are the symbols of emotions. In the same way, the inner consciousness also has a symbol.

Mudras appear to be physical gestures or positions made with the hands, eyes or the whole body, but mudra means a position taken by one's psychic attitude. The purpose of the mudras is to handle the problem of inner experience. So, in yoga and tantra mudra means 'the attitude of energy flow'. The spiritual meaning is to unite oneself with the inner being. But it is not enough to know this intellectually, the mudras have to be practised and thereby experienced. An ounce of practice is better than tons of theory.

Are mudras a form of body language?

Swami Niranjanananda: The Sanskrit word mudra is translated as 'attitude' or 'gesture'. Attitude is something which reflects mind in body, and body in mind. With a little observation, we can learn a lot about someone's mental state by the way they walk, sit, act, and so on. A person who is frightened will walk quite differently from someone who is angry. This 'body language' is a constant communication between the *annamaya kosha*, physical body, and the other koshas, via the network of nadis in the pranayama kosha. Even simple hand or facial gestures will have a corresponding 'gesture' in the subtle body.

Tantra has developed this knowledge into a system of mudras which are specific attitudes of the body relating to specific attitudes of mind. The mudra may be a whole body position or a simple finger position, but the effect is transmitted through all levels of the pancha kosha, and the appropriate 'signal' transferred from gross to subtle.

This flow of information through the pranamaya kosha is a two-way process. People experiencing altered states of consciousness have been known to perform mudras spontaneously, representing a transmission from subtle to gross. Conversely, we can reverse the signal and send a message to the mind by adopting a physical attitude or mudra. The effects are extremely subtle. It requires great sensitivity to perceive a change of consciousness simply by joining the thumb and index finger together, but with practise the mind becomes conditioned to this signal, and when this hand position is adopted the signal for meditation is transmitted.

Why is the channelling of prana so important in yoga?

Swami Niranjanananda: Yogis have always maintained that the different experiences of human consciousness can be easily monitored and controlled through the channelling of prana. A mental attitude can alter the movement of prana, and the external environment can influence the movement of prana, as everything is constantly and continuously influencing, affecting and altering the biorhythms. Thought and emotion alter one's physical and pranic biorhythms, and physical practices also alter the flows of prana. Due to an understanding of that process and its effects, the practices of yoga, including mudras, evolved for the conscious channelling of prana.

13

How do mudras act on prana?

Swami Satyananda: Mudras manipulate prana in much the same way that energy in the form of light or sound waves is diverted by a mirror or a cliff face. The nadis and chakras constantly radiate prana which normally escapes from the body and dissipates into the external world. By creating barriers within the body through the practice of mudra, the energy is redirected within. For example, by closing the eyes with the fingers in shanmukhi mudra, the prana being radiated through the eyes is reflected back. In the same way, the sexual energy emitted through vajra nadi is redirected to the brain through the practice of vajroli mudra.

Tantric literature states that once the dissipation of prana is arrested through the practice of mudra, the mind becomes introverted, inducing states of *pratyahara*, sense withdrawal, and *dharana*, concentration. Because of their ability to redirect prana, mudras are important techniques for awakening kundalini. For this reason they are incorporated extensively into kriya and kundalini yoga practices. In *Shiva Samhita* (4:13–14) it is written:

Suptaa guruprasaadena yadaa jaagarti kundalee;
Tadaa sarvaani padmaani bhidyante granthayopi cha.

Tasmaatsarvaprayatnena prabodhayitumeeshvareem;
Brahmarandhramukhe suptaam mudraabhyaasam samaacharet.

When the sleeping goddess Kundalini is awakened through the grace of guru, then all the lotuses and the bonds are readily pierced through and through. (13)

Therefore, in order that the goddess, who is asleep in the mouth of the brahmarandhra (the innermost hollow of sushumna) be awakened, the mudras should be practised with the greatest care. (14)

What methods does yoga use to control and channel prana and mind?

Swami Niranjanananda: Controlling the body by rebalancing the thought process is a mental approach; this is the approach of raja yoga, through the practices of pratyahara and dharana. In raja yoga one practises observation of the vrittis, thoughts and desires, and tries to control them. Gradually, by reducing their influence on behaviour and expression, greater balance and harmony are experienced in the mind-body complex.

Another approach is to work directly at the pranic level, on the nadis, chakras and pranas, using techniques for manipulating and raising the prana in order to alter the condition of the mind, thoughts and emotions, so that a physical technique can induce pratyahara or dharana, and a combination of physical techniques can induce dhyana. This is where mudras come in. By a change in physical posture, such as joining the fingers, pressing a certain part of the body, or closing certain areas of the body, the flow of prana being directed to that part can be diverted to another area. It is like shining a torch at night on a blank wall: the light will hit the wall and then spread out in all directions because there is a block. The theory of prana works in a similar way.

The nadis and chakras are like torches that are constantly shining and radiating their energy into infinity. How far that energy radiates is not known; maybe it gets lost or becomes invisible at some point. However, when one puts up a barrier within the field of the body, for example by closing the eyes with the fingers, the prana that is being radiated through the eyes hits that barrier and is reflected back; by closing the nostrils, the prana responsible for the expulsion of breath hits that barrier and bounces back; by closing vajra nadi, the sexual energy hits that barrier and rushes upward to the brain. In this way, each mudra has a purpose, which is to reverse that energy expression in one's being and divert it back into the body.

15

What is the scientific view of mudras?

Swami Satyananda: In scientific terms, mudras provide a means to access and influence the unconscious reflexes and primal, instinctive habit patterns that originate in the primitive areas of the brain around the brain stem. They establish a subtle, non-intellectual connection with these areas. Each mudra sets up a different link and has a correspondingly different effect on the body, mind and prana. The aim is to create fixed, repetitive postures and gestures which can snap the practitioner out of instinctive habit patterns and establish a more refined consciousness.

CATEGORIES OF MUDRA

What is the place of mudras in Indian culture?

Swami Satyananda: In India, mudras occupy an important place in the arts as well as the spiritual sciences. Mudras are often seen in the portraits, images and idols of saints, sages or gods and goddesses; for example jnana mudra, chin mudra, shankha mudra and abhaya mudra. *Abhaya mudra*, gesture of fearlessness, is seen in statues of Buddha.

In *bharat natyam*, Indian dance, there are the dance mudras; they are one group. In bhakti cults, there are devotional mudras; they are another aspect. Then there are the mudras for meditation, which are yet another aspect. There are also the yogic mudras such as vipareeta karani mudra, khechari mudra, yoga mudra, shambhavi mudra, nasikagra mudra and many others.

Why are mudras and bandhas sometimes classified together?

Swami Satyananda: If one makes a study of the different hatha yoga texts, there will surely be some confusion when it comes to mudras and bandhas. Some practices are referred to as mudras in one text and as bandhas in another. In different texts the same practices may be described, but they might also have different names. It is stated in *Hatha Yoga Pradipika* (3:6–7):

Mahaamudraa mahaabandho mahaavedhashcha khecharee;
Uddeeyaanam moolabandhashcha bandho jaalandharaabhidhah.

Karanee vipareetaakhyaa vajrolee shaktichaalanam;
Idam hi mudraadashakam jaraamarananaashanam.

Maha mudra, maha bandha, maha vedha, khechari, uddiyana, moola bandha and jalandhara bandha; (6)

Vipareeta karani mudra, vajroli and shakti chalana, verily, these are the ten mudras which destroy old age and death. (7)

In particular, one could easily be confused about jalandhara, uddiyana and moola bandhas. In the ancient tantric scriptures these practices were defined as mudras, not bandhas. Then during the periods when tantric practices were prevalent, it seems they were not considered as separate practices, but their combination was called *maha mudra*, 'the great attitude'.

When the system of hatha yoga was culled from the tantric practices, some of the practices were redefined and mudras and bandhas were separated. Now jalandhara, uddiyana and moola are defined as bandhas, but their combination becomes a mudra.

In this sloka, the most important mudras and bandhas have been listed: *maha mudra*, the great attitude, *maha bandha*, the great lock, *maha bhedha mudra*, the great piercing attitude, *khechari mudra*, the attitude of dwelling in Supreme Consciousness, *uddiyana bandha*, the abdominal retraction lock, *moola bandha*, perineum/cervix retraction lock, *jalandhara bandha*, throat lock, *vipareeta karani mudra*, the attitude of reversing, *shakti chalana mudra*, the attitude of moving or circulating the energy. One more important mudra of hatha yoga which is not listed here is *shambhavi mudra*, eyebrow centre gazing.

There are many groups of mudras – what differentiates the yoga mudras?

Swami Niranjanananda: There are many kinds of mudras, innumerable types of mudras; they cannot be counted. The various traditions, schools of philosophy and schools of sadhana use different groups of mudras to attain whatever goal they have set for themselves.

The nyasa system of tantra from which yoga nidra is derived involves profuse use of mudras, along with mantras, to make one aware of different areas of the body and to recognize the presence of shakti and devata in that particular organ. In dance, large numbers of mudras are used to express different sentiments, different *bhavas*, different attitudes, different moods, and they represent various responses to situations that are created in dance. The esoteric tantric sadhanas use still other sets of mudras to induce a different level of awareness. So there are a large number of mudras; mudras are not one specific category of practice like asana or pranayama.

In brief, those which are classified as yoga mudras help in the reversal of the prana shakti and in inducing states of concentration and awareness. With the regulation of prana shakti, mental activity is reduced, so that greater peace, greater concentration and broader awareness is experienced. In hatha yoga there are also mudras which help regulate the flow of prana through the body to eliminate various psychophysiological disorders. There are even mudras which rectify defects in the organs of the body. For example, if people who are having heart problems practise hridaya mudra, they experience a great deal of relief.

What are the categories of yoga mudras?

Swami Satyananda: The yoga mudras can be categorized into approximately five groups, which are described as follows.

1. *Hasta mudras*: hand mudras – The most commonly used hand mudras are meditative mudras. They redirect the prana emitted by the hands back into the body. Mudras

which join the thumb and index finger engage the motor cortex at a subtle level. They generate a loop of energy which moves from the brain down to the hand and then back again. Conscious awareness of this process rapidly leads to internalization. Some of the techniques included in this category are: jnana mudra, chin mudra, yoni mudra, bhairava mudra and hridaya mudra.

2. *Mana mudras*: head mudras – These practices form an integral part of kundalini yoga and many are meditation techniques in their own right. They use the eyes, ears, nose, tongue and lips. Some of the techniques included in this category are: shambhavi mudra, nasikagra drishti, khechari mudra, kaki mudra, bhujangini mudra, bhoochari mudra, akashi mudra, shanmukhi mudra and unmani mudra.

3. *Kaya mudras*: body mudras or postural mudras – These practices use physical postures combined with breathing and concentration. Some of the techniques included in this category are: vipareeta karani mudra, pashinee mudra, yoga mudra and tadagi mudra.

4. *Bandha mudras*: lock mudras – These practices combine mudra and bandha. They charge the system with prana and prepare it for kundalini awakening. Some of the techniques included in this category are: shakti chalini mudra, maha mudra, maha bheda mudra and maha vedha mudra.

5. *Adhara mudras*: perineal mudras – These techniques redirect prana from the lower centres to the brain. Mudras concerned with sublimating sexual energy are in this group. Techniques included in this category are: ashwini mudra, vajroli/sahajoli mudra, amaroli and vajroni mudra.

Between them these five groups engage substantial areas of the cerebral cortex. The comparatively large number of head and hand mudras reflects the fact that the operation and interpretation of information coming in from these two areas occupies approximately fifty percent of the cortex.

PURPOSE OF MUDRA

What is the purpose of mudras?

Swami Niranjanananda: *Mudras* are psychophysiological locks or psycho-energy locks. The practice of mudras helps stop the wastage of prana shakti. It has been shown by researchers that at the extremities of the body there is significant loss of prana shakti. There is a continuous discharge of prana shakti from the fingertips and also from the eyes. When one practises a mudra, one not only tries to contain the prana shakti, but also to reverse the flow of prana shakti.

There are also mudras related to different organs of the body. In the practice of hridaya mudra, for example, the fingers actually act as pressure points, stimulating the prana shakti in the heart and bringing about a calming effect. Many people have practised hridaya mudra for heart problems and felt that this practice has helped them. The practice of these mudras, apart from realigning the flow of prana in a particular organ, also activates the prana shakti.

The advanced asanas in hatha yoga are those asanas in which the body automatically triggers a particular bandha or mudra. One example is brahmacharyasana, where there is an automatic contraction of the perineal muscle, and therefore an automatic moola bandha occurs.

What is the aim of mudras?

Swami Niranjanananda: Mudras are different attitudes or subtle postures adopted by the body to induce a change in the pranic circulatory system. Ida, pingala and sushumna nadis flow along the spinal passage. Ida and pingala flow in a crisscross pattern, going from side-to-side, while sushumna flows along the centre. There are six junction points, where there is union of the three nadis. At these points of union, a chakra is created. Those six places are the six chakras from mooladhara up to ajna. From ajna, the three nadis become one: as one, they go up to sahashara.

The aim of mudras is to activate these three nadis and to ensure that the flow of prana takes place properly and without waste. To guide the prana towards a specific organ, a particular mudra is adopted. There are different types of mudras, and their whole purpose is to encourage the flow of energy back into the body or to stimulate a particular nadi.

For example, when sitting for meditation a hand mudra is used: either jnana mudra, with the palms down or chin mudra, with the palms facing upward. Other hand mudras may be used during meditation, such as hridaya mudra and yoni mudra. When mudras are performed with the hands, the energy is channelled back into the body.

There are also head mudras, such as *shambhavi mudra*, which is gazing at the eyebrow centre, and *unmani mudra*, which is gazing into space, keeping the eyes focused at least nine inches away from the body, on nothing. In the practice of shambhavi mudra the movement of the eyeballs pulls and pushes and stretches and contracts the eye muscles and nerves. After some time a pull is felt, stimulating a particular visual nadi which supplies prana to the sight, to the eyes. Also, by focussing the eyes together at the eyebrow centre sushumna nadi is stimulated.

Kirlian photography shows the aura, the electrical emission of the body. This shows how the body's stamina becomes depleted. The energy becomes less and less as the day goes by. But when mudras are practised, the same energy is redirected back into one's system. Then there is no wastage of shakti, no wastage of energy. Instead, it returns to the system.

How can the flow of prana in the body be most effectively regulated?

Swami Niranjanananda: How can one regulate the flow of prana in the body? Is breath the only method? People think that to regulate prana one should practise pranayama, one should practise prana vidya, one should practise other techniques, which can give the awareness and ability to

21

regulate the pranic flow. Within this context, mudra is as important as pranayama or prana vidya: pranayama uses the breath to direct the flow of prana in the body, to become aware of prana in the body, and prana vidya uses mental imagery and chakra visualizations. Mudra, however, is actually diverting the flow, the current of prana in the *nadis*, the channels within the body.

Mudras are therefore more important than even pranayama or prana vidya, because through the practice of mudra one ensures that the wires which conduct the energy in the body are proper, and that they can take the load as the intensity and quantity of shakti increases within, as the pranas become awakened within.

Mudras have been used to access the human psyche and to create a link, a bridge between the body, the external behaviour, function and performance of the senses, and the psyche, the internal expression of mind.

What is the role of mudras in meditation or other practices of contemplation?

Swami Niranjanananda: Many philosophies, religions and systems of thought in the world believe that it is necessary to completely detach oneself from the external world in order to experience some sort of spiritual or inner realization. The main aim of mudras and bandhas is to help attain an inner state in which external emotions and events do not scatter the mental state. One should be able to keep the mind one-pointed in prayer or meditation and not allow any negative feelings or reactions to manifest internally.

How can a physical practice, such as mudra or bandha, lead to spiritual experience?

Swami Niranjanananda: It is said in Vedanta that everything is transitory; it is all *maya*, illusion and delusion – leave it, and abide in the truth. But in yoga and tantra it is said that whatever state one is in should be used as a ladder to higher states. Yoga believes that if one wishes to attain one-pointedness and some sort of spiritual experience, that experience can be achieved through the medium of the senses also. The senses may be expanded and activated so much that the mind spontaneously becomes one-pointed. Mudras can play a role here; for example, khechari mudra is related to the senses.

One can activate, expand and absorb oneself in the sensations manifesting inside by adopting a particular technique. Making use of physical and psychic gestures activates the sensations of annamaya kosha, pranamaya kosha and manomaya kosha in order to go inside them. Mudras and bandhas play a significant role in this second process.

EFFECTS OF MUDRAS

How do mudras create a feeling?

Swami Niranjanananda: Mudras create and depict moods. From the gross point of view, mudra or gesture is a term meaning a particular mood or feeling. There are many kinds of mudras, but broadly speaking there are the *natya* or dance mudras, which express a particular state of mind, emotion or event, and the yoga mudras, which channel and reverse the flow of prana in the body. For example, in Indian dance the emotion of anger may be depicted through the eyes, the position of the hands and the body.

If a mudra is practised for a long time, the feeling of the mudra may be experienced, because the sensation it creates is imprinted in the body and mind. This also happens in daily life. For instance, when a person is angry, they may raise the eyebrows, tense the hands and clench the fists. If these actions are adopted when one is not angry, this feeling will gradually develop. This is because the physical stance brings a change in the brainwaves which influences the state of consciousness.

Mudras such as ashwini, vajroli and tadagi, are practised in kundalini yoga and influence pranamaya kosha and change the flow of prana. Their influence is felt on the brain as well, and they help in awakening a certain feeling inside chitta so that one becomes introverted and internalized. The practice of mudras is also helpful in achieving one-pointedness and concentration.

How do mudras create feelings of harmony?

Swami Niranjanananda: The literal meaning of the word *mudra*, according to the *Kularnava Tantra*, is 'one which brings happiness'. The word 'mudra' comes from the root *mudh*, which means pleasant, to be happy, to be content, to be at ease; in this context, mudra becomes that practice which brings a sense of ease and contentment to the body-mind unit by removing all the spikes and dissipations of prana and the corresponding states of mind which are experienced due to the pranic states.

Why are mudras so powerful?

Swami Satyananda: Many ancient yogis and sages are depicted displaying a characteristic mudra. These mudras have symbolic meaning and they also have the power to evoke forces within the individual. In other words, the individual dwells on, and tries to experience, the indescribable meaning contained within a mudra. In this way it is possible to call up inner forces which otherwise lie hidden and dormant. This is why mudras are so powerful.

How do mudras interact with the pranamaya kosha?

Swami Niranjanananda: Within the pranamaya kosha, these mudras represent a linking of various circuits within the network of nadis, creating a flow of prana which has gross and subtle implications. Mudras induce a change in the pranic circulatory system; they activate the nadis, ensuring a smooth flow of prana and eliminating wastage of prana. Therefore, they are able to guide prana towards a specific organ, as intended by a specific mudra. For example, the hand mudras in particular gradually rechannel the energy back into the system, while other mudras influence specific nadis and organs.

What happens when mudras occur spontaneously?

Swami Satyananda: Mudras can arouse specific emotions. When the pranic level is increased and the conscious mind withdraws, mudras occur spontaneously. The hands, feet, eyes, arms and legs move slowly into definite positions like those of Indian dancers. Through mudras, specific qualities of Shakti or Devi are invoked and one becomes overwhelmed by that power.

How do mudras affect the deeper layers of the personality?

Swami Niranjanananda: When prana is in the process of rebalancing itself, there is an automatic experience of mental tranquillity. Therefore, most of the mudras are used for going deep into a meditative state. They aid the processes of pratyahara and dharana. That is the superficial experience. At a deeper level of the personality something else happens.

The four basic instinctive tendencies are fear, sexual urge, desire for sleep and desire for food. These are the corresponding physical manifestations of the mental vrittis that are being experienced on the level of consciousness. For example, the sexual urge is a desire, a force, a thought and an expression. It is experienced in the region of mooladhara. That form of consciousness is actually activating that physical part of the body known as the mooladhara-swadhisthana region.

Sleep does not affect any one organ in the body. It slows down the activity of the nervous system. As the activities cease, one moves into another state of consciousness or sleep. One goes through different stages of drowsiness, lethargy and somnolence, from dream to deep sleep.

Hunger is not felt in the pancreas, kidneys or liver, it is felt in the stomach, the abdomen. The desire for food actually stimulates the digestive system. Therefore, that vritti can be controlled through the digestive system. By controlling the physical region of manipura, the solar plexus, that vritti can be controlled. Similarly, by controlling the autonomic nervous system, the vritti of fear which causes palpitation, secretion of adrenaline and rapid breathing can be controlled.

Mudras work within these areas in order to control the corresponding physical aspects of consciousness by altering and channelling the flow of prana, the energy that is manifesting in the body. Mudras become a process through which one begins to experiment with oneself, trying to see the relationship with the different koshas: annamaya kosha, manomaya kosha and pranamaya kosha. When harmony and integration of the various faculties of these koshas has taken place, then the psychic or spiritual aspect becomes known to us.

How can mudras alter consciousness?

Swami Satyananda: The subject of mudra is mainly centred on the possibility of altering the consciousness by certain means within the body. There are certain untapped secretions in the body. There are some secretions in the physical body which are dormant. There are certain centres in this physical body which are not functioning. There are certain areas in the brain which are not yet developed.

These centres in the brain may be ultrasonic or suprasonic; they are not of the nature of mind, they are not in the nature of thinking, they are in the form of what can be called frequencies or rhythms. The study of physics brings better understanding of this. In this universe there are rhythms or vibrations humans are not aware of. These are sometimes vibrating at many thousand times per second, but they can be registered.

It needs to be understood that there is more than is thought of in this physical body. There are areas in the brain which are not at all connected with daily life and experience. There are potential secretions in the physical body which are still closed, sealed; and there are certain centres in the physical body about which we have no idea. The subject of mudra concerns the process of unlocking, or arousing, these potentials.

26

How can mudra be used to balance the mind for meditation?

Swami Satyananda: There is an important mudra which yogis practise before meditation in order to balance the flow of breath. Often during meditation, the mind is out of gear for no apparent reason. This is usually due to an imbalance in the flow of the breath.

When the right nostril is flowing the mind plays games. This is because the right nostril is connected with the left hemisphere of the brain, which is the centre of *rajo guna*, dynamism.

At other times one feels relaxed and composed, as though under the influence of a tranquilliser. The mind refuses to act and goes to sleep. This is not a good condition either. It occurs when the left nostril is flowing. The left nostril is connected with the right hemisphere of the brain, which is the centre of *tamo guna*, inertia.

How can the brain be balanced? It is important to know how. If the right nostril is flowing, either the *yoga danda*, a special staff, or the left hand, must be pressed into the right armpit. Within a few minutes the left nostril will be clear. Likewise, if the left nostril is flowing, press the staff or the right hand into the left armpit. Within a few minutes the right nostril will be flowing. This mudra can also be practised by pressing both armpits at the same time and meditating. It is called *swara yoga mudra*. This helps create a smooth balance between the ida and pingala energy systems.

When both nostrils flow equally, the energy enters into sushumna nadi. Then meditation becomes a smooth experience and one has less problems. It is also possible to create this situation through pranayama, but that often takes more time.

How are mudras used to awaken the chakras?

Swami Satyananda: Mudra is a specific body position which channels the energy produced by asana and pranayama into the various centres, arousing particular states of mind. Some mudras are done separately after asana and pranayama, others are performed with asana and pranayama to help awaken the chakras and arouse kundalini shakti. It is stated in *Hatha Yoga Pradipika* (3:5):

Tasmaatsarvaprayatnena prabodhayitumeeshvareem;
Brahmadvaaramukhe suptaam mudraabhyaasam samaacharet.

Therefore, the goddess sleeping at the entrance of Brahma's door should be constantly aroused with all effort by performing mudra thoroughly.

How can mudras directly stimulate the chakras?

Swami Satyananda: Along with the mudras which affect the energy circuits, there are other mudras which directly stimulate the chakras. In shambhavi mudra, for example, the energy is concentrated between the eyebrows at bhrumadhya, the trigger point for ajna chakra. Nasikagra mudra focuses energy at the nosetip. This stimulates certain nerves which govern the sense of smell, thereby awakening mooladhara chakra, which is associated with this faculty.

Vipareeta karani mudra, the inverted psychic attitude of hatha yoga and kriya yoga, reverses the downward flow of energy. In the scriptures it is clearly stated that the moon (bindu) secretes nectar and the sun (manipura) consumes it. This leads to degeneration, decay and death. In vipareeta karani mudra, this downward process is reversed and the energy which is normally lost in external affairs is sucked back up to the higher centres in the brain.

What siddhis are attained through the perfection of mudras?

Swami Satyananda: The perfection of asana and pranayama result in minor *siddhis* or perfections, such as vitality, good health, mental and emotional equilibrium, and clairaudience. Perfection of mudras and bandhas, however, results in the attainment of major siddhis such as: *anima*, making the body small like an atom; *laghima*, making the body light; *mahima*, making the body large; *garima*, making the body heavy; *prapti*, the capacity to reach anywhere; *prakamya*, unobstructed fulfilment of desire; *vashitva*, control over all objects and *ishitva*; power to create and destroy. In *Hatha Yoga Pradipika* (3:8) Yogi Swatmarama says of mudras:

Aadinaathoditam divyamashtaishvaryapradaayakam;
Vallabham sarvasiddhaanaam durlabham marutaamapi.

Adinath said they are the bestowers of the eight divine powers. They are held in high esteem by all the siddhas and are difficult for even the gods to attain.

The *Yoga Sutras* of Sage Patanjali also list these eight siddhis, referring to them as *ashta siddhi*. However, Sage Patanjali emphasizes that siddhis should not be sought and, if they develop, they should virtually be ignored and definitely not exhibited.

According to him, they are obstacles on the path to samadhi and can completely hinder one's spiritual evolution. Therefore, although mudras and bandhas can bestow divine powers, they should not be practised for this purpose.

How do mudras affect the unconscious mind?

Swami Niranjanananda: Mudras and bandhas both work on the same principles as acupuncture. By performing certain mudras or physical locks, the flow of pranic energy either entering or going out of the body can be controlled and channelled.

For example, practices such as vajroli mudra, ashwini mudra and moola bandha are meant to block the downward flow of energy. With knowledge of the five pranas or their manifestation in the body, it can be understood that the force of apana, situated between the perineum and the navel, is a downward moving force controlling mooladhara and swadhisthana chakras. This means that control of the unconscious activities, the deep-rooted samskaras and inhibitions, desires, sense of security and sexual urge are being controlled by the apana force.

How do mudras bring stability?

Swami Niranjanananda: Mudras are gestures which focus pranic energy. By practising mudras, stability is attained. This means that the wavering mind and prana are controlled. With the practice of mudras the mind quickly becomes focused and internalized. In the *Gheranda Samhita* (1:10) it says:

> *Shatkarmanaa shodhanam cha aasanena bhaveddridham;*
> *Mudrayaa sthirataa chaiva pratyaahaarena dheerataa.*

Through shatkarmas, purification of the body is achieved; through asanas, firmness; through mudras, steadiness; and through pratyahara, patience is achieved.

Why are there so many mudras for the hands and head?

Swami Niranjanananda: Kirlian photography is a technique which shows the aura or energy field around a part of the body. Research has shown that there is a greater flow of pranic energy from the extreme ends of the body such as the hands, feet and head. In a Kirlian photograph an excessive flow of pranic energy is seen from the fingers and feet, but not from the back, thighs and calves. Yoga also teaches this, therefore, there are many mudras for the hands and head. Mudras stop the flow of pranic energy out of the body, rechannelling it into the body.

The sensitivity of these parts of the body is also reflected in the brain: in the motor cortex, the entire body is represented. The hands and the head alone take up about fifty percent of the cortex, and the rest is for all the other parts of the body. The sensory information and the motor output from the hands and head enable refined movements of the fingers, mouth and eyes. There are mudras for the eyes, hands and tongue. These techniques are aimed at controlling, and bringing the awareness to large areas of the cortex. Mudras cover most of the cortex and sensory motor area.

What is the difference between the effect of head and hand mudras?

Swami Niranjanananda: The head mudras involve the use of a sense organ like the eyes or tongue to directly affect the brain hemispheres and in this way have an effect at the mental level. With head mudras there is a relationship between the head, brain and mind. Head mudras, such as shambhavi mudra and nasikagra drishti, are used to focus the mind quickly.

With the hand mudras there is a relationship between the hands, the prana and the mind. Through the practice of hand mudras the flow of pranic energy out of the body can be stemmed and redirected back into the body. For example, in *jnana mudra* the hands are placed palm downward on the knees with the index finger curled into the root of the thumb. This causes the energy which is continuously flowing out of the index finger to re-enter the body. *Chin mudra* is similar to jnana mudra but with the palms on the knees facing upwards.

How does a hatha yogi use mudras to guide the power of kundalini?

Swami Sivananda: A hatha yogi brings down the prana by jalandhara bandha; by moola bandha he checks the downward tendency of apana; having accustomed himself to the practice of ashwini mudra, he makes the apana go upward with the mind intent on kumbhaka. Through uddiyana bandha, he forces the united prana-apana to enter the sushumna nadi along with kundalini, and through shakti chalana mudra, he takes kundalini from chakra to chakra. By this procedure a hatha yogi conquers *dehadhyasa*, identification with the body.

GUIDELINES FOR PRACTISING MUDRA

How important is concentration in the practice of mudra?

Swami Sivananda: Real success in mudras can only be had if there is intense concentration of mind.

When should mudras be performed?

Swami Satyananda: Mudras are performed either in combination with or after asana and pranayama.

What sequence is recommended for practising mudra as part of hatha yoga sadhana?

Swami Niranjanananda: In *Gheranda Samhita*, Sage Gheranda describes seven yogic techniques and their order of practice. The first one is purification of the body through practising shatkarmas. The second is the attainment of physical and mental stability and strength through asanas. The third is the experiencing of steadiness through mudras. After this, patience is achieved through pratyahara by separating the mind from the senses. These are followed by pranayama, meditation and samadhi.

Why does the tradition say that mudras should be kept secret?

Swami Satyananda: The traditional texts repeatedly mention that neither the practices, the siddhis, nor the sadhana should be divulged to anyone. It is the guru's decision who should be given the knowledge, and it can only be gained through experience. There is no merit in trying to share one's spiritual experiences with another. *Hatha Yoga Pradipika* (3:9) says of mudra:

> *Gopaneeyam prayatnena yathaa ratnakarandakam;*
> *Kasyachinnaiva vaktavyam kulastreesuratam yathaa.*

> These must remain secret just like precious stones, and not be talked about to anyone, just as one does not tell others about his intimate relations with his wife.

When is one ready for the practice of mudra?

Swami Niranjanananda: Mudras are techniques which require very subtle awareness. The practitioner comes to mudras after having practised and understood asana, pranayama and bandhas, which remove gross blockages.

32

When one comes to the practice of mudras, there needs to be an appreciation and feeling for what is going on at this highly subtle level. Whole body awareness and integration of the body parts has been experienced through the grosser practices, and now cellular level consciousness can be entered. The practitioner is coming out of the 'doing' techniques and coming into the 'being' techniques. Asanas and pranayama require a lot of manipulation and effort, a lot of 'doing'. Mudra techniques are much more within the scope of just 'being'. Now one can flow with the energy that has been created in the previous practice, and experiences can develop that come up into the consciousness.

Bandhas are used to slow down the physical and mental energy, thinking process, brainwaves and metabolism. Through mudras one enters the cellular level where energy, or *prana*, is manufactured, stored and used. The manufacture of energy is called anabolism, building up of tissue. The breakdown of energy is called catabolism, the using up of all the stores. The aim of yoga is to store prana, to build up and hold as much energy as possible. So the 'doing' techniques use more energy, while the 'being' techniques store it up.

What qualities are needed to achieve perfection in mudra?
Swami Satyananda: Mudras have been described as powerful practices which awaken kundalini shakti and bestow perfection by regular practice combined with self-control in life. It is stated in *Hatha Yoga Pradipika* (3:128):

Iti mudraa dasha proktaa aadinaathena shambhunaa;
Ekaikaa taasu yaminaam mahaasiddhipradaayinee.

Thus the ten mudras have been told by Adinath Shambhu. Each one is the bestower of perfection to the self-restrained.

Although ten mudras have been described, it is not necessary that all be practised. They are to be given as an initiation by the guru according to the nature and level of the aspirant.

33

The necessity of self-restraint and purification are repeatedly emphasized by Yogi Swatmarama. Self-restraint is an abiding quality of perfection.

How important are mudras in hatha yoga?

Swami Niranjanananda: After clarifiying the techniques and importance of all the mudras, Sage Gheranda concludes by once again alerting his disciple, the king, regarding their significance and usage. In *Gheranda Samhita* (3:94–100) he says,:

Idam tu mudraapatalam kathitam chandakaapaae;
Vallabham sarvasiddhaanaam jaraamarananaashanam.

Shathaaya bhaktiheenaaya na deyam yasya kasyachit;
Gopaneeyam prayatnena durlabham marutaamapi.

Rijave shaantachittaaya gurubhaktiparaaya cha;
Kuleenaaya pradaatavyam bhogamukti pradaayanam.

Mudraanaam patalam hyetatsarvavyaadhi vinaashakam;
Nityamabhyaasa sheelasya jatharaagnivivardhanam.

Tasya no jaayate mrityurnaasya vaardhakyamaayate;
Naagnijalabhayam tasya vaayorapi kuto bhayam.

Kaasah shvaasah pleehaa kushtham shleshmarogaashcha vimshatih;
Mudraanaam saadhanaachchaiva vinashyanti na samshayah.

Bahunaa kimihoktena saaram vachmi cha chanda te;
Naasti mudraasamnakinchid siddhidam kshitimandale.

O Chandakapali! Here I have told you about the various mudras, which all fulfil the desires of keeping away old age and death. (94)

Do not teach them to evil or undeserving people who lack devotion. These mudras are not even accessible to the gods. (95)

Both worldly enjoyments and liberation are attained through these mudras. They should only be imparted to those who have surrendered themselves to the guru, belong to a good family and whose minds are the abode of peace. (96)

With daily practice all diseases are eliminated and the digestive fire is activated. (97)

The worries of old age and death disappear. A practitioner is neither touched by death nor old age, nor has any fear of water, air or fire. (98)

Twenty types of kapha problems such as asthma and colds are eliminated by practising the described mudras. There is no doubt about this. (99)

O Chanda! I have explained to you everything about mudras and there is nothing else to tell you. There is no other practice in the world like mudra which enables you to achieve success and completeness. (100)

How important is the guru-disciple relationship for attainment through mudra?

Swami Satyananda: Once the disciple has chosen the guru and the guru has recognized the disciple, only the meaning and application of the guru's advice and instructions and the regularity of the practices have utmost importance in the disciple's life. The interaction with the inner and outer personality of the guru is all important in removing egocentricity. The deep-rooted and inherited *samskaras*, impressions, which stand as blockages to the greater flow of awareness and limit the expression of greater energy in the practices are to be systematically exposed and rooted out. *Hatha Yoga Pradipika* (3:130) clearly indicates the necessity of the guru-disciple relationship in attaining the fruits of mudra practice, namely siddhi and immortality:

Tasya vaakyaparo bhootvaa mudraabhyaase samaahitah;
Animaadigunaih saardham labhate kaalavanchanam.

By following explicitly his (guru's) words, and practising mudra, one obtains the qualities of anima, etc., and overcomes death/time.

How is the guru to be approached? The disciple has to use any and every means to bring himself into the light of the guru's awareness. His aspiration and efforts will be noted by the guru, who will give specific cues which the disciple must be attuned to receive. The greatest capacities for the aspirant are to be able to discriminate and so recognize a fine guru and guide, and then to surrender his ego and conditioning at the guru's feet.

Just as a sick person whose bowels are strangulated must soon find an accomplished surgeon, so the aspirant who wants to experience the greater consciousness has to submit his own psychophysiological personality before the guru. Only a fool will consent to an anaesthetic without trusting his surgeon. So the guru-disciple relationship must be established by a process of trust and surrender if the practices are to bear the greatest fruit.

What is the role of the guru in passing on the science of mudra?

Swami Satyananda: Perfection in mudra and awakening of the shakti through mudra depends upon the initiation of the guru and then the practice of the sadhaka. When mudra or any other practice is passed on from guru to disciple it is sure to bear fruit, because the guru's words themselves are the very shakti which manifests in concrete form. In *Hatha Yoga Pradipika* (3:129) it is written:

Upadesham hi mudraanaam yo dattte saampradaayikam;
Sa eva shreeguruh svaamee saakshaadeeshvara eva sah.

One who instructs mudra in the tradition of guru and disciple is the true guru and form of Ishwara.

The external guru is the only means to understanding your internal guru. He is considered as the manifestation of Ishwara. Of course, the inner guru, the atman, has no form or shape. In order to perceive it we have to give some form and identity to it. Atman with form is known as Ishwara.

Ishwara is the Supreme Being, the causal or sattwic body of the cosmic consciousness and Shakti. Ishwara is said to be the God presiding over the universe we know. Ishwara is commonly translated as God. To the yogi, however, God has no religious connotation, it is purely the highest state or experience. The *Yoga Sutras* of Sage Patanjali (1:24) state:

Kleshakarmavipaakaashayairaparaamrishtah purushavishesha eeshvarah.

God is a special soul untouched by afflictions, acts, their traces and their fruits.

Through guru that state of experience can be reached, therefore it is said that he is That. Externally, guru has a physical body, ego and mind, just like anyone else but his individual consciousness is illumined by the light of atma. He has realized his own inner guru, and therefore by contemplation on his form, by following his words and instructions, that experience can also come to the seeker. For the disciple, the guru represents the supreme experience and existence, Ishwara.

It is Lord Shiva who witnesses through the eyes of the guru established in sahaja samadhi. Those who can recognize this have perceived the true nature of their guru and joyfully pay homage and worship at his lotus feet.

2

Hasta Mudras: Hand Mudras

UNDERSTANDING HAND MUDRAS

What is the purpose of hand mudras?

Swami Satyananda: The hand mudras are methods of redirecting the prana inwards; the connections made by the fingers with the hands, and also the contact of the hands with the knees, closes circuits that keep the prana within the body instead of it being lost. Although the pranic body cannot usually be detected due to its subtlety, prana is nevertheless continually flowing within the physical body and some of this prana is discharged from the tips of the fingers.

Why are hand mudras so important?

Swami Satyananda: Experiments with Kirlian photography have shown that the fingers give out flares of energy. If the fingers touch the thumb, a circuit is produced. This allows energy that would normally be dissipated to travel back into the body and up to the brain.

The hand is directly connected to a large proportion of the brain's cortex. Therefore, the energy circuit created between the thumb and index finger has a powerful effect on the brain. Using both hands has the effect of bringing both hemispheres under conscious control.

What is the relationship between the hand mudras and the koshas?

Swami Niranjanananda: In relation to the five koshas, it is the prana which alters the brain functioning and helps tranquillize the mind. Annamaya kosha is the physical body and pranamaya kosha is the energy body. The pranamaya kosha is responsible for discharging energy throughout the whole physical system. Manomaya kosha is the mental body.

Hand mudras are associated with prana: whether one practises hridaya mudra, jnana mudra, chin mudra, prana mudra or any other hand mudras, they divert the flow of prana shakti which is being discharged through the extremities. A cause and effect sequence takes place: an action of the hands (part of annamaya kosha), alters the pranamaya kosha in order to balance, energize, harmonize and tranquillize the manomaya kosha.

How can hand mudras create the quality of stability?

Swami Niranjanananda: Hand mudras aim at providing greater concentration, awareness and internal physical relaxation, with the channelling of prana and the gentle opening up of the different muscles and cavities. Through the use of those mudras, the body is made more stable than when the fingers are left open.

How do hand mudras interact with the brain?

Swami Niranjanananda: In dealing with cellular level consciousness and the manipulation of the brain, awareness is brought into the cortex, into the conscious, from the unconscious. In the motor cortex, the entire body is represented. The area from the shoulder to the ankle is given only about a quarter or a fifth of the space that is designated to the hand. The hands and the head alone take up about fifty percent of the cortex, and the rest is for all the other parts of the body. The sensory information and the motor output from the hands and head enable refined movements of the fingers, mouth and eyes. There

39

are mudras for the eyes, hands, tongue and genitals. These techniques are aimed at controlling and bringing the awareness to large areas of the cortex. Mudras cover most of the cortex and sensory motor area.

Hand mudras, where the thumb and index finger are joined, engage the motor cortex at a highly subtle level. Once pingala nadi is engaged a signal goes back through ida nadi to the brain. By holding these incredibly sensitive areas in a certain fixed position, a loop of energy moves from the motor cortex down to the hand and then back to the brain. With this minimal use of energy, a large part of the sensory and motor cortex can be stimulated at the same time. After about one or two minutes, the brain habituates and blocks out the signal. Therefore, consciousness of the mudra needs to be maintained for a period of time, so that when the sensory information is dissolved into the general system, one can go with it consciously.

How can hand mudras be used in sadhana?

Swami Satyananda: There are many hand mudras, hundreds in fact. The hand mudras taught in yoga are particularly useful, for they can be used in daily meditation with little extra effort and no extra expenditure of time. They are ideally suited for integration with meditative techniques, for they intensify the power and the benefits that are obtained.

CHIN MUDRA: PSYCHIC GESTURE OF CONSCIOUSNESS
JNANA MUDRA: PSYCHIC GESTURE OF KNOWLEDGE

What are the literal meanings of the terms chin and jnana mudra?

Swami Satyananda: The word *jnana* means 'wisdom' or 'knowledge'. Thus, *jnana mudra* is the gesture of intuitive knowledge. *Chin*, on the other hand, is derived from the word *chit* or *chitta*, meaning 'consciousness'. *Chin mudra*, therefore, is the psychic gesture of consciousness.

40

What is the symbolism of chin and jnana mudras?

Swami Satyananda: The symbolic meaning of chin and jnana mudras is the same. Symbolically, the small, ring and middle fingers represent the three *gunas* or qualities of nature: *tamas*, stability; *rajas*, activity and creativity; and *sattwa*, luminosity and harmony. Due to the association between the mind and the gunas, the mind is always subject to the influence of these three states. In order for consciousness to pass from ignorance to knowledge, these three states must be transcended.

The index finger represents *jivatma*, the individual consciousness, and the thumb represents *paramatma*, the spirit of all-pervading consciousness or reality. In jnana and chin mudras the individual (index finger) is bowing down to the supreme consciousness (the thumb), acknowledging its unsurpassed power.

Yet at the same time, the index finger and the thumb touch each other, which shows that although they seem separate, the individual being is one with the Supreme. This symbolizes the ultimate unity of the two experiences and the culmination of yoga. The other three fingers are separated, symbolizing the separation between the individual consciousness and the three gunas of *prakriti*, nature.

When the individual consciousness separates itself from the three gunas of nature, of empirical existence, and unites itself with the central consciousness, that is the attitude of a yogi during the practice of chin mudra or jnana mudra.

When should chin and jnana mudras be used?

Swami Satyananda: One of these two mudras should be adopted whenever practising meditation, unless otherwise

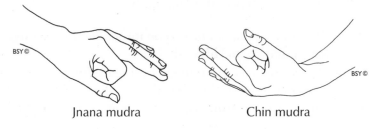

Jnana mudra   Chin mudra

41

specified. The effect of chin or jnana mudra is very subtle and it requires great sensitivity on the part of the practitioner to perceive the change established in consciousness. With practice, however, the mind becomes conditioned to the mudra and when it is adopted, the signal to enter a meditative state is transmitted.

Why are chin and jnana mudras the most important meditation mudras?

Swami Satyananda: Jnana mudra and chin mudra are simple but important psycho-neural finger locks which make meditation asanas more powerful. The palms and fingers of the hands have many nerve endings which constantly emit energy. When the index finger touches the thumb, a circuit is produced which allows the energy that would normally dissipate into the environment to travel back through the body and up to the brain.

When the fingers and hands are placed on the knees, the knees are sensitized, creating another pranic circuit that maintains and redirects prana within the body. In addition, placing the hands on the knees stimulates a nadi which runs from the knees, up the inside of the thighs and into the perineum. This nadi is known as the *gupta nadi*, or the hidden nadi. Sensitizing this channel helps to stimulate the energies at mooladhara chakra.

What is the difference between chin and jnana mudras?

Swami Satyananda: When the palms face upward in chin mudra, the chest area is opened up. The practitioner may experience this as a sense of lightness and receptivity, which is absent in the practice of jnana mudra.

How can chin and jnana mudras be understood in the light of the acupuncture meridians?

Swami Niranjanananda: An understanding of the relationship between prana and the ki energy of oriental acupuncture brings another interesting aspect to some of these mudras.

42

There are meridians of ki energy (related to prana in the nadis), which have their terminal points (*sei* or well points) in the fingertips.

The sei point of the lung meridian is located on the thumbs; the large intestine meridian at the tip of the index finger; the heart constrictor vessel at the tip of the middle finger; the triple heater meridian on the ring finger and small intestines and heart sei points on the little finger.

Energy is normally being discharged from the fingertips, and it has been suggested that the energy flowing along the lung meridians to the thumb while performing jnana or chin mudra is transferred to the large intestine meridian. The body's vital energy is therefore conserved. Chin mudra is said to have an influence on abdominal breathing, and here we can see a pranic connection between the lungs and abdomen through their respective meridians.

CHINMAYA MUDRA:
GESTURE OF MANIFESTED CONSCIOUSNESS

What is the meaning and symbolism of chinmaya mudra?
Swami Satyananda: The Sanskrit word *chinmaya* means 'manifested consciousness'; in other words, the phenomenal world around us that has arisen from the underlying consciousness.

The four folded fingers in chinmaya mudra represent the finite aspects of the world around us. The closed fist shows that the phenomenal world seems to be severely limited, blind and unconscious. The thumb pointing forwards indicates the consciousness and the transcendental aspect of existence that pervade everything.

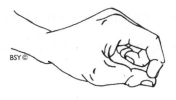

It is often regarded as different to or separate from the material world, yet in fact the manifested universe is really identical to and permeated with consciousness. The material world is linked intimately with consciousness. This is indicated by the contact between the index finger and the thumb.

Furthermore, the folded fingers represent the physical, energetic and mental aspects of life. This is not the complete picture of a human, for there is also consciousness. These aspects are intimately linked, yet it is the consciousness that is transcendental and capable of contacting infinity and the whole. This is indicated by the thumb, which points away from the finitude symbolized by the four fingers.

This mudra symbolizes yoga – the realization that the individual (four fingers) is identical to and connected directly with consciousness. The four fingers can also represent the gradual unfolding of higher states of awareness. That is, the little, ring and middle fingers represent different facets of the material world, from stones and trees to animals and birds, all becoming increasingly aware.

Eventually there is humanity, which appears to be no more than mind and body, yet as far as we know, humans alone can develop sufficient awareness to recognize their integral identity with consciousness. This is represented by the joining of the thumb and index finger.

How does chinmaya mudra affect the breath?
Swami Niranjanananda: Chinmaya mudra influences the prana and stimulates movement in the thoracic area creating subtle expansion of the breath in the middle lobes of the lungs. The acupuncture meridian points concerned here affect respiration.

ADI MUDRA: PRIMAL OR FIRST ATTITUDE

What is the meaning and effect of adi mudra?
Swami Niranjanananda: The Sanskrit word *adi* means primal, first or original. When held, this mudra influences the

breathing in the upper lobes of the lungs. While holding adi mudra one should observe the effect on the upper chest region and clavicles.

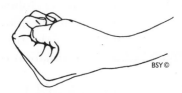

BRAHMA MUDRA:
ATTITUDE OF ALL-PERVADING CONSCIOUSNESS

What is the effect of brahma mudra?

Swami Niranjanananda: Brahma mudra helps to stimulate full yogic breathing, i.e. using the abdomen, chest and clavicles for each respiration. The knuckles, being pressed together, connect all the hand meridians. The tips of the fingers form another circuit as they touch the palm.

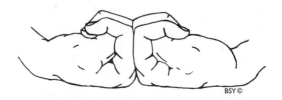

HASTA MUDRA PRANAYAMA:
HAND GESTURE BREATH

What is hasta mudra pranayama?

Swami Niranjanananda: From the pranic point of view *mudras* represent a linkup of specific nadis in the body, in this case, in the fingers, by which prana is redirected to different areas. *Hasta mudra pranayama*, the hand gesture breath, uses four specific hand positions known as *hasta* or hand mudras. These mudras are subtle techniques and their effects may not be immediately noticeable without awareness and sensitivity.

45

Hasta mudra pranayama uses hand mudras to ventilate the lower, middle and upper lobes of the lungs and influence other vital organs indirectly. The mudras used are: chin mudra for ventilation of the lower lobes of the lungs; chinmaya mudra for ventilation of the middle lobes of the lungs; adi mudra for ventilation of the upper lobes of the lungs; and brahma mudra, for ventilation of the total lung capacity.

The pancha pranas are activated by these practices. They are also therapeutic, as they relieve disorders related to specific areas of the body. All four should be practised in sequence, although for therapeutic purposes only the relevant practice need be applied.

HRIDAYA MUDRA: HEART GESTURE

How does hridaya mudra benefit the heart?

Swami Satyananda: This mudra diverts the flow of prana from the hands to the heart area, improving the vitality of the heart. The middle and ring fingers relate directly to nadis connected with the heart, while the thumb closes the pranic circuit and acts as an energizer, diverting the flow of prana from the hands to these nadis. Hridaya mudra is therefore beneficial for the heart. It is very simple and may be used safely and easily, even in acute situations. The heart is the centre of emotion. Hridaya mudra helps to release pent-up emotion and unburden the heart. It may be practised during emotional conflict and crisis.

46

BHAIRAVA AND BHAIRAVI MUDRA:
FIERCE OR TERRIFYING ATTITUDE

What is the meaning of bhairava and bhairavi mudras?

Swami Satyananda: *Bhairava* is one of the forms of Shiva, said to be fearsome and formidable. *Bhairavi* is his consort or Shakti, the power that manifests this particular aspect of existence. There is a distinct sect of tantra who worship this aspect of Shiva and Shakti. They are called bhairavis.

What is the difference between bhairava and bhairavi mudras?

Swami Satyananda: In bhairava mudra the right hand is placed on top of the left, so that the palms of both hands are facing upward. Both hands rest in the lap. When the left hand is placed on top of the right, the practice is called bhairavi mudra. Bhairavi is the female counterpart of Bhairava.

What do bhairava and bhairavi mudras represent?

Swami Satyananda: The two hands represent ida and pingala nadis, and the union of the individual with the Supreme consciousness.

When should bhairava or bhairavi mudra be used?

Swami Satyananda: During meditation and pranayama this is a particularly comfortable mudra. What is easier than placing the hands one on top of the other in the lap while sitting in a meditation asana? It is a mudra that people do almost automatically. Bhairava mudra is used in the practice of *prana mudra*, the invocation of energy.

SHANKHA MUDRA: GESTURE OF THE CONCH

What is the meaning of shankha mudra?

Swami Satyananda: The word *shankha* means 'shell' or 'conch', the type that one could so easily find on a quiet beach. Therefore, the English translation of this mudra is 'conch shell mudra'.

What does the conch symbolize?

Swami Satyananda: The conch is an integral part of religion: many of the deities, such as Vishnu, Lakshmi and Shiva are shown blowing or holding this symbolic object. In the opening chapter of the *Bhagavad Gita* (l:14) Sri Krishna and Arjuna blow their conches:

> *Tatah shvetairhayairyukte mahati syandane sthitau;*
> *Maadhavah paandavashchaiva divyau shankhau pradadhmatuh.*

Then also, Madhava (Sri Krishna) and the son of Pandu (Arjuna), who were seated in their magnificent chariot, yoked with fine white horses, blew their divine conches.

In ancient European traditions the conch is often used. For example, the tritons, a type of mermen in Greek mythology, used the conch as a trumpet.

The most obvious thing that this conch, or rather its sound, represents, is the cosmic, inner sound of each and every individual. This is the sound that links the individual with highest consciousness, like a puppet on a string. This is called *nada*, or *shabda*, in Sanskrit. It is known as 'logos' in some of the Western traditions. When the conch is blown it makes a penetrating sound like a long *Aum*. This is the reason it is sounded during religious ceremonies.

How can shankha mudra be used in meditation?

Swami Satyananda: While sitting for meditation the most comfortable method of holding shankha mudra is to simply rest the hands in the lap.

SHOONYA MUDRA: GESTURE OF EMPTINESS

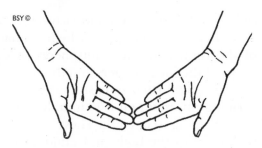

What is the meaning and significance of shoonya mudra?

Swami Satyananda: The word *shoonya* means 'voidness' or 'emptiness'. It is used by Buddhists to describe the indescribable state of *nirvana*, supreme enlightenment. In this context it does not mean, as so many people think, a state of nothingness; it means exactly the opposite: a state of totality, of oneness, devoid of ego, devoid of even the slightest turmoil, craving or dissatisfaction.

YONI MUDRA: ATTITUDE OF THE SOURCE

What is the meaning of yoni mudra?

Swami Satyananda: The word *yoni* means 'womb' or 'source'. Yoni mudra invokes the primal energy inherent in the womb or source of creation.

What are the effects of yoni mudra?

Swami Satyananda: The interlocking of the fingers in this practice creates a complete cross-connection of energies

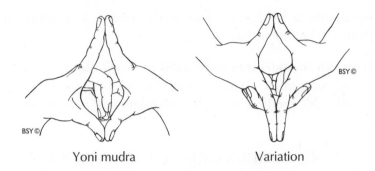

Yoni mudra   Variation

from the right hand into the left and vice versa. As well as balancing the energies in the body, it helps to balance the activities of the right and left hemispheres of the brain. Placing the tips of the index fingers and thumbs together in the form of a triangle further intensifies the flow of prana. While performing this mudra it is natural for the elbows to point sideways, helping to open the chest.

This mudra makes the body and mind more stable in meditation and develops greater concentration, awareness and internal physical relaxation. It redirects prana back into the body which would otherwise be dispersed through the hands and fingers.

MAHAYONI MUDRA:
GESTURE OF THE SUPREME SOURCE

What is the meaning of mahayoni mudra?
Swami Satyananda: This is a mudra that is widely practised in tantric circles. The word *maha* means 'great' or perhaps even better in this context, 'supreme'. The word *yoni* means 'womb', 'source' or 'origin'. Therefore, this *mahayoni mudra* can be called the 'gesture of the supreme source'.

What does mahayoni mudra symbolize?
Swami Satyananda: This is an important mudra as it symbolizes the unity between the individual and cosmic consciousness. It symbolizes the return of the individual to

his source, his origin. It is not only a symbol, for this mudra is used to help invoke this realization and experience. It is such a simple looking practice, but it possesses vast power of invocation when done under the correct circumstances.

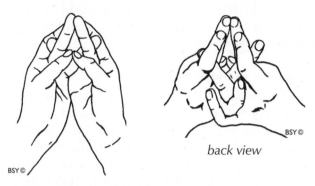

back view

How should mahayoni mudra be performed?

Swami Satyananda: To perform this mudra the fingers need to be wrapped and bent in a weird combination of directions. Having formed the mudra, the hands can either be held in front of the chest or rested on the lap. It is a personal choice.

PRANA VAYU MUDRAS: VITAL AIR GESTURES

How do the hands symbolize and activate the five elements?

Swami Niranjanananda: It is interesting to note how many ways the five common elements of earth, water, fire, air, and ether or space are not only macrocosmically but also microcosmically represented. These *pancha bhutas*, five elements, govern or dominate specific parts of the body and are also symbolized in each finger. This has significance when performing hand mudras, as different elements are symbolically joining together. The thumb represents fire; the index finger, air; the middle finger, ether; the ring finger, earth; and the little finger, water, although there is some variation in the classical texts.

51

The prana vayu mudras represent a subtle relationship between one's existence in gross matter and one's relationship to the more universal elements and forces, which interpenetrate all levels of creation. It reminds us to stop separating ourselves from the outside world, to stay still for a moment and feel the oneness vibrating and permeating all and everything.

What are the prana vayu mudras?

Swami Niranjanananda: The five different kinds of prana vayu are represented and invoked by hand mudras. When performing these mudras, it does not mean that particular vayu is automatically felt surging through its normally specified location in the body, but on a subtle or pranic level that particular energy will be stimulated. While dealing with prana and its subtleties, one should have knowledge of these mudras, until finally a deeper awareness dawns of the vital energies, and of those same energies pervading the cosmos. The prana vayu mudras are:

Prana mudra: The tip of the thumb (fire), middle finger (space) and ring finger (earth) are placed together. The mantra used with this mudra is *Om Pranaya Swaha*. Prana vayu centres in the chest area.

Apana mudra: The tip of the thumb, index (air) and middle fingers are placed together. The mantra is *Om Apanaya Swaha*. Apana vayu centres in the pelvic area.

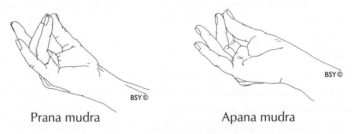

Prana mudra   Apana mudra

Samana mudra: The tip of the thumb, little finger (water) and ring finger are placed together. The mantra used is *Om Samanaya Swaha*. Samana vayu centres in the abdomen.

Udana mudra: The tip of the thumb, index and little fingers are placed together. The mantra is *Om Udanaya Swaha*. Udana vayu centres in the arms, legs, neck and head.

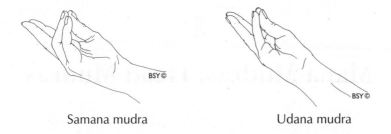

Samana mudra   Udana mudra

Vyana mudra: The tip of the thumb, index, middle, ring and little fingers are placed together. Its mantra is *Om Vyanaya Swaha*. Vyana vayu permeates the whole body.

Vyana mudra

When are the prana vayu mudras used?
Swami Niranjanananda: These mudras may be used with any pranayama or pre-pranayama practice, when alternate nostril breathing with nasikagra mudra is not used.

3

Mana Mudras: Head Mudras

UNDERSTANDING HEAD MUDRAS

What are head mudras?

Swami Niranjanananda: The head mudras are related to the eyes, ears, nose, tongue and lips. They are integral to kundalini yoga and many of them are used as advanced meditation techniques due to the powerful states of pratyahara and dharana they induce.

Why are head mudras used in hatha yoga?

Swami Niranjanananda: The head mudras work through the brain to influence the mind, to relax and internalize the mind and to sharpen the awareness.

In the brain, most of the cortex is given to the head, hands, tongue, eyes and voice. When any part of the body is used, the corresponding part of the brain is stimulated. Therefore, when mudras that use these areas are practised, the effect on the brain is significant. For example, when practising nasikagra drishti, gazing at the nosetip, nerves are activated which are connected to the left and right hemispheres of the brain. This harmonizes the brain hemispheres, inducing a more tranquil, peaceful, calm and quiet attitude.

NASAGRA MUDRA: NOSETIP POSITION

What is nasagra mudra?

Swami Niranjanananda: *Nasagra mudra* is one of the most common hand positions used in pranayama practice. It is sometimes known as *nasikagra mudra*. It is used to facilitate the smooth opening and closing of the nostrils required for alternate nostril breathing and therefore is of particular importance in nadi shodhana.

In one variation of nasagra mudra the index and middle fingers are bent or folded into the palm of the hand. However, this eliminates the added benefit of the index and middle fingers pressing the eyebrow centre, gently stimulating bhrumadhya, the *kshetram* or trigger point of ajna chakra.

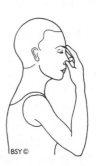

The right hand is used as it is more associated with giving on a pranic level, while the left is more associated with receiving. If, however, the right hand cannot be used for some reason, the left can be substituted.

NASIKAGRA MUDRA: NOSETIP GAZING

What is nasikagra drishti?

Swami Sivananda: Gazing steadily at the tip of the nose is known as *nasikagra drishti*.

What is the meaning and symbolism of nasikagra mudra?

Swami Satyananda: Another name for this mudra is nasikagra drishti. The word *nasika* means 'nose', *agra* means 'tip' and *drishti* means 'gazing'. This is an exact description of the technique, namely 'nosetip gazing'. It is also known as *agochari mudra*, which comes from the Sanskrit word *agocharam*, meaning 'beyond sensory perception', 'unknown', or 'invisible'. It is so named as this mudra

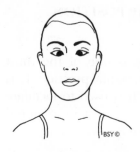

enables the practitioner to transcend normal awareness.

Symbolically, in nasikagra drishti the bridge of the nose is related to the spinal cord. At the top is the eyebrow centre, ajna chakra, while at the bottom is the nosetip, associated with mooladhara chakra. Just as shambhavi mudra aims to activate ajna chakra by gazing at the eyebrow centre, nasikagra drishti aims to activate mooladhara chakra by gazing at the nosetip.

What are the origins of nasikagra mudra?

Swami Satyananda: This mudra is one of the oldest recorded yogic practices. It is depicted in the ancient ruins of Mohanjodaro, which was a flourishing society many thousands of years ago, even before the Vedas were recorded.

The great archaeologist Sir John Marshall, who did much exploration of this ancient site, says: "It (the statue) represents someone seemingly in the pose of a yogi . . . the eyelids are more than half closed and the eyes are looking downwards to the tip of the nose." The ancient sculptor and the people of that time must have had great respect for this practice to depict it in stone for posterity.

Which of the classical yogic texts mention nasikagra mudra?

Swami Satyananda: Nasikagra mudra is mentioned in a number of ancient yogic texts, including the *Bhagavad Gita* and *Hatha Yoga Pradipika*. It seems so simple and inconsequential that one might easily regard it as insignificant. To the contrary, if practised for a long time with intensity it can induce high states of introspection and in turn, meditation. The *Bhagavad Gita* (6:13) refers to nosetip gazing:

Samam kaayashirogreevam dhaarayannachalam sthirah;
Samprekshya naasikaagram svam dishashchaanavalokayan.

Let him hold his body, head and neck erect and still,
gazing at the tip of his nose, without looking around.

This verse is from the chapter describing the method that
one should adopt in order to purify and steady the mind
to make it one-pointed. The *Bhagavad Gita* says that by
sufficient practice and by keeping the mind in a continual
state of balance and concentration one attains meditation
and higher illuminative knowledge.

Is nasikagra mudra a form of trataka?

Swami Satyananda: Nasikagra mudra is an excellent form of
trataka. It can be described as stage one of trataka.

How difficult is the practice of nasikagra mudra?

Swami Satyananda: At first nasikagra mudra will seem a
little strange and difficult, for it requires a fixed gaze at the
nosetip. The eyes have to assume a position to which they
are normally unaccustomed. With practice, however, the eye
muscles adapt themselves to their new role, strengthening
the eyes and in turn improving the eyesight. If practised for
some time with awareness, nosetip gazing can induce high
states of concentration and tranquillity of mind.

What is the purpose of nasikagra mudra?

Swami Satyananda: Nasikagra mudra is an excellent technique for calming anger and disturbed states of mind. It is
especially suitable in this respect, for it can be done at any
time during the day, which is when one is most likely to meet
stressful and disruptive situations. Most other techniques
require preparation and a special place of practice.

Although the eyes are open, the aim of nasikagra mudra is
to create introspection. The open eyes should not be aware of
the outside world. Focusing them on the nosetip concentrates
the mind, developing one's powers of concentration and

inducing meditative states. It takes the practitioner into the psychic and spiritual planes of consciousness.

When should nasikagra mudra be practised?

Swami Satyananda: The technique of nasikagra mudra can be practised at any time as it needs no preparation. This mudra can even be practised while sitting on a bus or a train.

The ideal times for its practice are early in the morning and late at night. Just before sleep is an especially good time, as the calmness of mind it induces prepares one for deep, restful sleep.

How is nasikagra drishti practised with breath retention?

Swami Niranjanananda: Nasikagra drishti is always practised with inner retention, not external retention. During inhalation and exhalation the eyes remain closed.

What is the connection between nosetip gazing and mooladhara chakra?

Swami Niranjanananda: While gazing at the nosetip one is actually activating mooladhara. The theory regarding this is that the bridge of the nose represents the spinal cord: just as different centres in the body are represented in the brain, the different psychic centres are also represented along the bridge of the nose. At the top of the bridge is ajna and at the tip is mooladhara.

What subtle experiences can arise with the practise of nasikagra mudra?

Swami Sivananda: When one concentrates on the tip of the nose *divya gandha*, divine aroma, is experienced.

Why is nasikagra mudra recommended for practice during meditation?

Swami Sivananda: Though the gaze is directed towards the tip of the nose when the eyes are half-closed and the eyeballs are steady, the mind should be fixed only on the Self. In the *Bhagavad Gita* (6:25) Sri Krishna says, "Having made the mind abide in the Self, let him not think of anything else." Gazing at the tip of the nose will soon bring about that concentration of mind.

What is the power of nasikagra mudra?

Swami Satyananda: Nasikagra mudra is a practice of hatha yoga which directly awakens the kundalini shakti in mooladhara. Sitting either in siddhasana or siddha yoni asana, one gazes steadily at the tip of the nose. The eyes become slightly convergent and the two sides of the nose are seen. Concentration should be centred right in the middle. At first the vision will be unsteady and the eyes will tire quickly. With a little practice each day the eyes become accustomed. While gazing at the nosetip, concentration is on the movement of breath in the nostrils so that it can be determined which nostril the breath is flowing through.

When both nostrils are open, i.e. sushumna is flowing, the practice is taking effect. After five to ten minutes one closes the eyes and looks into the dark space in front of the closed eyes, the *chidakasha*. When a light is seen in the darkness, one concentrates on it: that is the light which can completely absorb the consciousness. It is stated in *Hatha Yoga Pradipika* (4:41):

Chittam charati khe yasmaajjihvaa charati khe gataa;
Tenaishaa khecharee naama mudraa siddhairniroopitaa.

Mind steady, eyes semi-open, gaze fixed on the nosetip, the moon (ida) and sun (pingala) suspended, without any movement (physical or mental), that one attains the form of light (jyoti) which is endless and is complete, radiant, the Supreme. What more can be said?

By external gazing at the nosetip, vision of the inner light is aroused as the flow of shakti in the mind and body becomes concentrated. When the light switch is turned on, the light emanates from the bulb. The same applies in the physical body. When the kundalini shakti is released from mooladhara it is drawn up to ajna chakra, and there the inner light appears. That light, when seen, should be concentrated upon, as it is the essence of being, the inner light or *jyoti*. The purpose of practising nasikagra mudra is to arouse that experience.

KAKI MUDRA: GESTURE OF THE CROW'S BEAK

What is kaki mudra?

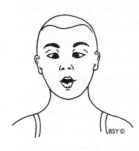

Swami Satyananda: The word *kaki* means 'crow'. Kaki mudra is so called because during inhalation the mouth is shaped like a crow's beak. It is claimed that regular practice of this mudra leads to the disease-free, long life that is associated with the crow.

Kaki mudra is also considered to be a pranayama practice because of its close similarity to sheetali and sheetkari pranayamas. Kaki mudra is described in *Shiva Samhita* (3:70):

*Kaakachanchvaa pibedvaayum sheetalam yo vichakshanah;
Praanaapaanavidhaanajnah sa bhavenmuktibhaajanah.*

When the skillfull yogi, knowing the laws of the action of prana and apana, can drink the cold air through the contraction of the mouth in the form of a crow's bill, then he becomes entitled to liberation.

How can one prepare for the practice of kaki mudra?

Swami Satyananda: Practitioners should be thoroughly familiar with nasikagra drishti prior to commencing this technique. The eyes must be kept open throughout the practice and nasikagra drishti should be continuous. If the eyes become tired, relax them for as long as necessary before recommencing the practice.

When should kaki mudra be practised?

Swami Satyananda: Kaki mudra is a cooling practice. It balances the temperature of the body when performed after heating pranayamas. It may be performed at any time of the day when the air is relatively pure, although it is best practised early in the morning or late at night. It should not be performed in cold weather. In *Shiva Samhita* (3:74–75) it says:

Kaakachanchvaa pibedvaayum sandhyayorubhayorapi;
Kundalinyaa mukhe dhyaatvaa kshayarogasya shaantaye.

Aharnisham pibedyogee kaakanchachvaa vichakshanah;
Pibetpraanaanilam tasya rogaanaam sankshayo bhavet;
Doorashrutirdooradrishtistathaa syaaddarshanam khalu.

When he drinks the air through the crow bill, both in the morning and in the evening twilight, contemplating that it goes to the mouth of the kundalini, consumption of the lungs is cured. (74)

When the wise yogi drinks the fluid day and night through the crow beak, his diseases are destroyed: he acquires certainly the powers of clairaudience and clairvoyance. (75)

What are the effects of kaki mudra?

Swami Niranjanananda: Kaki mudra cools the body and mind, soothing mental tensions and alleviating disorders such as high blood pressure.

The act of pursing the lips, together with the contact of the indrawn air on the membranes of the mouth, stimulates digestive secretions, aiding the digestive process and enhancing the digestive power. As a result it provides relief from many diseases. This practice also purifies the blood.

The benefits of kaki mudra are given in *Gheranda Samhita* (3:86–87):

Kaakachanchuvadaasyena pibedvaayum shanaih shanaih;
Kaakee mudraa bhavedeshaa sarvaroga vinaashinee.

61

Kaakee mudraa paraa mudraa sarvatantreshugopitaa;
Asyaah prasaadamaatrena kaakavanneerujo bhavet.

Inhale slowly through the mouth, shaping it like the beak of a crow. This is kaki mudra, the destroyer of all ailments. This great mudra should be kept secret by all means. (86)

By practising this mudra, relief from all disorders is achieved. Just like a crow, one becomes free from disease. (87)

MATANGINI MUDRA: ELEPHANT GESTURE

What is matangini mudra?

Swami Niranjanananda: *Matanga* means 'elephant'. Just as an elephant plays with water while sitting in it, the same actions are performed in this mudra. It is described in *Gheranda Samhita* (3:88–89):

Kanthamagnejale sthitvaa naasaabhyaam jalamaaharet;
Mukhaannirgamayetpashchaat punarvaktrena cghaaharet.

Naasaabhyaam rechayet pashchaat kuryaadevam punah punah;
Maatanginee paraa mudraa jaraamrityu vinaashinee.

Standing in water up to the throat, inhale deeply, drawing water up through the nostrils and expelling water out of the mouth. It should be practised repeatedly. This great mudra is known as matangini mudra. (88–89)

What are the benefits of matangini mudra?

Swami Niranjanananda: The practitioner becomes powerful and strong just like an elephant. It prevents the body from deteriorating and keeps death away. This is described in *Gheranda Samhita* (3:90):

Virale nirjane deshe sthitvaa chaikaagramaanasah;
Kuryanmaatanginee mudraam maatanga iva jaayate.

When it is perfected, there is no fear of old age and death, and a yogi becomes powerful like an elephant and always remains happy.

Matangini mudra is very important among the mudras, as a person practising it with effort and due care will attain *ananda siddhi*, mastery over bliss. This mudra can be perfected with only a little practice.

Where should matangini mudra be practised?

Swami Niranjanananda: Matangini mudra must be performed in a pure environment with uninterrupted concentration. This is specified in *Gheranda Samhita* (3:91):

> *Yatra yatra sthito yogee sukhamatyantamashnute;*
> *Tasmaat sarva prayatnena saadhayet mudrikaamparaam.*

It should be practised with concentration in a quiet, secluded place away from other people. This mudra should be perfected with sincere effort.

BHUJANGINI MUDRA: SERPENT GESTURE

What is bhujangini mudra?

Swami Niranjanananda: Bhujangini mudra is similar to kaki mudra. It is also known as *plavini pranayama*. In bhujangini mudra, air is sucked through the throat, keeping the mouth wide open. In this way, the air rotates in between the root of the palate and tongue, due to which the body experiences miraculous energy. One tries to fill the stomach as though drinking water, so that the stomach is expanded, and the lungs are not filled. The breath is held for as long as is comfortable, then the air is expelled by belching. It is described in *Gheranda Samhita* (3:92):

> *Vaktram kinchitsuprasaarya chaanilam galayaa pivet;*
> *Saa bhaved bhujangee mudraa jaraamrityuvinaashinee.*

Opening the mouth wide enough, suck air through the throat. This is known as bhujangini mudra.

What are the benefits of practising bhujangini mudra?

Swami Niranjanananda: This practice tones the whole stomach, removes stagnant wind and helps to alleviate abdominal disorders. It is particularly powerful when practised after shankhaprakshalana. The benefits are described in *Gheranda Samhita* (3:93):

> *Yaavachcha udare rogamajeernaadi visheshatah;*
> *Tatsarvannaashayedaashu yatra mudraa bhujanginee.*

> Once it is mastered, all abdominal disorders are removed; old age and death are eliminated.

Retaining air in the stomach enables the practitioner to float in water for as long as desired.

SHANMUKHI MUDRA:
THE ATTITUDE OF CLOSING THE SIX GATES

What is the meaning of shanmukhi mudra?

Swami Satyananda: The word shanmukhi is comprised of two roots: *shat* means 'six' and *mukhi* means 'gates' or 'faces'. Shanmukhi mudra involves redirecting the awareness inside by closing the six doors of outer perception: the two eyes,

the two ears, the nose and the mouth. This practice is also known as *baddha yoni asana*, the locked source pose; *devi mudra*, attitude of the great goddess; *parangmukhi mudra*, the gesture of inner focusing; *sambhava mudra*, the gesture of equipoise and *yoni mudra*, attitude of the source. Shanmukhi is described in *Shiva Samhita* (5:22):

Angushtaabhyaamubhe shrotre tarjaneebhyaam dvilochane;
Naasaarandhre cha madhyaabhyaamanaamaabhyaam mukham
dridham.

Let him close the ears with his thumbs, the eyes with
index fingers, the nostril with the middle fingers, and
with the remaining four fingers let him press together
the upper and lower lips. The yogi, by having thus firmly
confined the air, sees his soul in the shape of light.

What are the effects of shanmukhi mudra?

Swami Satyananda: Physically, the energy and heat from
the hands and fingers stimulate and relax the nerves and
muscles of the face. It is also good for those suffering from
vertigo. Mentally, it introverts the awareness. Spiritually, it
induces the state of pratyahara or sense withdrawal. This
state is described in *Shiva Samhita* (5:23–25):

Tattejo drishyate yena kshanamaatram niraakulam;
Sarvapaapavinirmuktah sa yaati paramaam gatim.

Nirantarakritaabhyaasaadhyogee vigatakalmashah;
Sarvadehaadi vismritya tadabhinnah svayam gatah.

Yah karoti sadaabhyaasam guptaachaarena maanavah;
Sa vai brahmavileenah syaatpaapakarmarato yadi.

When one sees, without obstruction, this light for even
a moment, becoming free from sin, one reaches the
highest end. (23)

The yogi, free from sin, and practising this (shanmukhi)
continually, forgets his physical, subtle and causal bodies,
and becomes one with that soul. (24)

He who practises this in secrecy, is absorbed in the
Brahman, though he had been engaged in sinful
works. (25)

65

How is shanmukhi mudra used in other branches of yoga?

Swami Satyananda: Shanmukhi mudra is a practice used in nada yoga to hear any internal manifestation of sound in the region of bindu chakra. There may be many sounds or none at all; one just listens without expecting to hear subtle sounds immediately. Practice is necessary. At first there may be no sound or a confused jumble of sounds. Upon hearing one distinct sound, focus the awareness totally upon it. This may take a few weeks of practice. As sensitivity develops, subtler sounds will be heard. The nada heard in shanmukhi mudra is described in *Shiva Samhita* (5:26–28):

> *Gopaneeyah prayatnena sadyah pratyayakaarakah;*
> *Nirvaanadaayako loke yogoyam mama vallabhah;*
> *Naadah sanjaayate tasya kramenaabhyaasatashcha vai.*

> *Mattabhringavenuveenaasadrishah prathamo dhvanih;*
> *Evamabhyaasatah pashchaat samsaaradhvaantanaashanam;*
> *Ghantaanaadasamah pashchaat dhvanirmegharavopamah;*
> *Dhvanau tasminmano dattvaa yadaa tishthati nirbhayah;*
> *Tadaa sanjaayate tasya layasya mama vallabhe.*

> *Tatra naade yadaa chittam ramate yogino bhrisham.*
> *Vismritya sakalam baahyam naadena saha shaamyati.*

This should be kept secret; it at once produces conviction; it gives nirvana to mankind. This is my most beloved yoga. From practising this (shanmukhi) gradually, the yogi begins to hear the mystic sounds. (26)

The first sound is like the hum of the honey-intoxicated bee, next that of a flute, then of a harp; after this, by the gradual practice of yoga, the destroyer of the darkness of the world, he hears the sounds of ringing bells; then sounds like the roar of thunder. When one fixes his full attention on this sound, being free from fear, one gets absorption, O my beloved! (27)

When the mind of the yogi is exceedingly engaged in this sound, he forgets all external things, and is absorbed in this sound. (28)

Shanmukhi mudra is also used to enhance visualization in other branches of yoga such as swara yoga, tattwa shuddhi and kriya yoga.

YONI MUDRA: ATTITUDE OF THE SOURCE

What is yoni mudra?

Swami Sivananda: Sit in padmasana or siddhasana. Inhale and retain the breath. Close the ears with two thumbs, eyes with the index fingers, nostrils with the middle fingers, the upper lips with the ring fingers and the lower lips with the little fingers. After some time, release the breath. Dive deep and meditate on the six chakras and kundalini.

This is not as easy as other mudras. Much effort is needed for success. One must be perfectly established in bhramacharya for success in this mudra. It is difficult to obtain even by the devas. Therefore realize the importance of this mudra and practise it cautiously.

How is the practice of yoni mudra different to shanmukhi mudra?

Swami Niranjanananda: For yoni mudra, once the physical position of shanmukhi mudra is assumed, but before closing the mouth with the fingers, the prana vayu is sucked inside by means of kaki mudra. *Kaki* means crow. The lips are pursed into a form like the beak of a crow, then one inhales through this beak.

Next, the breath is united with apana vayu, which is in the lower abdominal region, below the navel. To raise apana vayu means filling the abdomen and practising moola bandha, so that the normal flow of apana vayu, which is downward, is directed upward. Then the lips are closed, and the air is slowly exhaled through the nose.

67

Once this basic practice is comfortable, the awareness is rotated through the six chakras while antar kumbhaka is practised: the consciousness travels from mooladhara to swadhisthana, then manipura, anahata, vishuddhi and finally ajna. The breath is held inside for six seconds with moola bandha applied and the consciousness touching each psychic centre as the awareness passes through. When the consciousness reaches ajna chakra, one exhales.

The mantra *so* is mentally repeated while moving the awareness through the chakras, and *ham* is mentally repeated during exhalation.

This process is described in *Gheranda Samhita* (3:49–53):

Siddhaasanam samaasaadya karnachakshurnasaamukham;
Angushthatarjanee madhyaanaamaadyaih pidadheeta vai.

Praanamaakrishya kaakeebhirapaane yojayettatah;
Shat chakraani kramaaddhyaatvaa hum hamsamanunaa sudheeh.

Chaitanyamaanayeddeveem nidritaa yaa bhujanginee;
Jeevena sahitaam shaktim samutthaapya paraambuje.

Shaktimayo svayam bhootvaa param shivena sangamam;
Naanaasukham vihaaram cha chintayetparamam sukham.

Shivashaktisamaayogaadekaantam bhuvibhaavayet;
Aanandamaanaso bhootvaa aham brahmeti sambhavet.

Sit in siddhasana and close the ears with both thumbs, both eyes with the index fingers, both nostrils with the middle fingers and the mouth with the ring fingers and little fingers. (49)

With the help of kaki mudra, pull the prana and join it with apana, and keeping the awareness at the six chakras in the body, awaken kundalini shakti with the mantras *Hoom* and *Hamsa* and bring the jivatma (individual soul) along with it to sahasrara. (50–51)

There should be the silent feeling at that time that 'I am moving comfortably along with Shiva and enriched by Shakti. (52)

With the union of Shiva and Shakti I have become blissful Brahman too.' (53)

Why is yoni mudra so named?

Swami Niranjanananda: The word *yoni* means 'womb' or 'source'. It is not known why it came to be known as yoni mudra because this point has not been clarified in any yogic text. One can say that it came to be known as yoni mudra because the kind of awareness or consciousness which a human being has in the womb, that basic form of consciousness that exists, is the same experience of consciousness that occurs in this practice.

There is also a hand mudra known as yoni mudra.

What are the benefits of yoni mudra?

Swami Niranjanananda: Physically, the energy and heat from the hands and fingers stimulate and relax the nerves and muscles of the face. This practice helps in the treatment of eye, nose and throat infections, and alleviates vertigo. Mentally, it balances internal and external awareness.

In *Gheranda Samhita* (3:54–56) the purifying power of yoni mudra is described:

Brahmahaabhroonahaa chaiva suraapo guru talpagah;
Etaih paapairna lipyate yoni mudraa nibandhanaat.

Yonimudraa paraagopyaa devaanaamapi durlabhaa;
Sakrittu labdhasamsiddhih samaadhisthah sa eva hi.

Yaani paapaani ghoraani upapaapaani yaani cha;
Taani sarvaani nashyanti yonimudraa nibandhanaat;
Tasmaadabhyaasanam kuryaadyaadi muktim samichchhati.

This is yoni mudra. By means of this mudra one becomes liberated from sins like killing a brahmin or a foetus, drinking alcohol or polluting the bed of the teacher. (54)

Yoni mudra is a top secret kriya. It is not easily accessible even to the gods. Those who achieve mastery over it by regular practice attain samadhi. (55)

All the major sins, minor sins, etc., of the universe are erased by yoni mudra. Thus it should be practised by people seeking salvation. (56)

When should practising yoni mudra be avoided?

Swami Niranjanananda: This technique should not be practised if there is depression or too much introversion. Yoni mudra, and even shanmukhi mudra, are not mental therapies but skilful means to use and eventually transcend the healthy balanced state of mind which is achieved through extended sadhana.

What happens when pratyahara in yoni mudra becomes profound?

Swami Niranjanananda: The first experience in yoni mudra is a pratyahara state, as the consciousness loses contact with the senses. If just shanmukhi mudra is practised, the senses, which influence the mind and brain every moment by keeping them externalized, become peaceful. The external influences cease and the state of pratyahara is achieved.

In the state of pratyahara, the mind is internalized, consciousness is internalized and the inner senses awaken. Then, in yoni mudra, a mantra is practised along with kumbhaka. In this state of pratyahara, sensations are felt in the *pranamaya kosha*, the pranic body. In the region of prana, awakening is experienced. When the kumbhaka is released a little difficulty may be felt at the time of inhalation and exhalation because the body is not getting the usual amount of oxygen and carbon dioxide is accumulating. In this way the nervous system is activated. A state of drowsiness or a sort of sleepy state dawns and gradually the external consciousness starts vanishing.

Yogis purposely create this state through kumbhaka so that the external senses do not cause any distraction to the one-pointedness of consciousness. When the state of drowsiness arises inside consciousness, and the mind starts becoming internalized, then if the awareness is increased, one enters the state of meditation. When there is mental chanting of the mantra, the mental recitation takes one from gross to subtle *nada*, sound or vibration. Hearing or not hearing nada is dependent on how deep the one-pointedness is. When consciousness is engaged in a vibration, sound, or mantra in this kind of practice, eventually it is not just listening to external sounds through the ears, the vibration produced inside can be listened to. This sound is actually always there, but it cannot be heard with the ears.

How does yoni mudra help awaken the kundalini?
Swami Niranjanananda: Through the practice of yoni mudra an effort is made to awaken kundalini shakti by rotating the awareness around the six psychic centres with the additional help of breath retention and mantra awareness. Consciousness of the *jiva*, the individual self, is awakened with the mantra *Soham* made up of the syllables *sah* and *aham*, meaning 'That I am'. While meditating on this mantra, when Shakti is united with Shiva, the experience of awakening takes place in different states of consciousness.

These different states of consciousness are represented by the six chakras. In mooladhara chakra there is one state of consciousness; there is awareness, concentration and meditation on one element. In swadhisthana there is concentration and meditation on another element. In

71

manipura it is on a third element, and in this way finally, in the sixth chakra, union of the entire mind takes place with superconsciousness, Shiva. The purpose or aim of this mudra is to establish both Shiva and Shakti in the consciousness.

In *Gheranda Samhita* (3:52) it says, *naanaasukham vihaaram cha chintayetparamam sukham*, one has to meditate on this eternal blissful state while experiencing all types of pleasures. This may seem a bit odd. How is it possible? *Naanaasukham vihaaram* means moving through different pleasurable states towards *paramam sukham*, the highest pleasure of bliss. The achievement of all types of pleasures mentioned here is in fact the awakening of consciousness and prana in each chakra. To achieve and to absorb oneself in that experience which is hidden in the dimension of consciousness and prana in each chakra is the real spiritual pleasure. The reference to pleasures does not mean physical pleasures; it means the state of oneness which manifests, the experience of new dimensions of consciousness that takes place, and the pleasure and bliss that is achieved from this state.

What is the highest state that can be attained by practising yoni mudra?

Swami Niranjanananda: In *Gheranda Samhita* (3:53) it says, *Shiva-shaktisamaa-yogaat-ekaantam bhuvibhaavayet, Aanandamaanaso bhootvaa aham brahma-iti sambhavet*, one has to meditate on the blissful silent union of Shiva and Shakti and also on the concept 'I am Brahman'. The word *ekanta* has been used, which suggests peace and stability. Where consciousness is awakened, there is no movement, distraction or noise of any kind; inner peace, inner concentration and an experience of total absorption takes place. The same state has been explained here as *ekanta yoga*.

When the experience of all types of dualities ends internally, in the state of meditation, the experience of ekanta takes place and one becomes established in one's own form or nature. In this ekanta, one has to meditate on the union of Shiva and Shakti at sahasrara chakra. In this state, one is not even the witness or *drashta* of the union. There is no thought or idea that I am a sadhaka, sitting and imagining that the union of Shiva and Shakti is taking place at sahasrara. Rather, one is absorbed fully in the experience of it. This is the highest state of meditation.

How can one become absorbed in that *mahavakya*, great saying or teaching, *Aham Brahmasmi*, 'I am Brahman'? It is not looking at the two; because if I observe two, it means I am separate and that is separate. In the practice of yoni mudra the awakening of the feeling of *Soham*, 'That I am' is emphasized right from the start. When I am That, then I am not different from it. Thus one can attain the supreme state of consciousness.

In *Gheranda Samhita* (3:55) Sage Gheranda writes that the practice of yoni mudra is *paraa-gopyaa*, top secret. Even for the gods it is *durlabha*, hard to attain, but those who practise regularly can attain *samaadhisthah*, the state of samadhi. This is actually a description of one of the states of samadhi.

How can yoni mudra lead to samadhi?

Swami Niranjanananda: In *Gheranda Samhita* (3:56) Sage Gheranda writes of yoni mudra, *Tasmaat-abhyaasanam kuryaadyadi muktim samichchhati*, by its practice even liberation can be attained. People who are desirous of attaining *mukti*, liberation, should practise yoni mudra. Here, yoni mudra is mentioned in the context of attaining the state of samadhi due to *naadanubhooti*, the experience of nada in meditation. In the final chapter of *Gheranda Samhita*, Sage Gheranda describes various types of samadhi. One of these is nada samadhi; he once again mentions yoni mudra as a means to attain samadhi through nada anubhooti, the experience of the subtle nada. In *Gheranda Samhita* (7:12–13) it is written:

Yonimudraam samaasaadya svayam shaktimayo bhavet;
Sushringaararasenaiva viharetparamaatmani.

Aanandamayah sambhootvaa ekyam brahmani sambhavet;
Aham brahmeti chaadvaitasasamaadhistena jaayate.

73

Assuming yoni mudra, a yogi should create the feeling of shakti in himself and unite blissfully with param-atma. (12)

Thereafter, established in blissful oneness, one becomes one with Brahman and realizes 'I am Brahman'. This is non-dual samadhi (called laya siddhi yoga samadhi). (13)

While describing laya siddhi, Sage Gheranda says that first of all yoni mudra should be practised and one should see oneself in the form of shakti, i.e. at that time the feeling that one is male or female has to be discarded. With this attitude, there does not remain any kind of distinction according to sex. One may be a child, young man, young lady, old man or old lady, but one has to see oneself in the form of shakti, and also have the conviction that there is only one purusha (male) in the universe; all the rest are females in the form of shakti.

Sage Gheranda says, *Sushringaara-rasenaiva vihareta paramaatmani*. When something is dear to us, we decorate it and want to see it in a pleasing form. In childhood, dolls are played with. Every day there is a new feeling and so the doll's clothes and hairstyle are changed, and the doll is rocked with the feeling, "This is my doll". In the same way a feeling is awakened here that I might decorate and beautify my deity in whatever form I wish. However, this samadhi technique is suitable only for those sadhakas or aspirants who have already controlled their lower feelings and senses.

Each person has their own feelings. The inspiration may come from anywhere, but when there is a feeling of devotion, adorning the Lord is done on an inner form and one is totally lost in that. Just as a lady in love forgets everything for her lover, and because of that true love she is eventually successful in making him her own, aspirants or sadhakas are united with the limitless existence also on the strength of their feelings. No other knowledge except awareness of Brahman remains in the end. They are totally engrossed in bliss. This is the state of laya siddhi samadhi.

UNMANI MUDRA: THE ATTITUDE OF MINDLESSNESS

What is the meaning of unmani mudra?

Swami Satyananda: The word *unmani* literally means 'no mind' or 'not thinking'. It may also be translated as 'the attitude of thoughtlessness' or 'meditation'. Unmani implies that state which is beyond thought, a state where all attachment to the world of objects is dispelled. In this state, the awareness functions without the hindrance of conflicting thoughts and analysis. This is known as *unmani avastha*, the state of no thought.

How is unmani mudra practised?

Swami Satyananda: Sitting in any comfortable meditation asana with the eyes fully open, one inhales slowly and deeply. Whilst holding the breath inside, the awareness is focused at bindu for a few seconds. Exhaling, the awareness descends with the breath from bindu through the chakras in the spine: ajna, vishuddhi, anahata, manipura, swadhisthana, mooladhara. The eyes slowly close as the awareness descends. By the time the awareness reaches mooladhara, the eyes should be fully closed. Even when the eyes are open, the awareness is looking within. One must not try too hard, the process should be allowed to occur spontaneously.

What are the benefits of unmani mudra?

Swami Satyananda: Unmani mudra calms stress and agitation, and induces a meditative state.

SHAMBHAVI MUDRA/BHRUMADHYA DRISHTI: EYEBROW CENTRE GAZING

What is shambhavi mudra?

Swami Satyananda: In tantra there is a practice known as shambhavi mudra. *Shambhu* refers to Lord Shiva, 'the one born of peace', and *bhava* is 'divine emotion', or the elevation of human emotion into intense spiritual longing. *Shambhavi*

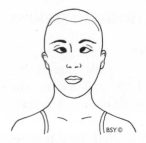

is the energy principle of Shambhu. The mudra instils peace. The practice is also known as bhrumadhya drishti. The word *bhrumadhya* means 'eyebrow centre', and *drishti* means 'gazing'.

Shambhavi mudra may be performed externally with the eyes open or internally with closed eyes. When the eyes are open, one tries to look at the mid-eyebrow centre. With the eyes closed, one concentrates on the mid-eyebrow centre.

When shambhavi mudra becomes effective there is light within. Concentration is on that point of light.

What are the origins of shambhavi mudra?

Swami Satyananda: Shambhavi is the name of the wife or consort of Shambhu, a name for Shiva. She has many other names, such as Parvati and Shakti, all of which have special significance in Indian mythology. It is believed that Shambhu taught Shambhavi the practice of shambhavi mudra and urged her to perform it diligently to attain higher awareness. It is said that the practice of shambhavi mudra will stir Shambhu (superconsciousness) and make him appear before you.

This infers that by practising shambhavi mudra for a sufficiently long period of time, one can transcend the fetters of the individual ego. Gradually there is withdrawal of the individual awareness. As the individual awareness withdraws, the higher, expanded awareness takes its place. In this way a significance and essence is seen behind everything, and it is realized that one's real nature is far more than can normally be conceived.

What other practices help one to master shambhavi mudra?

Swami Satyananda: In order to master shambhavi mudra, practise trataka. Trataka is not merely gazing at one point, although in the beginning the eyes must be kept fixed on something. Gradually the eyes become concentrated at the eyebrow centre and shambhavi mudra develops, bringing ida, pingala and sushumna into union and triggering the flow of kundalini energy.

How can eye strain and distraction be avoided when practising shambhavi mudra?

Swami Sivananda: In shambhavi mudra direct the eyes towards the ajna chakra with the eyes closed. If practised with open eyes, headache can result. Foreign particles such as dust may fall into the eyes, and there may be distraction of the mind. Do not strain the eyes. Practise gently.

What are the general benefits of shambhavi mudra?

Swami Satyananda: Physically, shambhavi mudra strengthens the eye muscles and releases accumulated tension in this area. Mentally, it calms the mind, removing emotional stress, anger and worries. As the practice develops, many beneficial effects are experienced at subtle levels.

What effect does shambhavi mudra have on the brain?

Swami Satyananda: One means of conducting prana to the frontal portion of the brain is by the practice of shambhavi mudra. When shambhavi mudra is practised, the pranas are sucked up by the force to irrigate the frontal area of the brain.

In the brain there are two important glands, the pineal gland and the pituitary gland. In yoga they are associated with ajna chakra and sahasrara chakra. Ajna chakra is related to the pineal gland and it has great control over the autonomic nervous system and the blood circulation.

When shambhavi mudra is practised, ajna chakra is influenced, and when this takes place there is illumination. When the gaze is directed between the two eyebrows, one begins to perceive the light. It can be seen with the eyes open in shambhavi for a long time.

What is the relevance of eye movements in sleep to the theory of shambhavi mudra?

Swami Satyananda: By watching a sleeping person it is possible to know if they are sleeping deeply or dreaming. The eye movements tell whether a sleeping person is worried, frightened, anxious, dreaming, thinking, sleeping or in samadhi. When a person is dreaming, there are fluctuations in the eyeballs, which can be seen, felt and also measured by machines.

In deep sleep the eyes may automatically assume shambhavi mudra. In states of profound meditation the eyeballs generally go straight up, they never stay at the centre. An anxious person's eyes are unsteady and by stilling the eyes the uncontrolled fluctuations of an anxious brain can generally be overcome.

What are the effects of shambhavi mudra on the mind and prana?

Swami Niranjanananda: Shambhavi mudra leads to control over the mind and prana. It develops concentration, mental stability and the state of thoughtlessness. With practice, the mind becomes capable of spiritual contemplation and absorption.

In kundalini yoga shambhavi mudra is a powerful practice to awaken ajna chakra, the centre which unites the lower consciousness with the higher consciousness. In *Hatha Yoga Pradipika* (4:36–37) it is written:

Antarlakshyam bahirdrishtirnimeshonmeshavarjitaa;
Eshaa saa shaambhavee mudraa vedashaastreshu gopitaa.

Antarlakshyavileenachittapavano yogee yadaa vartate;
Drishtyaa nishchalataarayaa bahiradhah pashyannapashyannapi;
Mudreyam khalu shaambhavee bhavati saa labdhaa prasaadaadguroh;
Shoonyaashoonyavilakshanam sphurati tattattvam padam shaambhavam.

78

Introverted, one-pointed awareness with an unblinking external gaze, this is shambhavi mudra which is preserved in the Vedas. (36)

If the yogi remains with the awareness and energy absorbed in the internal object (for concentration) while the external gaze is motionless, though looking one is not looking, that indeed is shambhavi. When it is given with the guru's blessing, the state of shoonyashoonya arises. That is the real state of Shiva (i.e. consciousness). (37)

Thus, the practice of shambhavi mudra turns the focus of awareness to the divine. Another point to consider is that Shambhavi is one of the names of Parvati, Lord Shiva's consort and disciple. According to the story, only one thinking process is present in Parvati – that although she may have to take many births, she must always have Shiva's company. The same thought existed when she took birth as Sati. It was expressed by Parvati at the time of her *tapasya,* austerities, that she would not be defeated, even if she had to take birth time and again: every time, it is her wish to attain the Shiva element.

How does shambhavi mudra awaken ajna?

Swami Satyananda: Shambhavi mudra relates to the control of a most important psychic centre in the body known as ajna chakra. To awaken ajna chakra and create union between the three conductors of energy in the body, shambhavi mudra should be practised.

Ajna chakra is situated in the midbrain at the very top of the spine, in the region of the pineal gland. *Ajna* is the centre which monitors and commands each and every function in the physical body. When this centre is healthy, the balance between the emotions and the body is maintained because the pineal gland is the stopcheck on the pituitary.

Shambhavi mudra directly awakens ajna. Both shambhavi and khechari cause the external mind to 'turn off' and inner awareness to awaken. In *Hatha Yoga Pradipika* (4:38) it says:

Rasanaamoordhvagaam kritvaa kshanaardhamapi tishthati;
Vishairvimuchyate yogee vyaadhimrityujaraadibhih.

Shambhavi and khechari states, though there is a difference in the place of concentration or influence, both bring about ecstasy, absorption in void, in the experience of chit sukha (the pleasure of consciousness).

Swami Muktananda states that during the period of his sadhana secretions sometimes flowed profusely from the cranial region and his eyeballs would spontaneously roll upwards into shambhavi. In deep meditation his tongue would automatically go upwards through the nasal pharynx, and a voice from within instructed that this would create a greater state of experience by opening the passage to sahasrara.

What subtle experiences can arise by practising shambhavi mudra?

Swami Sivananda: When the gaze is concentrated at ajna chakra one experiences *divya jyoti*, perception of supra-phenomenal lights. This is an experience to give encouragement, to push one up the spiritual path and convince the aspirant of the existence of transcendental or supra-physical things. One must not stop the sadhana.

How does shambhavi develop perfect concentration?

Swami Satyananda: Concentration becomes much easier through the practice of shambhavi, and the brainwaves can be controlled at will. The moment shambhavi mudra is practised, concentration takes place, and when concentration takes place there is union between ida and pingala nadis in ajna chakra. When these two nadis touch each other then there is an explosion of light.

Concentration is perfect when the totality of awareness knows only the object upon which it is concentrated. Perfect concentration is meditation, perfect meditation is samadhi. It is stated in *Hatha Yoga Pradipika* (4:39):

Taare jyotishi samyojya kinchidunnamayed bhruvau;
Poorvayogam mano yunjannunmaneekaarakah kshanaat.

With perfect concentration, the pupils fixed on the light by raising the eyebrows up a little, as from the previously described (shambhavi), mind is joined and instantly unmani occurs.

When shambhavi is practised for an extended period of time a small light appears. That light has then to be seen with the eyes closed and concentrated upon until nothing else exists. When samadhi is achieved through the practice it is called unmani.

How can shambhavi mudra be used to induce pratyahara during meditation?

Swami Sivananda: In bhrumadhya drishti the gaze is between the two eyebrows where the psychic centre known as ajna chakra is situated. This is described in the *Bhagavad Gita* (5:27) when Sri Krishna expounds the yoga of meditation:

Sparshaankritvaa bahirbaahyaamshchakshushchaivaantare bhruvoh;
Praanaapaanau samau kritvaa naasaabhyantarachaarinau.

Shutting out all external contacts and fixing the gaze between the eyebrows, equalizing the outgoing and incoming breaths moving within the nostrils.

External objects or contacts are the sound and other sense objects. If the mind does not think of the external objects they are shut out from the mind. The senses are the doors or avenues through which sound and other sense objects enter the mind. If the gaze is fixed between the eyebrows the eyeballs remain fixed and steady.

Rhythmic breathing is also described in this verse: the breath must be made rhythmic while practising bhrumadhya drishti. The mind becomes steady when the breath is rhythmic. When the breath is rhythmic there is perfect harmony in the mind and the whole system.

81

Why is shambhavi mudra so closely associated with deep states of meditation?

Swami Satyananda: The word 'shambhavi' is the name of the creative power of consciousness, Shiva. All the mudras expand consciousness, but for the aspirant whose mind remains disciplined, and whose awareness remains alert when all internal and external barriers have been dissolved in samadhi, shambhavi brings the greatest perfection. In *Hatha Yoga Pradipika* (3:125) it says:

> *Abhyaase tu vinidraanaam mano dhritvaa samaadhinaa;*
> *Rudraanee vaa paraa mudraa bhadraam siddhim prayachchhati.*

> For those who are alert and the mind one-pointed (disciplined) in samadhi, rudrani or shambhavi mudra is the greatest mudra for bestowing perfection.

Meditation becomes samadhi when awareness merges with the object of meditation and duality dissolves. In that state, sense perception is completely non-existent, and the eyeballs turn upwards, spontaneously fixed in shambhavi mudra. This is an external sign of the inner mental tranquillity.

Meditation is to remain one-pointed and disciplined in the midst of these inner experiences, and this discipline must continue through the succeeding stages of samadhi. For this purpose the inner gaze is fixed upon a particular psychic symbol (ishta devata) in shambhavi mudra.

This symbol is chosen by the aspirant according to his own inclination, or it may be assigned by the guru. That symbol becomes the focus of pure consciousness for the aspirant. It becomes a real illumined object in his consciousness by one-pointedness and discipline.

What are the stages of practising shambhavi mudra with dharana?

Swami Niranjanananda: According to the vedic system there are seven stages of shambhavi: with coordination of the breath, with breath retention, first dharana, second dharana, third dharana, fourth dharana and fifth dharana.

In stage one, the gaze is turned upward and inward whilst breathing normally. The mudra is released when the eyes begin to feel strained. After a few moments rest, the practice is repeated.

Stage two is commenced when the eye movement has been mastered. The eyes are raised whilst breathing in, and lowered whilst breathing out.

Once the eye movement is coordinated with the breath, gradually train the eye muscles to remain in shambhavi without any kind of tension. The movement continues to be coordinated with the breath. The mudra is maintained while breath retention is practised. During breath retention, concentration should be on the image of the self.

According to the vedantic approach there are five levels of experience in shambhavi through which the image of the self is developed. These experiences manifest as each stage is perfected. This kind of imagination or visualization also helps to focus the mind to a greater extent, so that sublimation can take place. The normal thoughts, ideas and visions which constantly distract one's concentration must be eliminated so that a different kind of experience can arise.

The remaining stages consist of the five dharanas:

1. *Agni mandala*, the first visualization, or dharana, is concentration on the entire body in the form of *agni*, fire. The whole body is to be viewed as agni mandala. Feel the body as fire. This is not just a visual or mental imagination, but a sensorial experience. The flames and heat can be experienced along the spine and the front of the body. The different experiences of fire must be felt in this body.

2. *Surya mandala*, the second dharana, is concentration on the image of the sun visualized in shambhavi mudra at the point between the eyebrows.

3. *Chandra mandala*, the third dharana, is also called ajna mandala. Here the symbol of ajna chakra is visualized at the gazing point in shambhavi.
4. *Prakasha mandala*, the fourth dharana, is visualization of light at the centre of ajna chakra. This light does not radiate any sensation of heat or coolness. It is pure, white light.
5. *Vidyut mandala*, the fifth dharana, is visualization of lightning within the white light.

These are the five levels of experience in shambhavi mudra.

Why is shambhavi mudra such a highly regarded practice?

Swami Niranjanananda: Shambhavi mudra is an extraordinary practice. Due to the different stages of experience that can be attained by this practice it is highly regarded in all yogic, tantric and vedantic texts. It has been stated that one who becomes proficient in this technique can awaken ajna chakra. This enables one to transcend the faculties of the lower mind and establish oneself in higher consciousness. It is described in *Gheranda Samhita* (3:76–79):

Netraantaram samaalokya chaatmaaraamam nireekshayet;
Saa bhavechchhaambhaveemudraa sarvatantreshugopitaa.

Vedashaastrapuraanaani saamaanyaganikaa iva;
Iyam tu shaambhaveemudraa guptaa kulavadhooriva.

Sa eva hyaadinaathashcha sa cha naaraayanah svayam;
Sa cha brahmaa srishtikaaree yo mudraam vetti shaambhaveem.

Satyam satyam punah satyam satyamaaha maheshvarah;
Shaambhaveem yo vijaaneeyaatsa cha brahma na chaanyathaa.

Steady the gaze at the eyebrow centre, on one's self, the atma or soul, and meditate. This is shambhavi mudra. It is a very secret tantric practice. (76)

The Vedas, shastras and puranas are like an ordinary woman and shambhavi mudra is like a bride. (77)

84

Practitioners of this practice are themselves Adinath, Narayana and Brahma, the creator of this world. (78)

Take this saying as absolutely true, that a person knowing shambhavi mudra is Maheshwara, is Brahman in reality. (79)

So few people know of shambhavi mudra that Sage Gheranda describes it using the simile of a bride from a well-to-do family who is carefully guarded and protected, while the status of ordinary women is compared to the Vedas, puranas and shastras – scriptures which everyone knows. Thus, for Sage Gheranda, shambhavi mudra occupies an even higher place than the Vedas, puranas and shastras.

In this mudra one meditates on *atma roopi Ishwara*, God in the form of the soul or spirit, uniting the individual soul with the trinity of Brahma, Vishnu and Mahesha, merging with the trinity and becoming one with them. Sage Gheranda considers a practitioner of shambhavi mudra to be *Mahesha* (also known as Lord Shiva or Shambhu), *Vishnu* (also known as Narayana) and *Brahma* (the creator of this universe). He emphasizes that a person who has attained perfection in shambhavi mudra is truly an incarnation of the Lord.

Shambhavi mudra is, therefore, a process of psychic union, and a meditative practice leading to a state of enlightenment.

How can shambhavi mudra become a practise of bhakti yoga?

Swami Sivananda: Yogis and bhaktas who meditate on Lord Shiva concentrate on the ajna chakra with bhrumadhya drishti. Choose whichever drishti suits you best. Whichever point is selected, visualize your own chosen deity there and feel his living presence.

How does shambhavi mudra help to bring about the state of samadhi?

Swami Satyananda: When the mind is absorbed in the point of concentration, the eyes spontaneously turn upwards. It requires no intellectual capacity or 'brainpower' to do this, only sincere application to the practice. Shambhavi mudra stimulates ajna chakra in the brain directly behind the mid-eyebrow point. Through this, samadhi develops, as the mind is absorbed and the nada perceived. In *Hatha Yoga Pradipika* (4:80):

Unmanyavaaptaye sheeghram bhroodhyaanam mama sammatam;
Raajayogapadam praaptum sukhopaayo'lpachetasaam;
Sadhyah pratyayasandhaayee jaayate naadajo layah.

In my opinion, contemplation on the eyebrow centre leads to a mindless state immediately. It is a suitable method even for those with less intellect to attain the state of raja yoga. The laya attained through nada gives immediate experience.

Spiritual life and experiences are independent of academic ability and intellectual or mundane knowledge. Spiritual knowledge, power and experience exist on a different plane altogether. Even a debauchee can perceive the nada and dwell in the greater experience. Anyone who hears it should listen intently, excluding other experiences and thoughts so that the mundane state of consciousness becomes illumined.

When Yogi Swatmarama says that in his opinion eyebrow centre gazing leads immediately to mindlessness, he is narrating from his own experience. Those who have become highly established in spiritual consciousness through hatha yoga and raja yoga, gain control of the mind and are able to transcend its modifications and enter into the samadhi states at will.

BHOOCHARI MUDRA: GAZING INTO NOTHINGNESS

What is bhoochari mudra?

Swami Satyananda: The word *bhoo* means 'earth', and *chari* means 'moving' or 'dwelling'. It cannot be sensibly translated into English in the literal sense, so it's known as 'nothingness gazing'.

When should bhoochari mudra be practised?

Swami Satyananda: Bhoochari mudra can be practised within the daily program and once it has been mastered, also in everyday life. It can be done in any position and almost any place, without others realizing a yogic technique is being practised. It can be done while standing, sitting or lying. It can be done in the privacy of one's own house or at work, whatever is convenient.

When practised at home in a sitting pose, it is best to face a blank wall, ensuring that there are no obstructions in the range of vision so that there is no distraction. It can also be practised facing an open space such as the sky or a body of still water. This is not essential, only preferable.

What are the benefits of bhoochari mudra?

Swami Satyananda: This is an excellent, simple, and effective practice which brings tranquillity and concentration of mind when done for a reasonable period of time with awareness. Bhoochari tranquillizes and introverts the mind and is particularly beneficial for calming anger and stress. It develops mental stability and the state of thoughtlessness. It helps awaken ajna chakra and induce meditative states, and takes the practitioner into the psychic and spiritual planes of consciousness.

Where should the awareness be held during bhoochari mudra?

Swami Satyananda: Whilst practising bhoochari mudra one is fully engrossed in gazing at a point of nothingness. Simultaneously, one should be aware of any thought processes. When the focus dissipates the hand is again raised and concentration is on the tip of the little finger. After some time the hand is lowered and again one gazes intently into the space, the nothingness. Awareness

is of space only; there should be no registration of outer events in the field of conscious perception.

How can bhoochari mudra be used for meditation?

Swami Satyananda: Bhoochari mudra may be performed as a preparation for meditation and as a meditation technique in its own right. It belongs to a group of techniques featuring gazing at an external focal point as a means to achieve dharana or the meditative state of relaxed concentration. It is allied to nasikagra drishti and shambhavi mudras, all three being forms of trataka.

AKASHI MUDRA: AWARENESS OF INNER SPACE

What is akashi mudra?

Swami Niranjanananda: The word *akashi* means 'inner space'. Akashi mudra is awareness of the inner space. This practice induces mental tranquillity by withdrawing the senses. It renders the mind free of thoughts and leads to states of trance. Akashi mudra is a combination of ujjayi, khechari, shambhavi and nasikagra.

How can one prepare to practise akashi mudra?

Swami Satyananda: It is recommended that the practitioner be completely familiar with the practices of ujjayi, khechari, nasikagra and shambhavi before commencing akashi mudra. At first, ujjayi pranayama may irritate the throat when performed with the head back. However, with practice, it becomes more comfortable.

What precautions should the practitioner of akashi mudra be aware of?

Swami Satyananda: As soon as faintness is felt, the practice must be stopped. This technique is to be practised slowly, under the guidance of a competent teacher. People suffering from high blood pressure, vertigo, brain disorders or epilepsy should not practise akashi mudra.

What are the benefits of akashi mudra?

Swami Satyananda: Akashi mudra combines the benefits of kumbhaka, ujjayi, shambhavi, nasikagra and khechari. It induces calmness and tranquillity, and develops control over the senses. When perfected, it arrests the thought processes and induces higher states of consciousness.

What are the physiological effects of akashi mudra?

Swami Niranjanananda: Akashi mudra aims at developing control over the senses. When one concentrates on the nose and the sense of smell, the attention is focused on the most primitive of all the senses, located deep down inside the primal brain. Vision, by contrast, is the most developed sense. When attention is taken to the eyes, there is movement from the lowest part of the brain to a highly developed part of the brain.

In the brain there are two main areas for vision. One is the occipital cortex, an area about the size of the hand which controls involuntary vision. A person has no choice but to keep moving the eyes in order to continue receiving sensory information and input. The second area, which is located in the frontal lobe, is involved in voluntary vision. It helps in directing the eyes where one wants them to look for a specific purpose, like looking ahead, in the same way as the purpose of the frontal lobes is thinking ahead, looking to the future. This is the physical level of the mental activity.

Akashi mudra fixes the eyes, stops involuntary movement, stops the use of energy and synchronizes the brainwaves. They go into a simple alpha rhythm. If the eyes are closed, there will be an alpha rhythm, which is a relaxed state in the back of the head. But when one focuses in these eye mudras, there is not only that relaxed rhythm in the back of the head, but also in the frontal lobes. This is the main

reason why mudras such as askashi are so tranquillizing. They stop the thinking process almost instantly. Thought and thought waves are connected to metabolic activity in the cells, the rate of breathing, the rate of movement of the eyes and also the rate of movement of the tongue. These activities have a reflex in the frontal lobes, so that when movement is slowed down the brain is also slowed down, for example, during meditation.

Akashi mudra involves different forms of manipulation, either looking upward at the eyebrow centre, directing the energy to the higher centres in the brain, or looking down at the nosetip, and fixing the attention on the lower, more primitive centres in the brain, whereas practices such as bhoochari mudra take one away from the point of focus. Just as shambhavi and nasikagra mudras increase concentration, bhoochari mudra takes one into a field of vision that is no longer focused on a point, but on the entire visual field.

Is akashi mudra a form of trataka?

Swami Satyananda: Akashi mudra is a form of trataka as it features gazing at an external focal point as a means to achieving dharana.

NABHO MUDRA: ATTITUDE OF THE SKY

What is nabho mudra?

Swami Niranjanananda: Nabho mudra is a simple form of khechari mudra. Folding the tongue upward and backward so that it lies in contact with the upper palate is called *nabho mudra*, which means the sky or space mudra. The intake of air can easily be stopped when the tongue is reversed like this. It can be practised with both internal and external breath retention.

Nabho mudra is an example of a simple raja yoga style technique. The mudras described in raja yoga are similar to those explained in hatha yoga. The practices of raja yoga, however, are given keeping in mind the normal physical condition of the body, and the care that it needs, whereas the practices of hatha yoga are carried out by exerting pressure on the body and by changing its physical state. Nabho mudra is described in *Gheranda Samhita* (3:32):

Yatra yatra sthito yogee sarvakaaryeshu sarvadaa;
Urdhvajihvah sthiro bhootvaa dhaarayetpavanam sadaa;
Nabhomudraa bhavedeshaa yoginaam roganaashinee.

Wherever one is and during all activities, a yogi should keep the tongue turned upward and retain the breath. Nabho mudra destroys all the disorders of a yogi.

What is the difference between khechari mudra and nabho mudra?

Swami Satyananda: The simple form of khechari mudra is also known as nabho mudra. To practise this form the tongue is simply rolled backwards so that the lower surface touches the soft upper palate. The tip is brought as far back as possible and kept there for as long as possible, from half a minute to ten or twenty minutes. It is suitable for most people, although it still takes a long time to perfect.

There is another form of khechari mudra in which the root of the tongue is slowly rubbed by friction and cut. When the simple form, nabho mudra, is done, day by day, week by week, month by month, year by year, the tongue becomes flexible and elongated. Once it can enter into the epiglottis, the same result can be achieved as with the actual khechari.

KHECHARI MUDRA:
THE ATTITUDE OF MOVING THROUGH SPACE

What is khechari mudra?

Swami Sivananda: This mudra can only be performed by one who has undergone the preliminary exercise under the direct guidance of a guru who is practising khechari mudra. The preliminary part of this mudra involves making the tongue so long that its tip might touch the space between the two eyebrows. Then, sitting in siddhasana the tongue is turned upwards and backwards so as to reach the palate and close the posterior nasal opening. The gaze is then fixed at the space between the two eyebrows. The respiration will stop. The tongue is on the mouth of the well of nectar. This is khechari mudra. It is described in *Shiva Samhita* (4:31):

> *Bhruvorantargataam drishtim vidhaaya sudridham sudheeh;*
> *Upavishyaasane vajre naanopadravavavarjitah;*
> *Lambikordhvam sthite garte rasanaam vipareetagaam;*
> *Sanyojayetprayatnena sudhaakoope vichakshanah.*
> *Mudraishaa khecharee proktaa bhaktaanaamanuroghatah.*

The wise yogi, sitting in vajrasana posture, in a place free from all disturbance, should firmly fix his gaze on the spot in the middle of the two eyebrows, and reversing the tongue backwards, fix it in the hollow under the epiglottis, placing it with great care on the mouth of the well of nectar. This mudra, described by me at the request of my devotees, is the khechari mudra.

What is the meaning of khechari mudra?

Swami Satyananda: *Khe* means 'in the sky' and *chari* means 'one who moves'. Therefore khechari means 'one who moves through akasha, space'. This name has been given as khechari produces a state of mind in which the astral body is detached from the physical body. In such a state, the consciousness dwells in the akasha, the space between the astral and physical bodies.

Why is khechari mudra so important?

Swami Niranjanananda: Khechari mudra, the tongue lock, is regarded as a very important practice in all the hatha yoga, raja yoga and vedantic texts because of its effect on the body and mind. It is generally combined with ujjayi pranayama and other meditation techniques. Its importance is revealed in *Shiva Samhita* (4:32–37):

Siddheenaam jananee hyoshaa mama praanaadhirkaaprayaa;
Nirantarakritaabhyaasaatpeeyoosham pratyaham pibet;
Tena vigrahasiddhih syaanmrityumaatangakesaree.

Apavitrah pavitro vaa sarvaavasthaam gato'pivaa;
Khecharee yasya shuddhaa tu sa shuddho naatra samshayah.

Kshanaardham kurute yastu teertvaa paapamahaarnavam;
Divyabhogaanprabhuktvaa cha satkule sa prajaayate.

Mudraishaa khecharee yastu svasthachitto hyatandritah;
Shatabrahmagatenaapi kshanaardham manyate hi sah.

Guroopadeshato mudraam yo vetti khechareemimaam;
Naanaapaaparato dheemaan sa yaati paramaam gatim.

Saa praanasadrishee mudraa yasminkasminna deeyate;
Prachchhadyate prayatnena mudreyam surapoojite.

O my beloved! Know this to be the source of all success, always practising it let one drink the ambrosia daily. By this one obtains vigraha siddhi (power over the microcosm), even as a lion over the elephant of death. (32)

Whether pure or impure, in whatever condition one may be, if success is obtained in khechari, one becomes pure. (33)

One who practises it even for a moment crosses the great ocean of sins, and having enjoyed the pleasures of the divine world, is born into a noble family. (34)

One who practises this khechari mudra calmly and without laziness counts as seconds the period of a hundred Brahmas. (35)

One who knows this khechari mudra according to the instructions of the guru obtains the highest end, though immersed in great sins. (36)

O, ye adored of gods! This mudra, dear as life, should not be given to everybody; it should be kept concealed with great care. (37)

Must one have a guru for the complete practise of khechari mudra?

Swami Satyananda: Khechari mudra should only be practised when the relationship between the guru and the disciple is very close.

What happens when khechari mudra is perfected?

Swami Satyananda: When the tongue reaches the upper passage of the nose, sweet stuff produced from the 'nectar glands' is tasted. The one who masters this technique is able to practice *kumbhaka*, breath retention, for as long as he wishes. All those yogis who go underground and are buried for five or ten days are using khechari mudra. They can only do it with khechari, not without. In *Shiva Samhita* (3:72) it is written:

> *Rasanaamoordhvagaam kritvaa yashchandre salilam pibet;*
> *Maasamaatrena yogeendro mrityunjayati nishchitam.*

> Pointing the tongue upwards, when the yogi can drink the nectar flowing from the moon (situated between the two eyebrows), within a month he certainly would conquer death.

Who is the traditional hatha yoga form of khechari mudra suitable for?

Swami Niranjanananda: It is stated clearly in the traditional texts that in order to perfect the practice of khechari mudra the first requirement in hatha yoga is that the tongue should be long. In order to increase the length of the tongue, the fraenum in between the palate and the tongue is gradually severed.

Khechari mudra must be learned at the age of twelve to sixteen years when the body is still developing. It is not usually taught after that. The process is described in *Hatha Yoga Pradipika* (3:32–36):

> *Kapaalakuhare jihvaa pravishtaa vipareetagaa;*
> *Bhruvorantargataa drishtirmudraa bhavati khecharee.*

94

Chedanachaalanadohaih kalaam kramenaatha vardhayettaavat;
Saa yaavadbhroomadyam sprishati tadaa khechareesiddhih.

Snuheepatranibham shastram suteekshnam snigdhanirmalam;
Samaadaaya tatastena romamaatram samuchchhinet.

Tatah saindhavapathyaabhyaam choornataabhyaam pragharshayet;
Punah saptadine praapte romamaatram samuchchhinet.

Evam kramena shanmaasam nityam yuktah samaacharet;
Shanmaasaadrasanaamoolashiraabandhah pranashyati.

Khechari mudra is turning the tongue backwards into the cavity of the cranium and turning the eyes inwards towards the eyebrow centre. (32)

The tongue should be exercised and milked and the underneath part cut away in small degrees. Indeed khechari is perfected when the tongue touches the eyebrow centre. (33)

With a clean thin blade, gently cut away the membrane under the tongue. Cut it by a fine hair's breadth each time. (34)

Then rub in a mixture of powdered rock salt and turmeric. After seven days, again cut a hair's breadth. (35)

One should continue doing this regularly for six months, then the membrane at the root of the tongue will be completely severed. (36)

The process is not actually cutting, it is rubbing by friction and then putting a little turmeric over the point which has been rubbed. Every day the tongue is massaged with butter. This has to be done very patiently. It takes four to five years until the tongue is completely disconnected from its connection to the floor of the mouth, and consequently elongated.

While practising khechari mudra, hatha yoga should also be practised, so that the body remains clean, and does not produce toxins. The elongated tongue is inserted into the epiglottis, and the breath is suspended.

This hatha yoga technique of khechari mudra, in which the fraenum under the tongue is cut, is not recommended for anyone needing to live an active life in society. Cutting the fraenum affects swallowing, making eating difficult and without a special diet, the health suffers. It can also make speech quite indistinct. Therefore, the hatha yoga technique was traditionally only done by those yogis who were totally dedicated to spiritual awakening and no longer involved in worldly life.

How is the tongue prepared for khechari mudra?

Swami Niranjanananda: In olden days yogis used to say that the fraenum should be severed with the help of the root of a tree, or a sharp edged leaf like tejpata (Cinnamomum tamala) which is put in tea and is pure, so that there is no infection. It is also sometimes severed with the help of a rice (paddy) plant. In the *Yoga Tattwopanishad* it states that each time this is practised, the severing should be equivalent only to the thickness of a hair. This means that it should be a mere touch, a slight stroke.

In modern times some people have had the tongue severed through surgery. In this process bleeding takes place, but according to the *Yoga Tattwopanishad* and other yoga scriptures oozing of blood should not take place at all while perfecting khechari. What the motive was behind this saying cannot be known exactly, but it can be inferred that it is cautionary. In those days if the region became septic, medicinal herbs might not always have been available. It would have been difficult for a person if there was no one close by with knowledge of medicinal herbs. For this reason it says that severing of the tongue should be just equal to the thickness of a hair and there should be no bleeding. It should be a process in which the fraenum is cut daily or weekly, bit by bit, only the thickness of a hair each time. This means it is just like drawing a line.

The tongue is to be gradually elongated by *dohan kriya*, the milking process.

Two methods of dohan kriya are explained. One is outward massage of the tongue using the fingers, and the other is using forceps. The tongue is massaged in the same manner as in the milking process and it is pulled daily with a pair of forceps. There is a possibility of vomiting if the tongue is held with the fingers during dohan kriya, so forceps or a pair of tongs can be used to hold it firmly but gently. This procedure is described in *Gheranda Samhita* (3:33–35):

Jihvaado naadeem samchhitya rasanaam chaalayetsadaa;
Dohayennavaneetena lauhayantrena karshayet.

Evam nityam samabhyaasaallambikaa deerghathaam vrajet;
Yaavadgachchhedbhruvormadhye tadaa sidhyati khecharee.

Rasanaam taalumoole tu shanaih shanaih praveshayet;
Kapaalakuhare jihvaa pravishtaa vipareetagaa;
Bhruvormadhye gataa drishtirmudraa bhavati khecharee.

The nadi connecting the tongue and the root of the tongue, which is located underneath the tongue, is to be severed and the tip of the tongue is to be moved continuously. By applying butter and with the help of dohan kriya (the milking process) it is to be pulled with iron forceps. (33)

With daily practice the tongue becomes elongated. Its length should be so increased that it can reach the eyebrow centre. Khechari mudra is then accomplished. (34)

In this way the tongue should gradually be inserted into the root of the palate. By folding the tongue upward and backward, it should be taken right up to the nasal cavity. Keep the awareness fixed at the eyebrow centre at that time. This is khechari mudra. (35)

Once the tongue has been elongated how is khechari mudra performed?

Swami Niranjanananda: Once the tongue has been sufficiently elongated and pranayama has been perfected, the tongue is folded back on itself and moved upwards into the nasal cavity. Here it can effectively control the flow of breath and energy in the left and right nostrils, directly influencing ida and pingala nadis and directly stimulating various centres within the skull. The instructions of the guru should be followed carefully at each step.

Why is it important to perfect pranayama before practising khechari mudra?

Swami Niranjanananda: It is essential to perfect pranayama prior to the practice of khechari, because when the tongue goes upward, the nasal cavities can be closed and breathing is not so easy.

In some of the yoga scriptures it is said that mastery of pranayama does not mean retaining the breath inside or outside. Not everyone can attain the capacity to retain the breath for hours at a time. Perhaps even yogis do not achieve this capacity, but a state very similar to it is attained. If there are normally ten to fifteen breaths per minute, then the breathing is reduced by half, which means only five to seven breaths per minute. Thus the speed and rate of breathing are reduced for hours at a time. This is what is meant by retention of the breath. The aim of yogis is to reduce the breathing rate gradually, so that in the state of perfection there is only one breath in and out in a minute. In this state there should be no compromise in the normal functioning of the body, no feeling of breathlessness and no lack of oxygen.

Therefore, for khechari it is essential to have control over the breath and to prepare the tongue. Finally, it should be realized that khechari should not be practised without the guidance and directions of the guru. This is the main rule of yoga.

What precautions should be taken when practising khechari mudra?

Swami Niranjanananda: In yogic texts it is also clearly instructed that khechari mudra should not be used until the tongue becomes long and thin. When the tongue is inserted upward and backward, a taste is experienced; juices are secreted from the taste glands (buds) located on the palate and *kapala kuhar*, hole in the forehead. At first the mouth may be filled with an extremely bitter taste. Next comes an astringent taste, then salty and after that it is filled with a sweet taste. That means all types of tastes are experienced while doing this practice.

When the tongue crosses the limits of the taste glands, various tastes are secreted which cannot be described. For instance, the taste of milk or butter – which is neither sweet, nor alkaline, nor salty, nor bitter, nor even sour – cannot be described. So the experience of these other tastes, which can be called natural flavours, occur as the glands become very active. The secretion of saliva in the mouth is also reduced while practising khechari so that saliva does not constantly need to be swallowed. These secretions are described in *Gheranda Samhita* (3:39–40):

Naanaarasasamudbhootamaanandam cha dine dine;
Aadau cha lavanam kshaaram tatastiktakashaayakam.

Navaneetam ghritam ksheeram dadhitakramadhooni cha;
Draakshaarasam cha peeyoosham jaayate rasanodakam.

Therefore, strange types of juices keep being produced, day in and day out, through the tongue of the practitioner. New blissful experiences manifest. In the beginning salty, alkaline, bitter and astringent tastes and then the taste of butter, ghee (clarified butter), milk, curd, buttermilk, honey, grapes or raisins and then nectar are produced. (39–40)

There is also a warning that khechari should not be practised by anyone who experiences a bitter taste in the mouth. If a bitter taste is produced and one keeps on practising khechari without paying any heed, that bitterness can become a poison for the body. If the bitter taste persists, it also means that all the toxins and disorders of the body are not yet fully removed. If this happens, it is imperative to practise the hatha yoga shatkarmas all over again.

It is important to make the body completely free from all disorders. The indication of being free from disorders is absence of bitterness in the mouth. On rising in the morning, there is often a persistent bitter taste in the mouth, which means that the digestive system is unhealthy. It has been observed that when the bowels are clear, the bitter taste automatically vanishes.

Cease the practice for at least one month if an extreme bitter taste is experienced. Take care with the diet and lifestyle, then try again.

How does the yogi benefit from practising khechari mudra?

Swami Sivananda: By practise of khechari mudra the yogi becomes free from fainting, hunger, thirst and laziness. He is free from diseases, decay, old age and death. As the body of the yogi is filled with the nectar, he will not die even by virulent poison: this mudra gives *kaya siddhi* to yogis. Khechari is the best of all mudras.

What are the effects and benefits of khechari mudra?

Swami Niranjanananda: Khechari mudra stimulates a number of pressure points located in the back of the mouth and the nasal cavity. These points influence the whole body. A number of glands are also massaged, stimulating the secretion of certain hormones and saliva.

The head, hands and tongue cover a large part of the sensory area of the cortex. In the motor area, the area given for the tongue is three or four times greater than that given in the sensory area. The area allocated to the lips, mouth and vocal cords for the communication of thought into words through vishuddhi is given tremendous importance. When nabho or khechari is practised, attention is brought into these important areas.

Folding the tongue back and holding it still has the effect of bringing it into consciousness. The tongue is an organ that moves a lot, often unconsciously, especially when talking. By folding it back into khechari mudra, it is stabilized and muscles that are normally never still are fixed. This act produces stillness and quiet through the whole system, and has a profound effect on the consciousness. Energy that would normally be used in cortical activity is free for other functions.

It is believed that by this practice one gains control over the major functions of the body. When the tongue is inserted into the nasal cavity, many tiny nerve endings, hormones and glands are activated, which give greater autonomic control. For example, khechari reduces the sensations of hunger and thirst, and induces a state of inner calm and stillness. These effects are shown by those yogis who practise underground samadhi. During that time they maintain khechari mudra so that they do not feel hunger and thirst.

Even in normal life, with continuous practice of the simple version of khechari called nabho mudra, the sensations of hunger and thirst are reduced. One does not feel like eating or drinking and gradually the body adjusts accordingly. This can be experienced by experimentation. In *Gheranda Samhita* (3:36–38) the benefits of khechari are described:

> *Na cha moorchchhaa kshudhaa trishnaa naivaalasyam prajaayate;*
> *Na cha rogo jaraa mrityurdevadehah sa jaayate.*
>
> *Naagninaa dahyate gaatram na shoshayati maarutah;*
> *Na deham kledayantyaapo dashenna bhujangamah.*
>
> *Laavanyam cha bhavedgaatre samaadhirjaayate dhruvam;*
> *Kapaalavaktrasamyoge rasanaa rasamaapnuyaat.*

The practitioner of khechari mudra is not troubled by unconsciousness, hunger, thirst, laziness, etc. Fear of any disorder or disease, old age and death vanishes as the body becomes divine. (36)

The physical body is neither burnt in fire nor dried up by wind. It can neither be made wet by water nor does poison have any effect as in the case of snake bite. (37)

The body becomes graceful and charming. Unshakeable samadhi is perfected. Various juices are produced as a result of the union between the forehead and the mouth through the tongue. (38)

It is also said that the full practice of khechari can separate the *karana sharira*, the causal body, from the *sthoola sharira*, the gross body, and enable the entry of *chetana*, consciousness, in the karana sharira. With this detachment one's mind or consciousness experiences the akasha tattwa.

In the ancient yoga scriptures, great importance has been accorded to this mudra. According to Sage Gheranda, the body of a person who has perfected khechari is not influenced by fire, water or air, because of the secretion of nectar from bindu visarga. When this nectar or elixir of life is taken in a proper way, the body cannot be influenced by old age, death or any kind of harm, and it becomes as hard as a *vajra*, thunderbolt, and unchanging.

Immortality is usually understood as indestructibility. In the yogic scriptures immortality means something else. Immortality here means that whatever one's age, fifty, eighty or a hundred years, the body does not age, its capacity is not reduced and the mental energy is not impaired in any way. According to kundalini yoga, a benefit attained through khechari is rejuvenation of the physical cells of the body.

Kundalini yoga states that *bindu visarga*, at the top back of the head, is an important centre. From there the *amrit*, the nectar or elixir of life, is secreted in tiny quantities which drip down into the body. When the lower centres metabolize this nectar the body undergoes the process of decay, old age, disease and death. With the practice of khechari mudra, yogis have tried to reverse this process by stimulating bindu visarga and trapping the drops of hormone or amrit at vishuddhi.

When that hormone is retained in the vishuddhi region, it becomes purified and creates a different effect on the body. It does not combine with the acids of the stomach and become poison. It retains its purity and is distributed throughout the body after being percolated by the mucus membranes and salivary glands lining the mouth. Once that happens, the nectar begins to rejuvenate the body. The lifespan can thus be increased through the practice of khechari mudra.

What is the aim of practising khechari mudra with ujjayi pranayama?

Swami Satyananda: The direct concern of this mudra is to activate the psychic, physiological and endocrine processes responsible for cellular revitalization and longevity. If khechari mudra is correctly practised in conjunction with ujjayi over a long period of time, the tongue goes into the upper nasal orifice – in the language of Kabir Das, the "cave of the sky", – where amrit, the nectar of immortality, flows constantly.

Just below the place where the Hindus used to keep the *sikha-chutia*, tuft of hair, there is a centre called bindu visarga, or sometimes, bindu chakra. *Bindu* means 'drop'. This centre is so-called because of a small gland there which produces a secretion that is converted into nectar. This crude secretion drops down into a refining centre in the throat called *vishuddhi chakra* where it is purified. By practising khechari mudra for two to five years, these two important centres can be stimulated. When this occurs nectar will flow, rejuvenating the body. About this Kabir has written: "When this nectar is tasted all fears, diseases, guilt and ignorance are burned away. Inside you will shine like the full moonlit night."

When the eyes are closed, what does one see? Only darkness. But if the eyes are closed when the nectar is flowing, only light is seen. The whole brain, the whole consciousness is illumined. This is the aim of practising ujjayi with khechari.

Why is the heat produced by khechari mudra important?

Swami Satyananda: By practising khechari mudra, heat is produced in the physical and subtle bodies. This is the same type of heat as that which may be produced through pranayama. It is stated in *Hatha Yoga Pradipika* (3:49):

Jihvaapraveshasambhootavahninotpaaditah khalu;
Chandraatstravati yah saarah saa syaadamaravaarunee.

When the tongue enters the cavity, indeed heat is produced and the nectar flows from the moon.

This heat is extremely important for the release of the 'nectar from the moon'. Just as metal becomes liquid when it is heated, ice becomes water and paraffin wax becomes liquid paraffin, so the nectar in the body which has 'solidified' begins to run like a fluid when it is heated. The release of this fluid within the body is extremely important for arousing a higher state of consciousness.

What is the fluid that is released by practising khechari mudra?

Swami Satyananda: The fluid released through the practice of khechari mudra is known as amrit. *Amrit* means 'nectar' or 'ambrosia', also, 'immortal': hence, the nectar of immortality.

When the tongue enters into the upper epiglottis, it touches a particular 'nerve ending'. That centre is in the nasal passage near lalana chakra. This particular centre, which the flexible tongue is able to reach, is connected with a higher centre in the brain. When the stimulus is transferred to that higher brain centre the fluid begins to flow. This particular brain centre is at a point called the cranial passage, known in yoga as bindu visarga. This is where many Hindus grow a tuft of hair, exactly at that centre.

Inside there is a tiny depression. In that depression is a small amount of fluid which in yoga is known as amrit. This fluid is not used, but close by there is another centre from which cerebrospinal fluid flows into the spine. If

104

that cerebrospinal fluid stops, one's consciousness cannot function.

This secretion known in yoga as amrit is the subject matter of khechari mudra. When the elongated and flexible tongue is able to reach a particular centre in the epiglottis then sometimes the nectar begins to flow down. It does not flow constantly, only for a fraction of a second, and the moment this fluid flows into the body, the body and mind begin to change. One may be sitting anywhere and the consciousness begins to change, even if there is no awareness of it.

Where does the secretion of amrit come from?

Swami Satyananda: Amrit is surely an endocrine secretion. It comes down and is assimilated by the body through the blood vessels. When it is properly assimilated, the body changes. Catabolism, the decaying process is arrested and a proper balance between anabolism, metabolism and catabolism is created, so that decay and degeneration in the blood vessels, cells and whole body is arrested. In this way the yoga practitioner achieves rejuvenation, *kayakalpa*. Kayakalpa means changing the total content of the body.

How are lalana and vishuddhi chakras affected by khechari mudra?

Swami Satyananda: The purpose of khechari mudra is to stimulate and awaken lalana chakra. Though it is a physical technique it induces subtle changes on a psychic level. *Lalana chakra* is a minor chakra that is closely associated with vishuddhi. It is located between bindu and vishuddhi, in the back of the naso-pharynx, the inner cavity above and beyond the soft palate into which the nasal passages open. When khechari mudra is performed, one is attempting to turn the tongue up and backwards into this cavity to stimulate the flow of nectar.

When the nectar trickles down from bindu it is stored in lalana, a sort of glandular reservoir, before reaching vishuddhi chakra. Although this fluid is known as ambrosia it actually has a dual nature which can act as poison as well as nectar. When it is produced in bindu and stored in lalana, it remains undifferentiated, neither poison nor nectar. As long as vishuddhi remains inactive, this fluid runs downward unimpeded, to be consumed in the fire of manipura, resulting in the processes of decay, degeneration and finally death in the body's tissues.

However, by certain practices such as khechari mudra, when the ambrosia is secreted from lalana it passes to vishuddhi chakra, the purifying and refining centre. When vishuddhi is awakened, the divine fluid is retained and used, becoming the nectar of immortality. The secret of youth and regeneration of the body lies in the awakening of vishuddhi. Life becomes a source of joyful experiences.

This signifies that even poison can be readily digested when vishuddhi chakra is awakened. It means that at higher levels of awareness, vishuddhi and above, even the poisonous and negative aspects of existence become integrated into the total scheme of being. They are rendered powerless, as concepts of good and bad fall away. In this state of awareness the poisonous aspects and experiences of life are absorbed and transformed into a state of bliss. Such is the importance of the vishuddhi-lalana chakras.

How does the perfection of khechari mudra make the body immune to toxins?

Swami Satyananda: 'Drinking the nectar of the moon' means drinking or assimilating the fluid released from bindu visarga. Bindu is always depicted as a full moon. The nectar produced in bindu is said to intoxicate the conscious mind and make the body resistant to toxins in the system.

At a certain stage of spiritual evolution this is an inevitable process which takes place irrespective of the type of yoga that is practised. There is a well known story about Mira Bai, one of the greatest saints and bhaktas of India. Her devotion to Lord Krishna was so intense that she lived

106

in constant ecstasy through remembering him. Even when her mother-in-law fed her deadly poison she remained unaffected. People say that Lord Krishna turned the poison into rose water or milk. Actually, her system was immune to it because of the 'flow of nectar from the bindu'. It is stated in *Hatha Yoga Pradipika* (3:45):

> *Nityam somakalaapoornam shareeram yasya yoginah;*
> *Takshakenaapi dashtasya visham tasya na sarpati.*

The yogi's body is forever full of the moon's nectar. Even if he is bitten by the king of snakes (Takshaka), he is not poisoned.

According to hatha yoga, if the practice of khechari mudra can be perfected, after two weeks the process of degeneration in the body is reversed. *Hatha Yoga Pradipika* (3:44) says:

> *Oordhvajihvah shtiro bhootvaa somapaanam karoti yah;*
> *Maasaardhena na sandeho mrityum jayati yogavit.*

With the tongue directed upwards, the knower of yoga drinks the fluid of the moon. Within fifteen days physical death is conquered.

However, it takes a long time to perfect khechari, but one should consider the fact that during the process of perfecting it, the body is slowly readjusting itself, and once it is perfected, it will only take a short time to release the fluid from bindu.

What is the effect of khechari mudra on ajna chakra?

Swami Satyananda: If the tongue can reach the eyebrow centre internally, the pineal gland, and also ajna chakra, will be stimulated. There is a close relationship between the pineal gland, vishuddhi chakra and lalana chakra. Bindu visarga, the psychic centre at the top back of the head, is also influenced by khechari mudra. Bindu is said to be the place where the moon resides, and when it is full it sheds its nectar or ambrosial fluid down to permeate the entire body, just as the external moon pours its light over the surface of the earth at the time of the full moon. In *Shiva Samhita* (3:73) it is written:

Raajadantabilam gaadham sampeedya vidhinaa pibet;
Dhyaatvaa kundalineem deveem shanmaasena kavirbhavet.

When, having firmly closed the glottis by the proper yogic method, and contemplating the goddess Kundalini, he drinks (the moon fluid of immortality), he becomes a sage or poet within six months.

What is the effect of khechari mudra on the body?

Swami Satyananda: Khechari mudra exerts a controlling influence upon the network of endocrine glands throughout the body. This is achieved by regulating the production of the powerful secretions of the brain itself, which are produced in tiny amounts to control the pituitary gland and thereby the whole orchestra of glands associated with the centres below ajna. These dependent glands include the thyroid, mammary, thymus, adrenal and reproductive glands, as well as many other dependent processes which continually go on in the body.

The practice of khechari mudra also influences the centres in the hypothalamus and brain stem which control autonomic breathing, heart rate, emotional expression, appetite and thirst. The hypothalamus is strongly connected with the thalamus and the RAS (reticular activating system), which assumes a vital role in the sleep and wake mechanisms and all degrees of central nervous system activities, including the ability to concentrate.

The practice also influences the salivary gland and the faculty of taste, which in turn are connected to the lower nerve plexuses involved in the digestive and assimilative processes. In *Hatha Yoga Pradipika* (3:38–39) the effects on the body are described:

108

Rasanaamoordhvagaam kritvaa kshanaardhamapi tishthati;
Vishairvimuchyate yogee vyaadhimrityujaraadibhih.

Na rogo maranam tandraa na nidraa na kshudhaa trishaa;
Na cha moorchchhaa bhavettasya yo mudraam vetti khechareem.

The yogi who remains with the tongue going upwards for even half a second is freed from toxins, disease, death, old age, etc. (38)

One who accomplishes this khechari mudra is neither troubled by diseases, nor death, lassitude, sleep, hunger, thirst or unconsciousness. (39)

Knowing the neuro-endocrinal functions of the brain helps one to understand this sloka concerning the powerful effects of khechari mudra on human psychophysiology and destiny.

Does khechari mudra help with the management of sexuality?

Swami Satyananda: Khechari mudra has a powerful effect on the endocrine system and the pineal gland. If one has control of the reproductive fluid, one has control of nature, the body and the mind. Of course, it is not easy to develop this control, but hatha yoga provides the methods. It is stated in *Hatha Yoga Pradipika* (3:42–43):

Khecharyaa mudritam yena vivaram lambikordhvatah;
Na tasya ksharate binduh kaaminyaah shleshitasya cha.

Chalito'pi yadaa bindu sampraapto yonimandalam;
Vrajatyoordhvam hritah shaktayaa nibaddho yonimudrayaa.

When the upper cavity of the palate is sealed by khechari mudra, the bindu or semen cannot be lost even if one embraces a beautiful woman. (42)

Even when there is movement of the bindu and it enters the genitals, it is seized by closing the perineum and is taken upward. (43)

Khechari mudra regulates hormonal production and activity in the brain centres while other practices directly control the secretory behaviour of the reproductive organs.

Does khechari mudra affect the psychological quality of the practitioner?

Swami Satyananda: Becoming established in khechari can bring about a change in consciousness so that one learns from a mistake and does not make it again, so that one learns how to manage these inner forces properly without any unnecessary residue of guilt or anxiety. It is stated in *Hatha Yoga Pradipika* (3:48):

> *Goshabdenoditaa jihvaa tatpravesho hi taaluni;*
> *Gomaamsabhakshanam tattu mahaapaatakanaashanam.*

> The word 'go' means tongue (and also means cow). When it enters into the upper palate, it is 'eating the flesh of the cow'. It (khechari) destroys the great sins.

The meaning of 'eating cow's flesh' is clarified by Yogi Swatmarama: *gomansa* is the tongue and should not be literally interpreted to mean 'cow's meat'. When the tongue is swallowed back up into the nasal cavity, that is called 'eating cow's meat' in hatha yoga. A Hindu considers a cow most sacred; it is worshipped as a form of Devi. For any Hindu, to eat cow's meat is one of the worst crimes, incurring the worst karma. Therefore, Yogi Swatmarama had to elucidate on the practice of eating cow's meat.

The practice of khechari is said to destroy 'the great sins'. What are these sins? The great sins are not overt crimes, but defects in character which are the cause of crimes. The defects are: lust, greed, anger, fear, ignorance and/or jealousy. These are also known as the 'six enemies' in some texts.

Khechari helps one to overcome gross emotions and passions that compel a person to react with anger, greed, etc. The very pattern of ones thoughts and desires can be overhauled, and in this way it can be said that the sins are destroyed. However, it's important not to misunderstand sin in this context due to its religious connotations.

Sin should be understood as something that is an obstacle to spiritual progress. These 'negative modes' of mind which grip the body and force one to act can become a powerful bondage to lower levels of awareness and can hinder further development. They are not to be suppressed, yet they have to be overcome and khechari mudra gives a direct method of doing so, by helping one recognize their subtle forms.

How does the absorption of amrit influence one's consciousness?

Swami Satyananda: This nectar, amrit, is responsible for the rejuvenation of the physical system, but it doesn't usually happen with the common man, nor is the purpose of this nectar to rejuvenate the physical body.

When the amrit is absorbed by the body during the practice of khechari mudra, the restless mind becomes quiet and one-pointed. Passions, desires, imaginations and dissipations just drop away.

When it flows and is absorbed by the body, one's state of consciousness changes, just as when cannabis, LSD, peyote, or even alcohol are taken, a change or an altered state of consciousness occurs.

How does science explain the nectar of immortality associated with khechari mudra?

Swami Satyananda: Yogic texts are pervaded by the theme of an immortal nectar and the techniques and practices by which it can be trapped and consumed within the human body. The divinization of man is considered to be a process of physiology rather than a philosophical or religious idea. In *Hatha Yoga Pradipika* (3:51) this nectar is associated with khechari mudra:

Moordhnah shodashapatrapadmagalitam praanaadavaaptam
hathaa-doordhvaasyo rasanaam niyamya vivare shaktim
paraam chintayan.
Utkallolakalaajalam cha vimalam dhaaraamayam yah pibe-
nirvyaadhih sa mrinaalakomalavapuryogee chiram jeevati.

Fluid drips into the sixteen-petalled lotus when the tongue is inserted into the upper throat cavity; the paramshakti (kundalini) is released and one becomes concentrated in the experience which ensues. The yogi who drinks the pure stream of nectar is freed from disease, has longevity, and has a body as soft and as beautiful as a lotus stem.

The sixteen-petalled lotus spoken of in the sloka is vishuddhi chakra. It describes the mechanism of consuming the nectarine flow by khechari mudra. When the tongue becomes flexible and can be inserted into the upper epiglottis, a nectarine secretion begins to flow. It drips from bindu visarga to soma, lalana and vishuddhi chakras. This is the technique of preservation and rejuvenation adopted by the yogis to gain radiant health, longevity and physical attractiveness.

This indicates the capacity of the yogi who has awakened vishuddhi chakra to assimilate both positive and negative aspects of life; to retain balance, health and equanimity in the midst of the dualities of pain and pleasure, light and dark, life and death, body and mind, etc. Physiologically, the symbology has relevance to the thyroid gland in the front of the neck and its relationship with the pituitary gland. The thyroid gland is responsible for regulation of the body's metabolic rate. It differs from other endocrine glands in that it has the capacity to secrete and store the hormones synthesized by its secretory cells within the follicles of the gland itself, and these pooled secretions can be understood as the nectar of vishuddhi.

Thyroxine is essential in maintaining the normal activities of the central nervous system, body growth and movement, memory, thought process and speech, and emotional and behavioural stability. It also exerts important effects on the biochemistry of the liver, heart and skeletal muscles, is essential in maintenance of the cells of the anterior pituitary, and has other important functions. Thus, thyroid imbalance has far-reaching effects on the whole body.

Symptoms of hyperthyroidism include tremulous personality, unstable emotions, poor memory, anxiety, palpitations and accelerated heart rate, accelerated gastric motility with diarrhoea and loss of weight. On the other hand, in hypothyroidism there is a general slowing of the mental and physical processes, including slowing of speech and thought processes, obesity and heaviness, reduced and slowed physical movements, and constipation.

It is interesting to note that Yogi Swatmarama mentions the body becoming as soft as a lotus stem with the trapping of nectar, as thyroxine maintains skin pliability and texture. In hypothyroidism the skin becomes dry and puffy, and with hyperthyroidism the skin becomes warm, moist and clammy. Correct proportion of thyroxine is clearly essential for balanced functioning of the body and mind. This is a part of the physiological aspect of the 'dripping of nectar', a phenomenon associated with the practice of khechari mudra.

What do the different flavours experienced during khechari mudra signify?

Swami Satyananda: The particular tastes attributed to the nectar are related to the *pancha tattwas* the five elements: earth, water, fire, air and ether. Each creates a definite flavour when it predominates. *Tattwas* represent specific pranic flows associated with the five vayus and each can be tasted when it is active. According to the flavour, the active tattwa can be known, as each tattwa is characterized by a particular flavour: earth has a sweet flavour, water is astringent, fire is bitter, air is acidic and ether is pungent or hot. These flavours are listed in *Hatha Yoga Pradipika* (3:50):

Chumbantee yadi lambikaagramanisham jihvaarasasyandinee;
Sakshaaraa katukaamladugdhasadrishee madhvaajyatulyaa tathaa;
Vyaadheenaam haranam jaraantakaranam shastraagamodeeranam;
Tasya syaadamaratvamashtagunitam siddhaanganaakarshanam.

When the tongue constantly presses the cavity, the moon's nectar flows and has a saline, pungent and acidic flavour. It is like the consistency of milk, ghee, honey. Fatal diseases, old age and weapons are warded off. From that, immortality and the eight siddhis or perfections manifest.

How does khechari help to deepen meditation?

Swami Satyananda: Methods such as shatkarma, asana and pranayama are intended to awaken sushumna nadi. By that time, everything is set properly. The chakras are clear, the pathways of the nadis are unblocked, and awakening can take place. Mudras and bandhas are intended to awaken kundalini, which arouses meditation spontaneously. It is stated in *Hatha Yoga Pradipika* (4:43–46):

Savyadakshinanaadeestho madhye charati maarutah;
Tishthati khecharee mudraa tasminsthaane na samshayah.

Idaapingalayormadhye shoonyam chaivaanilam graset;
Tishthate khecharee mudraa tatra satyam punah punah.

Sooryaachandramasormadhye niraalambaantare punah;
Samsthitaa vyomachakre yaa saa mudraa naama khecharee.

Somaad yatroditaa dhaaraa saakshaat saa shivavallabhaa;
Poorayedatulaam divyaam sushumnaam pashchime mukhe.

When the prana which is in the right and left nadis moves in the middle nadi (sushumna) that is the condition for khechari mudra. (43)

The fire (of shakti) being swallowed (suppressed) midway between, ida and pingala, in that shoonya (of sushumna), is in truth the condition for khechari mudra. (44)

114

The middle of the sun (pingala) and moon (ida) is the 'unsupported', in which is situated vyoma chakra or the centre of ether (void). This mudra is called khechari. (45)

In the flow from the moon (bindu) is the beloved of Shiva (consciousness). The opening of the unequalled divine sushumna should be filled from behind (by the tongue). (46)

Even if one does not know how to meditate, or does not have sufficient willpower, if khechari mudra is practised, after some time a 'serum' flows into the body. When it mixes with the blood and other secretions, the state of mind and flow of prana changes. One begins to feel 'high', and the brainwave patterns alter. Even with the eyes open, one can have an altered experience. With the eyes closed one is able to have inner experience. Music can be heard internally. The beauty of flowers can be seen in any season, anywhere. The moon can be seen even when there is none. It is not hallucination, it is a real and conscious experience. The body becomes quiet and the mind steady. It is stated in *Hatha Yoga Pradipika* (4:47):

Poorastaachchaiva pooryeta nishchitaa khecharee bhavet;
Abhyaastaa khecharee mudraapyunmanee samprajaayate.

The sushumna being completely filled at the rear (upper palate) also is khechari. The practice of khechari mudra is followed by the state of unmani (consciousness devoid of mind).

Mudra is one of the most important aspects that hatha yoga has inherited from tantra to expand the consciousness. Meditation may be a spiritual practice but its effects on the body are definite and physiologically verified. Alpha waves become intense, respiration becomes minimal, consumption of oxygen decreases, blood pressure and temperature drop. The rishis realized these effects and therefore instructed the use of particular asanas for meditation and also the use of mudras, especially khechari.

When sushumna is active, the heart rate and blood pressure drop, and at that time khechari must be employed. Mudras definitely affect the quality of meditation. This can be verified by experiment: one can practise meditation of a passive type for six months, then change the practice to an active type incorporating mudras like maha vedha, and others, especially khechari mudra. The nature of the experiences will definitely alter.

How is khechari mudra used to influence the flows of ida, pingala and sushumna?

Swami Satyananda: Once the tongue has been sufficiently elongated, it has to be inserted into the nasal cavity at the back of the throat. This is not an easy process and at first it is necessary to push the tongue into position with the fingers. When the tongue is strengthened, it can be pushed right into the back of the nasal cavity by itself, and when prana is awakened in the body, the tongue will move into that position spontaneously. It is stated in *Hatha Yoga Pradipika* (3:37):

Kalaam paraanmukheem kritvaa tripathe pariyojayet;
Saa bhavetkhecharee mudraa vyomachakram taduchyate.

Having turned the tongue back, the three channels of ida, pingala and sushumna are controlled. This is khechari mudra and it is called the centre of ether.

When the tongue is inserted right up into the nasal cavity, the breath can be directed into either nostril by the tip of the tongue. The tip of the tongue will be able to block the right or left passage or be placed a little lower so that both nostrils are open. To actually elongate the tongue to the extent that it can move up to the eyebrow centre takes many years of consistent practice.

116

What chakras and nadis are stimulated by khechari mudra?

Swami Satyananda: When the tongue extends into the nasal cavity through the practice of khechari mudra, then four chakras in that area are affected: *ajna* – in the medulla oblongata; *lalana* – just below ajna and opposite the uvula (the fleshy appendage which projects from the soft palate); *manas* – directly above ajna; and *soma* – above manas, in the mid-cerebrum above the sensorium.

The five nadis which convene in this cavity are ida, pingala, sushumna, gandhari and hastijihva, which all merge into ajna. This is stated in *Hatha Yoga Pradipika* (3:53):

> *Sushiram jnaanajanakam panchastrotahsamanvitam;*
> *Tishthate khecharee mudraa tasminshoonye niranjane.*

> Five nadis convene in this cavity and it is the source of knowledge. Khechari should be established in that void, untainted (by ignorance).

Why is khechari an important practice during samadhi?

Swami Satyananda: Through the practice of khechari mudra the prana is maintained in the body even while the consciousness moves into the higher realms during samadhi. This is achieved by channelling the total pranic force through sushumna. It is stated in *Hatha Yoga Pradipika* (3:46):

> *Indhanaani yathaa vahnistailavarttim cha deepakah;*
> *Tathaa somakalaapoornam dehi deham na munchati.*

> Just as fuel kindles fire and oil a lamp, so the indweller of the body does not vacate while the body is full of the moon's nectar.

The process involves the release of the body fluid the yogis call amaravaruni. *Amara* refers to immortality or the moon and *varuni* is wine. *Amaravaruni* is the wine of immortality or of the moon. This wine is the fluid secreted by bindu visarga.

117

It is the nectar of pure consciousness. It is stated in *Hatha Yoga Pradipika* (3:47):

Gomaamsam bhakshayennityam pibedamaravaaruneem;
Kuleenam tamaham manye chetare kulaghaatakaah.

By constant swallowing of the tongue he can drink amaravaruni. I consider him of high lineage (heritage). Others destroy the heritage.

Just as the result of the union between a man and a woman is the release of reproductive secretions, so the union of ida and pingala with sushumna in ajna chakra releases the fluid from bindu. At that time one experiences the climax of spiritual experience which is more fulfilling than any empirical experience. With the release of amaravaruni the body is impregnated with spiritual or cosmic force and gives birth to higher consciousness or *atman*.

The physical body is the feminine principle of Shakti. Mind is the masculine principle of Shiva, consciousness. The union of the two is realization of the indweller, the Self.

Yogi Swatmarama says that the person who can drink amaravaruni is from a worthy or high lineage. Those who live, procreate and die without attaining any spiritual knowledge have not been fulfilling the purpose of life or evolution. They are only continuing the generations of families.

However, once a person endeavours to know the spirit or pure consciousness, the whole physical structure undergoes a rearrangement and even the genes of that person change. Consequently, the generations that follow are influenced by the achievements made in sadhana. The children of such a person, and their children, have a greater chance of achieving the same perfections. Therefore, the person who can drink amaravaruni is truly venerable to his family.

What are the spiritual benefits of khechari mudra?
Swami Satyananda: The benefits attributed to khechari mudra are those which result from the experience of

supraconsciousness or samadhi. It is stated in *Hatha Yoga Pradipika* (3:40–41):

Peedyate na sa rogena lipyate na cha karmanaa;
Baadhyate na sa kaalena yo mudraam vetti khechareem.

Chittam charati khe yasmaajjihvaa charati khe gataa;
Tenaishaa khecharee naama mudraa siddhairniroopitaa.

One who knows khechari mudra is unafflicted by disease, unaffected by the laws of cause and effect (karma) and free from the bonds of time (death). (40)

Mind moves in Brahman (khe) because the tongue moves in space (khe). Therefore, the perfected ones have named this mudra khechari, moving in space, or Brahman. (41)

Here we are told that khechari is so powerful that the practitioner can reach a state beyond *karma* (i.e. cause and effect), time, death and disease, which are all aspects of the influence of Shakti or *maya*. The state of supraconsciousness is that of universal awareness, beyond duality and the finite mind. It is called *kaivalya*, *nirvana*, *moksha*, *samadhi* or *Brahma* – these are all synonymous terms indicating the final stage or accomplishment of raja yoga

Khechari mudra directly influences brain functions and awakens the higher centres of awareness. Our mind functions within the confines of time and space, ida and pingala, but it is possible to transcend these two poles of duality. Normal brain functions have to undergo a transformation and restructuring so that supernormal functioning takes place.

Time and space are concepts of the finite mind and perception. In yoga and tantra they are said to be the tools of maya, prakriti or Shakti. They are the laws of nature, and finite mind is the product of nature. If consciousness can be expanded beyond the awareness of finite mind and natural phenomena, it will enter the realm of the infinite.

How is khechari mudra linked with cosmic consciousness?

Swami Satyananda: *Bindu* is the seed of creation and khechari mudra maintains bindu in the brain centre. This leads to the expansion of finite consciousness and realization of Shiva, Brahman, atman. This is a state that transcends the mind; it is samadhi. In *Hatha Yoga Pradipika* (3:54) it is written:

Ekam srishtimayam beejamekaa mudraa cha khecharee;
Eko devo niraalamba ekaavasthaa manonmanee.

There is only one seed of creation and one mudra – khechari; one deva independent of everything, and one state – manonmani.

This sloka indicates the experience of oneness, union with the Supreme, which is realized by the yogi. There is an experience of oneness which is to be realized. There is unity amidst seeming diversity; the many fragmentary experiences, seeming realities, individuals and distinctions one confronts, are only elements of a greater Self, which includes all diversities and relative contradictions within itself. A yogi gains this experience by grasping within himself the bindu of consciousness. The unity of consciousness, creation and mind is comprehended by one who realizes the bindu; the seed from which all thoughts, minds, bodies, deities, devas and mudras spring forth.

The one who has steadied the bindu comprehends in a single eternal crystalline experience all the scattered and fragmentary pieces of individual and collective perception, knowledge and aspiration. He alone sees the world through the eye of Lord Shiva, the one who wishes well to all beings and sees only unity amidst apparent diversity.

Different men appear separate and distinct from one another, with distinguishing features and characteristics. However, from a greater standpoint these distinctions fall away and we can see that all men are essentially the same – all are born by the same process, with the same hopes and aspirations, fears and desires. Similarly, individual minds and personalities can be endlessly defined by their differences, but it is to their similarity that a yogi directs his attention. All minds are only minute parts and expressions of a single collective mind. To realize this collective mind in operation is called *manonmani*.

How is the yogi to realize within himself the entire creation in all its diversity, which has been studied in a thousand disciplines? Physics, chemistry, history, biology and geology are just a few of them. Even a lifespan of academic study could not hope to keep abreast of all these fields of research. Yogically, these types of knowledge are not absolute, but are the various aspects of a single creative seed and source, like rays emerging from the sun. The realization of creation, time and space, including his own body and mind, as the outpouring of the one cosmic maha bindu, is the attainment of a yogi.

Similarly, all the mudras and other practices of hatha yoga lead towards khechari, the attitude of unsupportedness in space; consciousness existing alone and independently; without a second. In the same way, all the devas, deities, gurus and evolved personalities are to be realized as the work pieces of a single absolute consciousness and experience.

How is the yogic aspirant to gain this experience of yoga? How to realize the one containing the many, and the unity within diversity? How to realize that he is none other than all names, forms, ages, times and personalities which have ever existed or will ever exist, to have the experience that all these are already within himself? How to span the seemingly infinite chasm between the individual and cosmic awareness? By realizing the bindu, the seed, the nada within his own body, mind and consciousness. By the outpouring of the bindu, one has become many. By its retention, many again become one.

4

Kaya Mudra: Postural Mudras

YOGA MUDRA: ATTITUDE OF PSYCHIC UNION

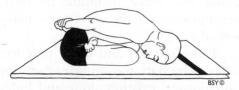

What is the meaning of yoga mudra?

Swami Satyananda: Yoga mudra is so called because it unites the individual consciousness with the Supreme Consciousness, or the outer nature with the inner nature.

What is the difference between the hatha yoga and the kundalini yoga versions of yoga mudra?

Swami Niranjanananda: In the hatha yoga technique one sits in padmasana, closes the eyes and clasps the left wrist with the right hand. Inhaling deeply in the upright position, the breath is released while slowly bending forward, bringing the forehead to the floor. This position is held for as long as is comfortable, with concentration on manipura chakra. Then the body is slowly raised to the starting position while inhaling.

In the kundalini yoga technique, sitting in padmasana, the right wrist is held with the left hand, or the left wrist with the right hand. The hand that is held should always be opposite to the nostril which is flowing more freely. If the right nostril is flowing more freely, then the left wrist is held with the right hand. If the left nostril is flowing more freely, then the right wrist is held with the left hand. The purpose is to balance the swara.

In the starting position, one inhales deeply and then exhales. With the breath held out, the awareness is brought to mooladhara chakra, and 'mooladhara' is mentally repeated five times with concentration at the perineum. Then, while slowly inhaling, the awareness is taken up the spinal passage from mooladhara to ajna. At this point, the awareness is at ajna, at the top of the spine, just below the bindu centre. Beginning to exhale, one bends forward until the head touches the floor. While bending forward, the awareness is moved from the back of the head to the forehead. As the forehead touches the floor the awareness should be at bhrumadhya. The breath is retained outside while mentally repeating 'ajna' five times. There should be total relaxation of the entire body in the pose. The body should be loose like a rag doll. Inhaling, the body is lifted upright with the breath, bringing the awareness from bhrumadhya to ajna in the centre of the head. Slowly exhaling, the awareness is taken down along the spine from ajna to mooladhara. Holding the breath outside, and with the awareness at mooladhara, the word 'mooladhara' is mentally repeated five times. This is one round.

During the practice the movement of the body should be coordinated with the breath and the movement of the consciousness up and down the spine. This is very important.

Can other sitting postures be used by those who cannot sit in padmasana?

Swami Niranjanananda: If it is not possible to sit comfortably in padmasana, yoga mudra can be practised in vajrasana. This is like the technique of shashankasana with the hands clasped behind the back. If there is difficulty bending forward due to stiffness in the back, it will be easier to bend

123

forward into shashankasana. If it is difficult to bend forward in vajrasana, because of the legs supporting the entire trunk, then the knees can be separated slightly, allowing the chest to come closer to the floor. That is also a very comfortable posture and similar results are experienced.

What are the general benefits of yoga mudra?

Swami Niranjanananda: Yoga mudra is the best antidote for anxiety, tension, mental pressure, fatigue, lethargy, drowsiness or dullness.

When is the best time to practise yoga mudra?

Swami Niranjanananda: It should be practised first thing in the morning, so that the prana begins to flow through the chakras and the entire chakra system becomes active.

Why is yoga mudra a comforting practice?

Swami Niranjanananda: There are a few reasons why yoga mudra is so comforting. Firstly, it brings the body in touch with the ground. Touching the front of the body against the legs is deeply comforting. The resulting pressure along the abdomen and chest has a calming effect on the adrenal system, as in shashankasana. Also, in this posture the front of the body is protected while the back is exposed. The back of the body is harder; it is the soft front that one feels the need to protect. So, in yoga mudra a highly protective attitude is created, in which there is contact with the earth, and with the back to the world, one's connection with the external is closed off.

SWARA YOGA MUDRA:
BREATH BALANCING GESTURE

How is swara yoga mudra practised?

Swami Satyananda: Place the right hand under the left armpit and the left hand under the right armpit and press. The arms should be relaxed. This mudra is also known as padadhirasana.

Why is swara yoga mudra a useful preparation for meditation?

Swami Satyananda: Swara yoga mudra is used to make both nostrils flow freely. At the time of meditation both nostrils must flow freely. If they do not, part of the brain remains inactive and it is impossible to meditate properly. When both nostrils flow freely, both hemispheres of the brain are equally active and meditation can be accomplished without any difficulty.

TADAGI MUDRA: WATER POT MUDRA; BARRELLED ABDOMEN TECHNIQUE

What is the meaning of tadagi mudra?

Swami Satyananda: The word *tadagi* literally means 'water pot', which resembles the shape of an extended abdomen.

What happens during tadagi mudra?

Swami Niranjanananda: The forward bend blocks the lower part of the large and small intestines; this means that during deep inhalation, as the diaphragm contracts downward, the upper abdomen expands. On exhalation, the diaphragm relaxes upward, creating pressure throughout the trunk of the body. Tension stored in the diaphragm and pelvic floor is released. This practice tones the abdominal organs and stimulates blood circulation to these areas.

Imagine a pot half filled with water. When the pot is moved, the water rushes first to one side then to the other. The same effect is created inside the abdomen during this practice. It is essential that the stomach is empty. The abdomen is expanded while slowly drawing the breath in. The action of breathing in this way is similar to that of water in a moving pot. This analogy is used in *Gheranda Samhita* (3:73):

Udaram pashchimottaanam kritvaa cha tadaagaakritih;
Taadaagee saa paraamudraa jaraa mrityu vinaashinee.

Sit in paschimottanasana and expand the abdomen as if it were full of water. This is an important mudra which removes the fear of old age and death.

What are the benefits of tadagi mudra?
Swami Niranjanananda: Tadagi mudra improves digestion and helps to alleviate diseases in the abdominal region. The nerve plexuses in the visceral area are stimulated and toned.

This practice is also taught to rectify incorrect breathing, or thoracic breathing and to promote abdominal breathing. Many people believe the chest should expand on inhalation and try to forcefully expand the chest while keeping the abdomen tucked in. This exerts too much pressure in the upper portions of the lungs and creates tension in the lower parts, which can result in breathing problems. The muscles of the lower lungs become weak and the lungs begin to lose their capacity.

Spiritually, tadagi mudra stimulates manipura chakra, the centre of energy distribution, and raises the level of prana generally, which is needed for higher sadhana.

PASHINEE MUDRA:
FOLDED PSYCHIC ATTITUDE; NOOSE MUDRA

What is the meaning of pashinee mudra?
Swami Satyananda: The word *pash* means 'noose'. Pashinee therefore means, 'bound in a noose'.

What are the benefits of pashinee mudra?

Swami Niranjanananda: Pashinee mudra brings balance and tranquillity to the nervous system and induces *pratyahara*, sense withdrawal. It stretches the spine and back muscles and stimulates all the spinal nerves. It massages the abdominal organs and directs energy to the reproductive organs. Pashinee mudra strengthens the body.

The successful practitioner can become capable of fulfilling all desires, because this mudra is also helpful in awakening energy, especially in mooladhara and vishuddhi chakras. It is described in *Gheranda Samhita* (3:84–85):

Kanthaprishthe kshipetpaadau paashavad dridhabandhanam;
Sa eva paashinee mudraa shakti prabodhakaarinee.

Paashinee mahatee mudraa balapushti vidhaayinee;
Saadhaneeyaa prayatnena saadhakaih siddhikaankshibhih.

Taking both the legs behind the neck, hold them together firmly like a noose. This is pashinee mudra for awakening energy. (84)

It provides strength and vitality. A yogi desirous of siddhi should practise it with effort. (85)

MANDUKI MUDRA: GESTURE OF THE FROG

What is the meaning of manduki mudra?

Swami Niranjanananda: The word *manduki* means 'frog', so *manduki mudra* is the frog attitude. It was given this name because the sitting pose resembles the natural position of the frog.

127

What is manduki mudra?

Swami Satyananda: Manduki mudra is an advanced variation of *nasikagra drishti*, nosetip gazing: while sitting in manduki asana one performs *nasikagra drishti*. It should be performed in mild light so that the tip of the nose can be seen clearly.

Why is nosetip gazing used in manduki mudra?

Swami Satyananda: The purpose of gazing at the tip of the nose is to calm the disturbances and fluctuations of the mind, and to balance ida and pingala, creating harmony between extroversion and introversion.

This is exquisitely and lucidly described in the Chinese scriptures called *T'ai Chin Hua Tzung Chih* translated by Wilhelm: "What then is really meant by this? The expression 'tip of the nose' is very cleverly chosen. The nose must serve the eyes as a guideline. If one is not guided by the nose either one opens the eyes too wide and looks into the distance so that the nose is not seen, or the lids shut too much so that the eyes are not seen. But when the eyes are opened too wide, one makes the mistake of directing them outwards, thereby one is easily distracted (by outer events). If they are closed too much, one makes the mistake of letting them turn inwards, thereby one easily sinks into a dreamy reverie (lost in thoughts; unawareness). Only when the eyelids are lowered properly, halfway, is the tip of the nose seen in just the right way. Therefore, it is taken as a guideline . . ."

Thus, there is great significance and reason behind nosetip gazing. It balances the ida and pingala nadis and leads to the awakening of sushumna, leading directly to meditation if it is perfected: this is the reason for nosetip gazing in manduki mudra.

Where is the awareness placed during manduki mudra?

Swami Satyananda: Physical awareness is at the nosetip; spiritual awareness is at mooladhara chakra.

What are the effects of manduki mudra?

Swami Satyananda: Manduki mudra activates mooladhara chakra. It calms the disturbances and fluctuations of the mind and balances ida and pingala nadis, leading directly to meditation.

What are the different methods of practising manduki mudra?

Swami Niranjanananda: Generally manduki mudra is an advanced practice of nasikagra drishti. In the kriya yoga practice of manduki mudra, awareness of the sense of smell is included, as one imagines the fragrance of sandalwood, the smell of the astral body.

In *Gheranda Samhita*, however, nosetip gazing is not included. While keeping the mouth closed, the tongue is rotated from right to left and up and down. This stimulates a secretion known as *shuddha* or *amrita*, nectar. Drinking this nectar can only be perfected by practice. In this mudra the rotation of the tongue to all sides is just like the jumping of a frog, hence it has been named the frog mudra. It is described in *Gheranda Samhita* (3:74):

> *Mukham sammudritam kritvaa jihvaamoolam prachaalayet;*
> *Shanairgrasedamritam taam maandukeem mudrikaam viduh.*

> Keeping the mouth closed, the tongue should be rotated inside the palate and nectar flowing from sahasrara should be slowly tasted by the tongue. This is called manduki mudra.

What are the benefits of manduki mudra?

Swami Niranjanananda: According to Sage Gheranda those who practise this mudra never grow old. The nectar provides strength and vitality to the body. Wrinkles do not appear and the hair does not turn grey, the cells of the body are not destroyed, and maximum grace is achieved. In *Gheranda Samhita* (3:75) it is written:

Valitampalitam naiva jaayate nityayauvanam;
Na keshe jaayate paako yah kuryaannityamaandukeem.

By this practice wrinkling of the body and greying of the hair cease and permanent youth is attained.

In kundalini yoga, the physical posture is an important practice for awakening mooladhara chakra, which is linked to perceiving divine scents in the state of meditation.

VIPAREETA KARANI MUDRA: INVERTED PSYCHIC ATTITUDE

What is vipareeta karani mudra?
Swami Satyananda: The practice of vipareeta karani is similar to the shoulder stand pose, *sarvangasana*. The major difference is the angle of the back to the floor. In sarvangasana the back and legs should be perpendicular, in vipareeta karani the back is maintained at a forty-five degree angle to the floor and legs. This means the throat

is not completely blocked and allows unrestricted blood flow to the brain. Vipareeta karani mudra is the first practice in kriya yoga. In kriya yoga a particular concentration and visualization is used in the practice which is omitted in the hatha yoga technique.

What is the meaning of vipareeta karani mudra?
Swami Satyananda: In Sanskrit *vipareeta* means 'inverted', *karani*

130

means 'one who does', and *mudra* is usually interpreted as a gesture that symbolizes, by means of the body, an inner feeling or attitude. Hence, it is called the inverted psychic attitude. English names of the asana, though not direct translations of the Sanskrit name, include: the half-shoulder stand pose, the inverted gesture, and the inverted pose.

Though its name signifies that it is a mudra, vipareeta karani is generally classified as an asana by present day authorities, possibly due to its close resemblance to sarvangasana. Classical hatha yoga texts attach great importance to this mudra.

What is the postural difference between vipareeta karani asana and vipareeta karani mudra?

Swami Niranjanananda: There is a version of vipareeta karani mudra which is taught as an asana for the considerable physical benefits of the inverted posture. In this method the legs are kept straight and perpendicular to the floor, rather than being tilted forward over the upper body. The feet are not brought in line with the line of sight. It is a much simpler technique. One simply breathes normally in the final position. This practice is known as vipareeta karani asana, but it is not exactly the correct position for the mudra.

How is vipareeta karani described in classical hatha yoga texts?

Swami Satyananda: No detailed description of the method of performing vipareeta karani is given in old texts. The brief descriptions that are given – legs upwards, arms and head on the ground – describe all the inverted poses. The ancient treatises say that vipareeta karani should be learnt from a guru, which is presumably the reason why its technique is not described. For example, in *Hatharatnavali* (2:66–68) it is written:

Yatkinchitsravate chandraadamritam divyaroopinah;
Tatsarvam grasate sooryastena bandham jaraayutam.

Tatraasti divyam karanam sooryasya mukhabandhanam;
Guroo padeshato jneyam na tu shaastraardha kotibhih.

Oordhvam naabhiradhastaaluroordhvam bhaanuradhah shashee;
Karanee vipareetaakhyaa guruvaakyena labhyate.

All the nectar that flows from the splendid moon (in the throat) is swallowed up by the sun (at the navel) and it is for this reason that the body gets old. (66)

There is a superb practice which binds the mouth of the sun in the navel. It can only be known from the instructions of a guru, not from millions of discussions. (67)

The practice in which the navel is above and the palate below, the sun above and the moon below, is known as vipareeta karani. It can only be learnt from the words uttered by the guru. (68)

It is possible that the practice as it is known and understood today is but one version of a number of possibilities, including perhaps sirshasana and sarvangasana. It other words, it is plausible that vipareeta karani mudra was originally a collective name of all the inverted poses, the names sirshasana and the others being of recent origin. This would certainly explain why an asana as important as sirshasana is not even mentioned in the old books.

Why is vipareeta karani called a mudra while sarvangasana is an asana?

Swami Niranjanananda: To understand this, the differences in the practices of sarvangasana and vipareeta karani need to be looked at. The position in vipareeta karani seems similar to that of sarvangasana. There is only a slight change in the position of the spinal column. The trunk is raised from the ground making an angle of forty-five degrees, and the buttocks are supported by the hands, whereas in sarvangasana the trunk is kept perpendicular to the ground

132

to make an angle of ninety degrees. In the practice of sarvangasana, jalandhara bandha is automatically practised, because the chin presses against the chest, but while practising vipareeta karani there is no jalandhara bandha. The pressure which is exerted on the chest in sarvangasana is absent in vipareeta karani, so the physical position is not uncomfortable.

Also, in the practice of sarvangasana the load and pressure is exerted on the neck and shoulders, in vipareeta karani it is distributed onto the arms and hands, i.e. the weight of the body is distributed from the elbows right up to the region of the head. The feeling of the weight of the body pressing down, especially on the neck, which is experienced during sarvangasana, is not present in vipareeta karani mudra. Vipareeta karani mudra gives a gentle inversion without hard compression of the neck. Physiologically, there is a greater flow of blood to the cerebral capillaries and blood vessels, which helps to activate the brain. Therefore, it is believed that the posture gives a fresh charge to the brain.

During the practice of sarvangasana, the whole neck is compressed and contracted. Breathing continues in a normal way, although with slight difficulty due to the compression of the throat. In vipareeta karani the throat is not contracted. This is an important difference as it means that the flow of both blood and prana to the brain is not restricted. It is the flow of prana, however, which has the greatest relevance to the quality of the practice as a mudra. The physical position is briefly described in *Gheranda Samhita* (3:47):

Bhoomau shirashcha samsthaapya karayugmam samaahitah;
Urdhvapaadah sthiro bhootvaa vipareetakaree mataa.

Place the head on the ground, provide support with both hands and raise both legs; this is vipareeta karani mudra. (3:47)

Why is vipareeta karani mudra an important hatha yoga practice?

Swami Niranjanananda: It is helpful to understand vipareeta karani from the viewpoint of hatha yoga. In hatha yoga, vipareeta karani mudra is explained in the context of the sun and moon. The word vipareeta means 'inverted'. The centre of *surya*, the sun, is manipura chakra in the solar plexus, and the centre of *chandra*, the moon, is the region of the brain or ajna, lalana and bindu chakras. In this practice, the position of the sun (manipura), and the moon (bindu), is reversed, so that the sun is above the moon. In *Gheranda Samhita* (3:45–46) this symbolism is used:

> *Naabhimoole vasetsooryastaalumoole cha chandramaah;*
> *Amritam graste sooryastato mrityuvasho narah.*

> *Urdhvam cha yojayetsooryam chandram chaapyadha aanayet;*
> *Vipareetakaree mudraa sarvatantreshu gopitaa.*

> The sun plexus is located at the root of the navel and the moon plexus is located at the root of the palate. A person dies when the sun consumes nectar secreted by the moon, but when the chandra nadi consumes the nectar, there is no fear of death. (45)

> Therefore, the sun is to be brought up and the moon is to be brought down. This is vipareeta karani mudra, which is secret by all standards. (46)

These verses say, *taalumoole cha chandramaah*, "the moon resides behind the palate," i.e. where lalana and bindu chakras are located. The sutras also say, *Amritam graste sooryastato mrityuvasho narah*, "the sun digests the nectar, due to which man is in the grip of death."

In vipareeta karani mudra the positions of the sun and the moon are reversed, so that the sun is above the moon, as the navel region goes up and the head is down on the ground. Normally, the life-giving nectar flows downward from bindu to manipura, where it is burnt up by physical

134

activities. In vipareeta karani, however, the process is reversed. The nectar of subtle life force is redirected from manipura back to bindu, its source, which leads to the expansion of consciousness and revitalization of one's entire being. It is even said that the aged can regain their youth and vitality by this practice.

Why have the details of vipareeta karani mudra traditionally been kept secret?

Swami Niranjanananda: In *Gheranda Samhita*, the asana or position of the body is described but which technique or method to follow while in the posture is not mentioned at all. This is because this sadhana or scripture is extremely secret, *sarva tantreshu gopitaa*. In this practice an effort is made to change the activities or processes of the body and the chemicals produced inside the body. Even if this is achieved by everyone who practises it, there will be those who do not understand what is happening to them. For this reason, it has been described as a secret process.

In vipareeta karani mudra, first the inverted posture reverses the flow of prana. Then, continual rotation of awareness and breath between the chakras takes this practice from being just an asana to being a mudra where one increases the awareness of, and redirects prana. When it is used as a mudra, the pranic dimension is augmented. With the rotation of awareness, the concentration and mental faculties are directed to a particular pathway in one's being. As one's awareness evolves, one can feel the actual movement happening at various levels.

Hatha yogis also combine the practices of khechari mudra and ujjayi pranayama with this practice. With ujjayi the breath is taken up from vishuddhi to bindu in a sudden rush, or ejection: one imagines that the awareness is flowing from vishuddhi to bindu, just as a jet of liquid flows out from an injection.

What are the physical benefits of vipareeta karani mudra?

Swami Niranjanananda: Vipareeta karani mudra balances a hypoactive thyroid and acts as a preventive for coughs, colds, sore throat and bronchial disorders. It stimulates the appetite and digestion, so a healthy and plentiful diet should be taken. It helps relieve constipation, particularly if water is drunk just before the practice. Regular practice prevents atherosclerosis by restoring vascular tone and elasticity. It relieves prolapse, haemorrhoids, varicose veins and hernia, all of which are exacerbated by the downward pull of gravity. Circulation to the brain is enhanced, especially to the cerebral cortex and pituitary and pineal glands. Cerebral insufficiency and senile dementia are counteracted and mental alertness increased.

The inverted posture sustained in this mudra is used to reverse the downward and outward movement of energy and redirect it back to the brain. When this happens, the whole being is revitalized and awareness expands. As the practice is perfected, the flow of prana in ida and pingala nadis becomes balanced. This state manifests as an equal flow of breath in the nostrils. The balancing effect of the practice also helps prevent disease from manifesting on the physical and mental planes.

Sage Gheranda says that whoever practises the sadhana of this mudra daily attains victory over old age and death, achieves siddhi in all the *lokas* or dimensions and is not destroyed even at the time of dissolution. This is written in *Gheranda Samhita* (3:48):

Mudraam cha saadhayennityam jaraam mrityum cha naashayet;
Sa siddhah sarvalokeshu pralaye'pi na seedati.

By practising it daily, old age and death are eliminated. The practitioner of this mudra attains siddhi (perfection) in all the lokas (worlds) and is not grieved even at the time of dissolution (of the universe).

What are the dietary guidelines for the serious practitioner of vipareeta karani mudra?

Swami Satyananda: There are a number of basic rules which have to be followed when practising any of the hatha yoga techniques. It is therefore important to learn under expert guidance. The practices have a specific effect on the body and mind which has to be watched by the person who is guiding you.

All the practices of hatha yoga will release an internal heat in the course of time. Swami Muktananda of Ganeshpuri describes how, as a result of asana, pranayama, mudra, bandha and meditation, a type of fire was liberated in his body. No matter what he did to cool himself, still his body burnt internally. Consequently his body became emaciated. He had to adjust his diet, taking boiled rice water rather than solid food. This reiterates that yoga practices are very powerful and the sadhaka must be guided by a guru.

One of the initial positive effects of vipareeta karani is an increased capacity to digest and assimilate food. Digestive secretions and appetite are definitely increased, therefore, a moderate diet should be taken at regular intervals.

Food should be taken after practising hatha yoga. If food is not taken, if one fasts, the gastric acids and digestive enzymes will burn the lining of the stomach and duodenum. However, this is unlikely to happen when vipareeta karani is practised for only a few minutes. Regularity of meal timings and quantities is necessary for the advanced hatha yogi, and fasting is contra-indicated. The effect of vipareeta karani mudra on the digestion is described in *Hatha Yoga Pradipika* (3:80–81):

Nityamabhyaasayuktasya jatharaagnivivardhinee;
Aahaaro bahulastasya sampaadyah saadhakasya cha;
Alpaahaaro yadi bhavedagnirdahati tatkshanaat.

Adhahshirashchordhvapaadah kshanam syaatprathame dine;
Kshanaachcha kinchidadhikamabhyaasechcha dine dine.

Digestion is strengthened by continual, regular practice and therefore, the practitioner should always have sufficient food. If one takes only a little food, the heat produced by the digestion will destroy the system. (80)

Therefore, on the first day, one should only stay a moment with the feet up and head down. The practice should be done daily, gradually increasing the duration. (81)

Why are practitioners of vipareeta karani mudra advised to eat well?

Swami Niranjanananda: The metabolic rate may increase when this mudra is practised for periods of half an hour or more. If this happens, the food intake should be adjusted accordingly. In *Hatharatnavali* (2:69–70) it says:

Karanee vipareetaakhyaa sarvavyaadhivinaashinee;
Nityamabhyaasayuktasya jatharaagni pravardhinee.

Aahaaro bahulastasya sampaadyah saadhakasya cha;
Alpaahaaro yadi bhavet agnirdeham dehat kshanaat.

This vipareeta karani destroys all sorts of diseases. It increases the gastric heat of a regular practitioner. (69)

One who practises it (daily) should procure and eat ample food. If he eats insufficient food, the increasing fire soon consumes his body. (70)

When and for how long should vipareeta karani mudra be practised?

Swami Satyananda: Vipareeta karani mudra should be done daily at a consistent time, preferably early in the morning. The position should only be held for a few seconds in the beginning or until discomfort arises. Over the period of a few months the duration of practice can slowly be increased. When pressure builds up in the head, slowly come down. Count the number of respirations taken during the practice and increase by an extra breath each day. In *Hatharatnavali* (2:71) it advises:

Adhah shiraa oordhvapaadah kshanam syaat prathame dine;
Kshanaachchetkinchidadhikam abhyasechcha dine dine.

On the first day one should remain for a very short time with one's head below and feet above. The duration of this practise should be increased day by day.

According to *Hatha Yoga Pradipika* (3:82):

Valitam palitam chaiva shannmaasordhvam na drishyate;
Yaamamaatram tu yo nityamabhyaset sa tu kaalajit.

After six months of practise, grey hairs and wrinkles become inconspicuous. One who practises it for a yama (three hours) conquers death.

Do not practise for such a long duration on this basis, however, because the body will be unable to cope with its influence. It takes years of sadhana to reach this stage. Most important is that during the practice the position is perfect and concentration is one-pointed.

To gain full benefit from the practice it is necessary to go slowly. Gradually build up the duration and adhere to the rules of the practice.

What are the subtle effects of inverting the body?
Swami Satyananda: In *Hatha Yoga Pradipika* (3:78–79) Yogi Swatmarama says:

Tatraasti karanam divyam sooryasya mukhavanchanam;
Guroopadeshato jneyam na tu shaastraarthakotibhih.

Urdhvanaabheradhastaaloroordhvam bhaanuradhah shashee;
Karanee vipareetaakhyaa guruvaakyena labhyate.

There is a wonderful means by which the nectar is averted from falling into the opening of the sun. This is obtained by the guru's instructions and not from the hundreds of shastras (treatises). (78)

With the navel region above and the palate below, the sun is above and the moon below. It is called vipareeta karani, the reversing process. When given by the guru's instructions, it is fruitful. (79)

The moon emits its nectar, and due to the natural body processes the nectar falls into the sun. The moon not only represents bindu visarga, but also consciousness. The sun not only represents manipura but also prana, the body. From this it can be understood that the consciousness streams into the body and is wasted through the sense organs.

The practice of vipareeta karani mudra is directly concerned with reversing the flow of a fluid from the brain. This is possible by reversing the natural upright body position. The force of gravity naturally pulls all body fluids down to the lower parts. By inverting the body so that the head is down and the feet are up, all the fluids flow back towards the head without undue force or pressure.

There are various asanas which also do this, but the two most effective are vipareeta karani and sirshasana. The effects of vipareeta karani differ from sirshasana, as vipareeta karani creates pressure in the throat which stimulates the thyroid and awakens vishuddhi chakra, while sirshasana directly affects the cerebrum and sahasrara chakra. Vipareeta is also a simpler posture than sirshasana but it should be learnt from the guru directly.

What are the different methods of practising vipareeta karani mudra?

Swami Niranjanananda: Hatha yoga and kundalini yoga techniques for vipareeta karani mudra are described in the Upanishads. In vipareeta karani mudra, the inverted posture is used to reverse the flow of prana. In both techniques the asana is assumed and ujjayi breathing is used. The asana becomes a mudra by directing the prana through rotation of awareness around different psychic passages.

There are two hatha yoga versions. In one, the awareness is taken to mooladhara chakra, which is the starting point of every round. While inhaling, the breath flows from mooladhara to manipura. While exhaling, the breath flows from manipura to vishuddhi. The awareness is then brought straight back to mooladhara, and the next round continues. In this practice one becomes aware of three regions: (i) mooladhara, the perineal base, (ii) manipura, the lumbar base, and (iii) vishuddhi, the base connecting the body to the brain. The consciousness is moved from one base to the next with inhalation and exhalation. The movement of consciousness is always from mooladhara to vishuddhi, not the reverse. There is awareness of these bases when one stops momentarily between inhalation and exhalation.

In the other hatha yoga version, the starting point is manipura chakra. The awareness is focused at manipura, then, while breathing in with ujjayi, the breath and awareness move together along the spine to vishuddhi. While exhaling, the awareness is held at vishuddhi. When the exhalation is complete, the awareness is immediately returned to manipura. This makes one round.

The kundalini technique is only given after preparatory techniques have made the system ready.

How does vipareeta karani mudra affect prana and the brain?

Swami Niranjanananda: In vipareeta karani mudra, the inverted posture is used to reverse the flow of prana. Physiologically this links the limbic system with the cortex. The limbic system controls all the activities which go on automatically, including the experience of pleasure, sexuality, breathing and heartbeat.

These brain centres are very powerful. The brain is a kind of hologram of the whole body. It is like a little mirror of everything that is in the body. Continually rotating the awareness and breath along a fixed pathway takes the practice from being just a posture to being a mudra; as the intention is to manipulate the prana, the pranic dimension is added. With the rotation of awareness, the concentration and mental faculties are directed to a particular pathway in one's being. As awareness evolves, the actual movement of prana can be felt happening at various levels. This shows the intensity of mind working at the pranic level.

When vipareeta karani mudra is practised for a period of time, the attention moves from the limbic system through the thalamus towards the cortex, the region of the brain associated with consciousness. In this way, awareness of these various functions develops, and gradually they become mentally and neuronally linked. This is, in general, what happens. By this process, control over pleasure, sexuality and all the other basic involuntary functions of the body develops.

PRANA MUDRA: INVOCATION OF ENERGY

What is the attitude associated with prana mudra?

Swami Niranjanananda: Prana mudra is also known as *shanti mudra*, or the attitude of peace. This attitude of the whole being is one of supplication to receive the radiations of the sun and the heavens, both physical and imaginary.

What is the effect of prana mudra on the chakras?

Swami Niranjanananda: Prana mudra pranayama develops awareness of the seven chakras: mooladhara, swadhisthana, manipura, anahata, vishuddhi, ajna and sahasrara, and the subtle movement of energy associated with their activation.

When is the best time for practising prana mudra?

Swami Niranjanananda: Prana mudra can be practised at sunrise, facing the sun, if desired. However, this is unnecessary because the practice actually awakens the prana shakti from within. Prana mudra is best practised after asana and pranayama, and before meditation: it is an excellent pre-meditative technique. It can, however, be performed at any time.

What are the effects of prana mudra?

Swami Satyananda: Prana mudra awakens the dormant *prana shakti*, vital strength, and distributes it throughout the body, increasing strength, health and confidence. It develops awareness of the nadis and chakras, and the subtle flow of prana in the body. It instills an inner attitude of peace and equanimity by adopting an external attitude of offering and receiving energy to and from the cosmic source.

143

How should the awareness be directed during prana mudra?

Swami Satyananda: The awareness should move in a smooth and continuous flow from mooladhara to sahasrara and back to mooladhara, in coordination with the breath and the movement of the hands.

When the practice has been perfected, the breath can be visualized as a stream of white light ascending and descending within sushumna nadi.

5

Bandha Mudra: Lock Mudras

UNDERSTANDING LOCK MUDRAS

What are lock mudras?

Swami Niranjanananda: These practices are a combination of mudras and bandhas. They charge the whole system with prana and prepare it for kundalini awakening.

What posture is used for the lock mudras?

Swami Niranjanananda: Shakti chalini mudra is best performed while sitting in siddhasana or siddha yoni asana. Otherwise, any comfortable meditation asana can be used.

In maha mudra and maha bheda mudra, utthanpadasana is used as the sitting posture. One leg is stretched forward and the other leg is bent with the heel pressed against the perineum, exerting direct pressure on mooladhara. Maha vedha mudra is performed from padmasana.

Why is the posture an important aspect of the mudra?

Swami Niranjanananda: Both maha mudra and maha bheda mudra are performed in the same posture, sitting in half vajrasana with one leg outstretched in front of the body and the knees together. The heel of the folded leg is pressed against the perineum, exerting pressure directly on mooladhara. As the body bends forward the spine is extended and held straight.

In this position, the prana from the hands goes into the toes, creating a circuit. Pressure is exerted on vajra nadi and there is focusing on the ocular nerves. Along with contraction, a circuit is created in the movement of energy from mooladhara to ajna. Therefore, these mudras stimulate the channels of prana, circulate the movement of prana within the body, and awaken prana.

What are the physiological effects of the locked mudras?
Swami Niranjanananda: The locked mudras combine bandhas, eye mudras and kumbhaka. In this process of bringing the body into alignment and stopping these organs, the entire brain is affected. When performing bandhas with kumbhaka, the body is squeezed like a bag of fluid.

Stimulation of mooladhara chakra affects the area of the upper brain stem, where the reticular activating system is located. By squeezing the perineum, an immediate reflex of energy comes up and illumines the whole brain. As so many different structures are stopped simultaneously, the cortex is rapidly pushed into a single, pulsating unit. In meditation practice, the brainwaves are synchronized but normally this is a slow process. With these locked mudras, the brain and the catabolism are slowed down immediately, like putting the brakes on too quickly. This has a powerful effect on the metabolism, which can be disturbing if the constitution or psyche is weak.

How often should the bandha mudras be performed?
Swami Satyananda: According to the yoga shastras, the twenty-four hours of a day is divided into sixteen parts, each of ninety minutes, called *ghariya*; or eight periods of three hours, called *yama*. In each period the flow of energy throughout the body varies and different organs function more actively. Also, as the brain hemispheres alternate their functioning every sixty to ninety minutes, one's mode of thinking also changes.

Yogi Swatmarama specifies that maha mudra, maha bandha and maha vedha mudra should be practised during each three-hour period. As this means they are being performed during different phases of the brain's cycle, they must surely induce radical changes in the brain and psychological structure of the practitioner. This instruction is given in *Hatha Yoga Pradipika* (3:30–31):

> *Etattrayam mahaaguhyam jaraamrityuvinaashanam;*
> *Vahnivriddhikaram chaiva hyanimaadigunapradam.*
>
> *Ashtadhaa kriyate chaiva yaame yaame dine dine;*
> *Punyasambhaarasandhaayi paapaughabhiduram sadaa;*
> *Samyakshikshaavataamevam svalpam prathamasaadhanam.*
>
> These are the three great secrets which destroy old age and death, increase the digestive fire and bestow the siddhis of anima, etc. (30)
>
> They should be done daily at every yama (three-hour period). They bring out the virtues and destroy vices. Those who have perfect instructions should practise them gradually. (31)

It is obviously impossible for the average person to practise so frequently, and it is not really recommended. It is quite sufficient to practise in the morning and again in the evening if time allows. It must be kept in mind that the specifications laid down in this text are for a recluse who lives away from society, free from family and social obligations, and who is practising directly under the guidance of a guru. If a householder were to perform these practices so frequently, there would by little time and energy for anything else.

People today do not need to practise hatha yoga for hours and hours together. They are dynamic and need to express themselves through action and various relationships with others. Yoga must meet the demands of the various elements of one's personality, and for this reason a balanced combination of hatha yoga, karma yoga, bhakti yoga and jnana yoga are needed.

Therefore, when the yoga texts are read they must be viewed in a practical manner. The techniques can be practised according to the instructions given, but which techniques to do and how much they should be practised has to be decided upon according to one's physical and mental capacity, and the amount of time that can be devoted to sadhana. Of course, it is preferable if one has a guru to make the decisions, and this is always advised by the texts themselves.

MAHA MUDRA: GREAT PSYCHIC ATTITUDE

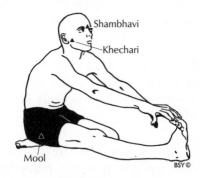

What is the meaning of maha mudra?
Swami Niranjanananda: Maha mudra is formed from two Sanskrit words: *maha* means, 'the greatest' and *mudra* means, 'a technique to create a particular attitude or mental modification'. Therefore, *mahamudra* means both the technique referred to here and the actual state by which the human consciousness travels in the highest level. This is revealed in *Shiva Samhita* (4:16):

Mahaamudraam pravakshyaami tantre'sminmama vallabhe;
Yaam praapya siddhaah siddhim cha kapilaadyaa puraagataah.

My dearest, I shall now describe to you the maha mudra, from whose knowledge the ancient sages Kapila and others obtained success in yoga.

148

What does the practice of maha mudra involve?

Swami Satyananda: Although maha mudra is a technique of hatha yoga it is also one of the kriya yoga practices. It involves asana, kumbhaka, mudra and bandha and makes a powerful pranic lock which spontaneously arouses meditation. It is described in *Hatha Yoga Pradipika* (3:10–13, 15):

Paadamoolena vaamena yonim sampeedya dakshinam;
Prasaaritam padam kritvaa karaabhyaam dhaaryeddridham.

Kanthe bandham samaaropya dhaaryedvaayumoordhvatah;
Yathaa dandahatah sarpo dandaakaarah prajaayate.

Rijveebhoota tathaa shaktih kundalee sahasaa bhavet;
Tadaa saa maranaavasthaa jaayate dviputaashrayaa.

Tatah shanaih shanaireva rechayennaiva vegatah;
Mahaamudraam cha tenaiva vadanti vibudhottamaah.

Chandraange tu samabhyasya sooryaange punarabhyaset;
Yaavattulyaa bhavetsamkhyaa tato mudraam visarjayet.

Press the left heel into the perineum (or vagina), straighten the right leg, and with the hands, firmly take hold of the outstretched foot. (10)

By locking the throat and retaining the breath, the prana rises straight, just like a snake beaten with a stick becomes straight. (11)

So the kundalini shakti becomes straight at once. Then the two (ida and pingala) become lifeless as the shakti enters sushumna. (12)

Then exhale slowly and gradually, not quickly. Indeed this is described as maha mudra by the great siddhas. (13)

After practising on the left side, practise on the right side. When the number of rounds is even, discontinue and release the mudra. (15)

The kriya yoga practice of maha mudra incorporates ujjayi pranayama, khechari mudra, awareness of arohan and awarohan passages and the chakras, and unmani mudra. The hatha yoga variation is a good preparation for the kriya yoga technique which should not be attempted without the guru's instruction.

What are the physical benefits of maha mudra?

Swami Satyananda: Maha mudra increases one's vitality and harmonizes all bodily functions. Through the practice of maha mudra, digestion and assimilation of both food and prana are stimulated. The benefits of maha mudra are equal to and above those of mayurasana, and it is essentially more dynamic on a pranic and psychic level. In *Hatha Yoga Pradipika* (3:16–17) it says:

Na hi pathyamapathyam vaa rasaah sarve'pi neerasaah;
Api bhuktam visham ghoram peeyooshamapi jeeryati.

Kshayakushthagudaavartagulmaajeernapurogamaah;
Tasya doshaah kshayam yaanti mahaamudraam tu yo'bhyaset.

For one who practises maha mudra, there is nothing wholesome or unwholesome. Anything can be consumed, even the deadliest of poisons is digested like nectar. (16)

Abdominal disorders, constipation, indigestion and leprosy, etc., are alleviated by the practice of maha mudra. (17)

Why is maha mudra beneficial for physical and mental health?

Swami Niranjanananda: Physically, digestion is improved and diseases relating to the stomach are reduced. With the practice of maha mudra, disorders such as excess kapha, piles, tuberculosis, ailments of the spleen and throat, fever, etc., which are linked with the digestive process, also show improvement. The sympathetic and parasympathetic nervous systems are balanced, establishing peace and tranquillity in the sensory and motor nerves connecting the senses, body and mind. Sensory experiences are reduced, thereby reducing excitement and calming the activity in the brain. Slowly the brainwaves become peaceful, inducing spontaneous meditation.

This mudra stimulates the energy circuit linking mooladhara with ajna chakra. The whole system is charged with prana, which intensifies awareness. The effects are described in *Shiva Samhita* (4:18):

Anena vidhinaa yogee mandabhaagyopi sidhyati;
Sarvaasaameva naadeenaam chaalanam bindumaaranam;
Jeevanantu kashaayasya paatakaanaam vinaashanam;
Savarogopashamanam jatharaagnivivardhanam;
Vapushaa kaantimamalaam jaraamrityuvinaashanam;
Vaanchhitaarthaphalam saukhyamindriyaanaancha maaranam;
Etaduktaani sarvaani yogaaroodhasya yoginah;
Bhavedabhyaasato'vashyam naatra kaaryaa vichaaranaa.

In this way, even the most unfortunate yogi might obtain success. By this means all the vessels of the body are roused and stirred into activity; the life is increased and its decay is checked, and all sins are destroyed. All diseases are healed, and the gastric fire is increased. It gives faultless beauty to the body, and destroys decay and death. All fruits of desires and pleasures are obtained, and the senses are conquered. Through practice, the yogi fixed in meditation acquires all the above-mentioned things. There should be no hesitation in doing so.

What are the subtle benefits of maha mudra?
Swami Satyananda: From the practice of maha mudra the combined benefits of shambhavi mudra, moola bandha, kumbhaka and paschimottanasana or utthanpadasana are gained. Physiologically it stimulates the digestive capacity; pranically it generates circulation of energy in the chakras; psychologically it develops the mind and inner awareness, and psychically it arouses receptivity.

151

Maha mudra clears the nadis and particularly stimulates the flow of sushumna. It increases one's awareness and brings about clarity of thought. Maha mudra stimulates the shakti in the energy circuit from mooladhara to ajna chakra and its effects can be strongly felt on a psychic level. This powerful effect on the pranic system is described in the *Yoga Chudamani Upanishad* (v. 65):

Shodhanam naadijaalasya chaalanam chandrasooryayoh;
Rasaanaam shoshanam chaiva mahaamudraa abhidheeyate.

The method taught for purification of the entire nadi structure governing the movement of the moon and the sun and absorption of the vital fluid is maha mudra.

Maha mudra rapidly eliminates mental depression as it removes all energy blockages which are the fundamental cause of the problem. The practice stills the mind and body and increases one's sensitivity to subtle experiences. It is therefore a highly recommended and powerful preparatory practice for meditation. These effects are described in *Hatha Yoga Pradipika* (3:14,18):

Iyam khalu mahaamudraa mahaasiddhaih pradarshitaa;
Mahaakleshaadayo doshaah ksheeyante maranaadayah;
Mahaamudraam cha tenaiva vadanti vibhudhottamaah.

Kathiteyam mahaamudraa mahaasiddhikaraa nrinaam;
Gopaneeyaa prayatnena na deyaa yasya kasyachit.

Maha mudra removes the worst afflictions (the five kleshas) and the cause of death. Therefore it is called 'the great attitude' by the ones of highest knowledge. (14)

Thus maha mudra has been described as the giver of great siddhis. It must be kept secret and not disclosed to anyone. (18)

Why is maha mudra recommended as a pre-meditation practice?

Swami Niranjanananda: From a practical point of view, maha mudra can be practised prior to meditation to reduce restlessness in chitta, making it calm and peaceful, and making the mind one-pointed. Maha mudra introverts the mind: when shambhavi mudra is performed, restlessness of the mind quickly subsides; when the eyes are closed, the mind becomes introverted, and the number and speed of the thoughts and feelings are reduced. After practising for some time, the mind attains *shoonya avastha*, a vacuum state. In this one-pointed or focused state there are no thoughts or feelings. With the removal of energy blockages, mental turmoil quickly vanishes.

When moola bandha and constriction of the throat are practised, both prana vayu, which is influenced by jalandhara bandha, and apana vayu, which is influenced by moola bandha, are brought to the middle of the body at manipura chakra, where they unite, and activation of prana shakti is experienced. When prana shakti is awakened properly inside the body, then the two flows of ida and pingala come into a balanced state and sushumna is awakened.

It is said in the yoga scriptures that awakening of sushumna is necessary if one is to succeed in meditation and gain mastery over it. Its power is described in the *Yoga Chudamani Upanishad* (v. 70):

Kathiteyam mahaamudraa mahaasiddhikaree nrinaam;
Gopaneeyaa prayatnena na deyaa yasya kasyachit.

The maha mudra, which was mentioned earlier, is the bestower of great powers for men. It should be kept secret, with care, and not taught to anyone.

What is the meaning and significance of maha bheda mudra?

Swami Niranjanananda: *Maha bheda mudra* means the 'great separating attitude'. This is a powerful practice for uniting with the inner being or self.

What are the different versions of maha bheda mudra?

Swami Niranjanananda: *Gheranda Samhita* describes maha bheda mudra under hatha yoga, but another version is practised in kriya yoga.

In hatha yoga, while sitting in utthanpadasana and holding the big toe, bahir kumbhaka is performed along with maha bandha and nasikagra drishti. Holding this position, the awareness is rotated through the three chakras where the locks are applied: in moola bandha energy is locked into mooladhara, in uddiyana bandha, awareness is of manipura, and in jalandhara bandha, awareness is of vishuddhi. This practice is described in *Gheranda Samhita* (3:41–44):

> *Roopayauvanalaavanyam naareenaam purusham binaa;*
> *Moolabandhamahaabandhau mahabedham vinaa tathaa.*

> *Mahaabandhamsamaasaadya kumbhakam chareduddeena;*
> *Mahaabedhah samaakhyaato yoginaam siddhidaayakah.*

> *Mahaabandhamoolabandhau mahaabedhasamanvitau;*
> *Pratyaham kurute yastu sa yogee yogavittamah.*

Na mrityuto bhayam tasya na jaraa tasya vidyate;
Gopaneeyah prayatnena vedho'yam yogipungavaih.

In the same way that the beauty, youth and elegance of a woman are useless without a man, similarly moola bandha and maha bandha are also fruitless without maha bheda. First practise maha bandha, then while performing uddiyana bandha retain the air through kumbhaka. This has been called maha bheda. (41–42)

The yogis who perform maha bandha and moola bandha along with maha bheda daily are considered the best of all yogis. They are neither affected by old age nor the fear of death. The best of the yogis should keep it secret. (43–44)

Bheda also means 'piercing'. In the kriya yoga practice, just as the beads of a *mala*, rosary, are pierced with a needle in order to thread them, in exactly the same manner the seven chakras are pierced. This piercing is through consciousness. In each chakra there is a state of prana and also a state of consciousness which is as yet unknown to the practitioner. In every chakra there is a state of consciousness which may be called an expanded form of consciousness. In mooladhara, the form of consciousness reflects the qualities of mooladhara; in swadhisthana, the consciousness takes a swadhisthana form; in manipura, anahata, vishuddhi and ajna, the form of consciousness relates to each particular chakra. Thus, one moves through the sequential development of consciousness, experiencing new forms of consciousness at each progression. The idea is to traverse each state while maintaining one's present awareness and state of perception.

The most important principle of kundalini yoga is that while crossing all the chakras or psychic centres, the awareness, the consciousness and the state of perception should remain the same. This state of perception is one-pointed, the end of being scattered. It can be called an 'unscattered mind', where there is no dissipation or deflection. It is a fully focused and one-pointed state, in which the mind is not influenced by any quality. This is the basic form of consciousness. In maha bheda mudra, all the chakras or psychic centres should be pierced by this one-pointed state.

How can one prepare for practising maha bheda mudra?

Swami Satyananda: Before commencing this practice, the practitioner should be familiar with the techniques of jalandhara, uddiyana and moola bandhas and bahir kumbhaka. This practice should be attempted only under the guidance of a competent teacher.

What are the benefits of maha bheda mudra?

Swami Niranjanananda: The benefits of maha bheda mudra are similar to maha mudra. It has a profound influence at a pranic level, specifically influencing mooladhara, manipura and vishuddhi chakras, manipulating and harnessing the energies within them to induce concentration of mind and meditation.

Maha bheda supplements and follows maha mudra; together they supercharge the whole body-mind complex which enables a very powerful flow at the physical, mental and pranic levels. There is circulation of fresh energy in the body, mind and senses. Consciousness becomes extremely subtle and deep.

One of the main benefits of this mudra is to achieve a high state of consciousness while maintaining awareness of consciousness in a normal form. This is the aim and purpose of maha bheda mudra. Maha bheda enables yogis to become *siddhas*, perfect and knowledgeable. A person who does all three practices of maha bandha, moola bandha and maha bheda daily is known as a *yogavit,* or yoga specialist.

MAHA VEDHA MUDRA: GREAT PIERCING ATTITUDE

What is maha vedha mudra?

Swami Satyananda: *Maha vedha mudra* means 'the great piercing attitude'. The purpose of maha vedha mudra is to pierce mooladhara chakra and channel the kundalini energy upwards by gently beating the buttocks on the floor.

The technique belongs to hatha yoga and is a preparatory technique for the kriya yoga practice of *tadan kriya*, 'the beating action'. It should not be confused with the kriya yoga practice of maha bheda mudra which is similar to maha mudra. Maha vedha mudra is described in *Hatha Yoga Pradipika* (3:27–28):

Samahastayugo bhoomau sphichau santaadayechchhanaih;
Putadvayamatikramya vaayuh sphurati madhyagah.

Somasooryagnisambandho jaayate chamritaaya vai;
Mritaavasthaa samutpannaa tato vaayum virechayet.

Placing the palms of the hands on the ground, one should slowly beat the buttocks gently on the ground. The prana (then) leaves the two nadis (ida and pingala) and enters into the middle channel (sushumna). (27)

Ida, pingala and sushumna become united and verily, immortality is attained. A death-like state occurs; then the breath should be exhaled. (28)

What are the benefits of maha vedha mudra?

Swami Satyananda: This is a powerful practice for introverting the mind. It awakens psychic faculties and the kundalini which resides in mooladhara chakra. The effect of maha vedha on *brahma granthi*, the psychic knot in the region of mooladhara, is revealed in *Shiva Samhita* (4:23–24):

Apaanapraanayoraikyam kritvaa tribhuvaneshvari;
Mahaavedhasthitau yogee kukshimaapoorya vaayunaa;
Sphichau santaadayeddheemaanvedho'yam keertito mayaa.

Vedhenaanena sambidhya vaayunaa yogipungavah;
Granthim sushumnaamaargena brahmagranthim bhinattyasau.

Oh goddess of the three worlds! When the yogi, while performing maha bandha, causes the union of the prana and apana vayus, and filling the viscera with air drives it slowly towards the buttocks, it is called maha vedha. (23)

The best of the yogis having, through the help of the vayu pierced the knot which is in the path of sushumna, should then pierce the knot of Brahma. (24)

How does maha vedha mudra influence the ageing process?

Swami Satyananda: All the practices of hatha yoga which help relax the body and mind, and which stimulate pranic capacity, slow down the ageing process. Maha mudra and maha vedha mudra are powerful techniques that introvert the mind and awaken psychic faculties. They affect the pineal and pituitary glands and thus the whole endocrinal system. By activating the pineal gland, the pituitary is kept under control, hormonal secretions are regulated and catabolism is curtailed: consequently, the symptoms of old age are either annihilated or reduced. In *Hatha Yoga Pradipika* (3:29) it says:

Mahaavedho'yamabhyaasaanmahaasiddhipradaayakah;
Valeepalitavepaghnah sevyate saadhakottamaih.

This is maha vheda, and its practice bestows great perfections. Wrinkles, grey hair and the trembling of old age are evaded, thus the best of practitioners devote themselves to it.

SHAKTI CHALINI MUDRA:
ATTITUDE OF MOVING THE ENERGY

What is the difference between shakti chalini mudra in hatha yoga and kriya yoga?

Swami Satyananda: Shakti chalini is widely mentioned in yogic scriptures. It is well described in the *Yoga Chudamani Upanishad* (verses 107–108), *Gheranda Samhita* (3:61–72) and the *Hatha Yoga Pradipika* (3:104–120). All the descriptions, however, are different. None of the hatha yoga techniques resemble the practice of shakti chalini that is used in kriya yoga. Kriya yoga uses mental visualization whereas hatha yoga does not. Of course, this does not mean it may not be incorporated.

In kriya yoga, whilst performing certain mudras, bandhas and pranayamas, one visualizes a thin green serpent in the arohan and awarohan passages, with the mouth biting its own tail. This serpent is then visualized rotating through the arohan and awarohan passages until the breath can no longer be held.

The practice in hatha yoga is different. The techniques used in hatha yoga are: siddhasana/siddha yoni asana, moola bandha, antar and bahir kumbhaka, and nauli. In *Gheranda Samhita* ash is smeared on the body and ashwini mudra is used. In *Hatha Yoga Pradipika* moola bandha is used instead. In *Hatha Yoga Pradipika* (3:112), the practice of shakti chalini is carefully undisclosed:

> *Avasthitaa chaiva phanaavatee saa praatashcha saayam praharaardhamaatram;*
> *Prapoorya sooryaat paridhaanayuktyaa pragrihya nityam parichaalaneeya.*

Breathing in through the right nostril (pingala) the serpent (shakti) should be seized through kumbhaka and rotated constantly for an hour and a half, morning and evening.

This version includes antar kumbhaka with moola bandha, then jalandhara bandha, uddiyana bandha and nauli with bahir kumbhaka. Though it is stated in the text that shakti chalini should be practised for ninety minutes, this will not be possible, nor is it advisable.

Shakti chalini is described using naumukhi mudra in *Yoga Chudamani Upanishad* (v. 107):

Dvaaraanaam nava samnirudhya marutam baddhvaa dridhaam dhaaranaam;
Neetvaa kaalam apaanavahni sahitam shaktyaa samam chaalitam;
Aatmadhyaanayutastvanena vidhinaa vinyasya moordhni sthiram;
Yaavattishthati taavadeva mahataam sango na samstooyate.

Closing the nine gates properly and retaining the breath, intensify the concentration. Performing shakti chalini mudra correctly, take the divine element, kundalini, along with apana vayu and fire (samana vayu) to the (crown of the) head. By this method become absorbed in meditation on the Self. When steadiness and stillness are achieved, while remaining in that state, the company of great men is not needed.

Why is shakti chalini mudra regarded as an important practice of kundalini yoga?

Swami Niranjanananda: The principle of kundalini yoga is briefly explained by Sage Gheranda in his verses on shakti chalini mudra, which say that this mudra is one of the yogic techniques for awakening kundalini. In *Gheranda Samhita* (3:61–63) it says:

Moolaadhaare aatmashaktih kundalee para devata;
Shayitaa bhujagaakaaraa saardha trivalayaanvitaa.

Yaavatsaa nidritaa dehe taavajjeevah pashuryathaa;
Jnaanam na jaayate taavatkotiyogam samabhyaset.

160

Udghaatayetkavaatam cha yathaa kunchikayaahathaat;
Kundalinyaah prabodhena brahmadvaaram prabhedayet.

In mooladhara, kundalini sleeps in the form of a serpent
with three and a half coils. (61)

A living being remains in the state of an animal
(ignorance) as long as the kundalini remains sleeping.
Therefore, one should keep on practising until such
time as knowledge manifests. (62)

Just as a door opens only when the lock is opened with
a key, in the same way brahmarandhra can only be
opened when kundalini is awakened. (63)

Sage Gheranda explains to his disciple, King Chandakapali,
that *atma shakti*, spiritual energy, resides in mooladhara
chakra as kundalini and is in the form of a serpent with
three and a half coils. As long as this *shakti*, energy, remains
dormant or sleeping inside a human being, that person's life
is just like that of an animal. This means one's consciousness
is not developed and one treads the path of the *vrittis*,
modifications of the mind, like an animal. Just as an animal
eats when it feels hungry, sleeps when sleep overtakes it and
does not think or discriminate, such a person eats when he
feels hungry, indulges in sex when he craves it and sleeps
when he feels like sleeping. He remains under the influence
of the gunas and in the grip of lust, passion and desires. In
this state a human being cannot achieve knowledge; the
consciousness cannot be expanded.

Sage Gheranda says that just as a lock cannot be
opened without a key, in exactly the same way *brahmadvara*,
sahasrara, or literally, the door to Brahman, cannot be
opened without awakening kundalini. According to the yogic
viewpoint *brahmadvara* means the door which exists between
the *para* and *apara* worlds, between the experiences of the
spiritual and materialistic worlds. Only when that door opens
after the awakening of kundalini shakti does a human being
attain knowledge.

Due to its power the practice or kriya is top secret. It is a destroyer (remedy) for old age and death, and those yogis who wish to attain *siddhi*, mastery, should practise it with sincerity.

How is shakti chalini mudra described in *Gheranda Samhita*?

Swami Niranjanananda: Sage Gheranda specifies that shakti chalini mudra should be practised in a quiet, secluded place, not in the open.

He says to secure a clean, soft piece of white cloth of a certain size to the navel region by tying it around the waist with a thin cotton or jute thread, so that it does not slip. Knotting the cloth is prohibited as the size of the knot would interfere with the practice. Instead of tying the cloth with a knot, one must ensure that it is wrapped tightly but without obstructing the blood circulation, and then secure it by tying it in place with a thread.

One sits in siddhasana with holy ash applied on the body, inhales deeply, taking the breath not into the chest but into the abdomen, the region of apana vayu. Next, with the help of uddiyana bandha, the apana vayu is moved upward, uniting it with the prana vayu. Due to tying the cloth over the navel region, the pressure of the air inside the body will start moving towards the rectum, where ashwini mudra is also directing the energy upwards.

Sage Gheranda says that this practice should be done until kundalini shakti is raised upward. This process is described in *Gheranda Samhita* (3:64–68):

Naabhim samveshtya vastrena na cha nagno bahih sthitah;
Gopaneeyagrihe sthitvaa shaktichaalanamabhyaset.

Vitastipramitam deergham vistaare chaturangulam;
Mridulam dhavalam sookshmam veshtanaambaralakshanam.

Evamambarayuktam cha katisootrena yojayet;
Samlipya bhasmanaagaatram siddhaasanamathaacharet.

162

Naasaabhyaam praanamaakrishyaapyapaane yojayedbalaat;
Taavadaakunchayedguhyamashvineemudrayaa shanaih.

Yaavadgachchhetsushumnaayaam hathaadvaayuh prakaashayet;
Tadaa vaayuprabandhena kumbhikaa cha bhujanginee.

It should be practised in a secluded place with the navel covered with a piece of cloth tied around it. Practising this mudra naked in the open is prohibited. (64)

A soft piece of cloth (about 10 cm wide and 23 cm long) is secured around the navel by a thread tied around the waist. (65)

Smear ash on the body, sit in siddhasana and while pulling the prana, merge it with apana. Keep the anus contracted by means of ashwini mudra as long as the sushumna passage is not cleared or lighted. (66–67)

Thus, with the air held by kumbhaka, kundalini in the form of a serpent awakens and stands upright in the passage. (68)

What is the recommended sequence of practice for shakti chalini mudra?

Swami Niranjanananda: Sage Gheranda's advice is to first practise shakti chalini mudra, and then practise yoni mudra. This is specified in *Gheranda Samhita* (3:69–70):

Baddhashvaasastato bhootvaa chordhvamaarga prapadyate;
Vinaa shaktichaalanena yonimudraa na sidhyati.

Aadau chaalanamabhyasya yonimudraam tato'bhyaset;
Iti te kathitam chandakapaale shaktichaalanam.

Yoni mudra cannot be perfected without the practice of shakti chalini mudra. First practise shakti chalini mudra, then practise yoni mudra. (69–70)

How often should shakti chalini mudra be practised, and for how long?

Swami Niranjanananda: Shakti chalini can only be perfected by daily practice. In *Gheranda Samhita* (3:71) it is written:

Gopaneeyam prayatnena dine dine samabhyaset;
Mudreyam paramaa gopyaa jaraamarananaashinee.

O Chandakapali! Thus practise this shakti chalini mudra daily which I have told you of, and keep it secret as far as practicable.

In *Hatha Yoga Pradipika* the instruction is to practise for one and a half hours. This instruction is aimed at adepts. If one has been taught the practice, up to seven or nine rounds is enough for several years. According to *Shiva Samhita* (4:57), correct practise is essential for the desired results:

Muhoortadvayaparyantam vidhinaa shaktichaalanam;
Yah karoti prayatnena tasya siddhiradooratah;
Yuktaasanena kartavyam yogibhih shaktichaalanam.

He who practises shakti chalini properly for two seconds, and with care, is very near to success. This mudra should be practised by the yogi in the proper posture.

What are the benefits of shakti chalini mudra?

Swami Niranjanananda: Sage Gheranda states that those who practise this mudra daily will achieve many siddhis, are relieved of all physical disorders and the power of reception is highly developed. In *Gheranda Samhita* (3:72) it is written:

Tasmaadabhyasanam kaaryam yogibhih siddhikaankshibhih;
Nityam yo'bhyasate yogee siddhistasya kare sthitaa;
Tasya vigrahasiddhih syaadrogaanaam sankshayo bhavet.

Whosoever practises it attains all the siddhis, including vigraha siddhi, and all diseases are destroyed or overcome.

6

Adhara Mudra: Perineal Mudras

AMAROLI MUDRA:
ATTITUDE AROUSING IMMORTALITY

What is amaroli mudra?

Swami Satyananda: The various hatha yoga texts have different views as to what constitutes the practice of amaroli. *Amara* means 'immortal', 'undying' or 'imperishable'. Thus *amaroli* is the practice leading to immortality. *Hatha Yoga Pradipika* (3:96–97) says that amaroli is the practice of drinking the midstream urine:

> *Pittolbanatvaatprathamaambudhaaraam vihaaya*
> *nihsaaratayaantyadhaaraam;*
> *Nishevyate sheetalamadhyadhaaraa kaapaalike*
> *khandamate'marolee.*
>
> *Amareem yah pibennipyam nasyam kurvandinedine;*
> *Vajroleemabhyaset samyaksaamaroleeti kathyate.*

According to the Kapalika sect, amaroli is practised by drinking the cool midstream of urine. The first part of the urine is left as it contains bile, and the last part is left as it does not contain goodness. (96)

One who drinks amari, takes it through the nose and practices vajroli, is said to be practising amaroli. (97)

The *Shiva Samhita* states that amaroli is the practice of withdrawing the seminal fluid from the woman after it has been released. However, this is generally described as vajroli. Amaroli is most commonly accepted as the drinking of midstream urine.

Why is amaroli a controversial practice?

Swami Satyananda: Urine has been used for centuries as a healing agent in many cultures but little has ever been spoken about it, as urine is generally considered to be 'unclean'. Definitely the urine of people who take an unwholesome diet, and those whose bodies are impure, will be offensive because it contains toxins and metabolic wastes that are harmful to drink, or even apply on the body. However, the midstream urine of a yogi is pure and inoffensive.

In tantra and yoga, amaroli is also known as *shivambhu*, i.e., the basic element of one's self. The drinking of the midstream of urine is highly regarded in yoga. There is also a science of urine therapy but medical science has yet to look more deeply into it.

The *Jnanarnava Tantra* (Ch 22) states that:

After realizing the exact knowledge of dharma and adharma (healthy and unhealthy lifestyle), every aspect of the (material) world becomes holy: stool, urine, nails, bone, all are holy aspects in the sight of that person who has explored mantra. O Parvati, deities (divine powers) are living in that water from which urine is made, then why is urine said to be contaminated?

People believe urine to be dirty because they think of it as a waste product of the same quality as the stool (solid wastes). We should review this concept thoroughly. Both anatomically and physiologically, it is not correct to class urine and stool together, because the two are produced in completely different ways and leave the body by distinct and separate portals.

166

Urine is an ultra-filtrate of the blood. It contains water, hormones, enzymes, electrolytes, minerals and byproducts of protein and fat breakdown, which exceed the body's capacity to recycle them at that time. Therefore, these may be termed wastes only in the same sense that grains harvested by a farmer are surplus because they exceed the capacity of the granary to store them for later use. It is not that they are wastes in the sense of being unclean, but only that their potential value has had to be sacrificed. Vital biomolecules such as hormones, amino acids and enzymes are synthesized at great metabolic cost to the body and their loss from the body must indeed be considered as a waste.

Furthermore, the human bloodstream is an absolutely clean living substance, from which the urine is filtered and collected in sterile conditions by the kidneys. Nor is there any question of bacterial contamination in the ureters, bladder or urethra, provided of course, no infection is present. Therefore, which part of this process can be termed 'dirty'? Medical scientists will have to consider this carefully if they wish to understand the rejuvenating power of amaroli.

The solid wastes are formed in an entirely different way. The digestive tract is unsterile from the mouth to the anus, and at no time has this solid matter actually entered inside the body, or into the general circulation. It has remained only within the hollow digestive pipe, yielding up its nutrients without itself being assimilated into the body.

What is the effect of diet on amaroli?

Swami Satyananda: What is offensive about urine? Urine which contains a high concentration of urea, uric acid and bile salts has a definite pungent taste and objectionable quality. These constituents are the byproducts of protein and fat metabolism and are contained in only small amounts in the urine of a yogi who consumes a diet low in protein and devoid of animal products.

That is the first requirement for amaroli. The diet should be completely fresh and natural, without excess salt, spices and condiments. Highly refined and processed foods should also be avoided. Under these circumstances, the quality of the urine is transformed. It is not that the practice becomes ineffective or prohibited by a heavy, rich diet. However, objectionable qualities of the urine are avoided if the lighter diet is adopted.

How can mental resistance to practising amaroli be overcome?

Swami Satyananda: It is not possible to overcome mental conditioning about urine just by thinking intellectually. However, practising amaroli rapidly dissolves subconscious blockages. If one feels that one's own urine is impure, it betrays a deep subconscious belief about one's body and its origin. Subconsciously, the conviction that the body is impure has been inherited. This deep-rooted defect must be eradicated, and if amaroli is practised for a fixed period of time according to the guru's instruction, this surely occurs.

Why is amaroli practised using the first urine passed in the morning?

Swami Satyananda: Scientists who study the body's biorhythms have discovered that during the day and night, various hormones are secreted sequentially. For example, pituitary hormones such as growth hormone are released during sleep, while ACTH which activates the adrenal glands and TSH which activates the thyroid, become prominent during daytime activity. Pineal hormones follow a similar diurnal pattern.

The various hormones are filtered into the urine over the nocturnal sleep period and are reassimilated into the blood when amaroli is practised on rising in the morning.

This urine will accurately mirror the hormonal activities which have occurred during sleep. In this regard, it is the hormones secreted at night, and more specifically, in the very early morning hours, which are of most value, as during this physiological 'lull' period, consciousness is withdrawn from the lower centres and the secretions of the cerebral glands become prominent.

Why has amaroli traditionally been kept secret by yogis?

Swami Satyananda: It must be remembered that amaroli has always been a closely guarded secret revealed to yogis by initiation, but not to others. It is part of a system which evolves the human body into an illumined state over a number of years.

What is the overall effect of long-term practise of amaroli upon the human psychophysiology? Medical science has yet to establish it, but we can postulate that it rectifies the inherent imbalance between the process of production and consumption of hormones in the body which is the fundamental cause of the ageing process. Scientists have always dreamed of a 'perpetual motion machine' which would run indefinitely on its own products, thus conserving energy for other purposes, but they have been unable to create it. Amaroli is based upon this principle.

What are the rules for practising amaroli?

Swami Satyananda: There are a few rules for those who wish to practise amaroli. First of all, amaroli sadhana is not suitable for all and, therefore, it should be adopted according to a guru's instructions. Second, the amount and duration of the practice will be indicated by the guru. Third, regular habits and lifestyle are necessary. Finally, amaroli is a secret sadhana: it should not be discussed in public. Certain experiences will come in yoga sadhana: these are known to the guru and can be discussed with him, but not with others.

What is the effect of the oli mudras on the pranas?

Swami Satyananda: The purpose of vajroli, sahajoli and amaroli is to reverse the natural downward flow of apana so that the vayu flows upward through sushumna. When this is achieved the external mind becomes instantly tranquil and the awareness enters the inner dimensions. Mental equanimity means a steady mind, peaceful and unflinching in every circumstance. It is stated in *Hatha Yoga Pradipika* (4:14):

Chitte samatvamaapanne vaayau vrajati madhyame.
Tadaamarolee vajrolee sahajolee prajaayate.

When the mind is in equanimity and (prana) vayu proceeds through sushumna, then amaroli, vajroli and sahajoli are attained.

Reversal of apana vayu through sushumna is the primary aim, yet it is difficult to cope with that experience and positively sustain it. In this sense, vajroli, sahajoli and amaroli are not physical practices but indwelling attitudes or states of perfection.

VAJRONI MUDRA: THUNDERBOLT ATTITUDE.

Is vajroni mudra also an asana?

Swami Niranjanananda: This mudra is linked with an asana called *brahmacharyasana*, celibate's pose. When classified as an asana, it is called brahmacharya asana and when classified as a mudra, it is called vajroni mudra.

During the practice of this asana the entire body, including the urinary tract, rectum, muscles of the thighs, all muscles of the legs and feet, and that of the waist are contracted and moolabandha occurs spontaneously. A strong locking of moolabandha is important. This locking influences vajra nadi giving the practice its name, *vajroni mudra*. Vajroni mudra is described in *Gheranda Samhita* (3:57):

> *Dharaamavashtabhya karayostalaabhyaam urdhvam kshipetpaada yugamshirakhe;*
> *Shakti prabodhaaya chirajeevanaaya vajronimudraam munayoh vadanti.*

Place both hands firmly on the ground and lift both the feet and head into the sky. Learned ones have named it vajroni mudra which enables the flow of energy and provides life to us.

What is the significance of vajroni mudra?

Swami Niranjanananda: In tantra the practice of vajroni mudra carries great significance. The *panchamakara* sadhana, the tantric sadhana involving five Ms: *madya*, wine; *matsya*, fish; *mudra*, grain; *maithuna*, intercourse, and *mamsa*, meat, prescribes vajroli mudra for men, sahajoli mudra for women and vajroni mudra for celibates. This sadhana is greatly misunderstood, as these elements are highly symbolic. With these mudras the downward flowing energy can be converted into upward flowing energy.

Why is vajroni mudra recommended for celibates?

Swami Niranjanananda: Yogis have linked vajra nadi with the digestive process and the retention of semen. In *Gheranda Samhita* (3:58–60) it says:

> *Ayam yoge yoga shreshtho yoginaam muktikaaranam;*
> *Ayam hitaprado yogo yoginaam siddhidaayakah.*

> *Etadyogaprasaadena bindusiddhirbhaveddhruvam;*
> *Siddhe bindau mahaayatne kim na sidhyati bhootale.*

> *Bhogena mahataa yukto yadi mudraam samaacharet;*
> *Tathaapi sakalaa siddhirbhavati tasya nishchitam.*

This mudra provides mukti, liberation to the yogis, is favourable and a provider of siddhi or perfection and is the best. (58)

A sadhaka becomes competent in urdhvaretas tattwa due to siddhi of bindu as a result of its prasad and once bindu siddhi is achieved, then what work cannot be accomplished on this earth? (59)

Even if a bhogi, a householder, perfects this mudra, he can achieve all the siddhis. (60)

Etad yoga prasaadena bindu siddhir-bhaved-dhruvam means, the practice of yoga which enables siddhi or perfection of bindu is *veerya siddhi* or control over the semen. *Urdhvaretas* refers to a yogi whose seminal fluid has been converted and turned upwards into spiritual energy. There are also other aspects to this practice.

It is normal for men to have night emissions, which is certainly not a physical problem but can cause disturbance in the mind. During sleep, when there is no longer control over thoughts and feelings, sexual thinking sometimes arises and passionate and lustful feelings surface. The senses are influenced and night emissions occur. This is a natural process, it is not a disease or disorder, but it is said that when sense control remains weak, especially in the reproductive sense, mental turmoil and ejaculation occur.

Some men fear that energy or power from their body is wasted in this way, but from a physical viewpoint there is no defect or disorder. The problem lies in the feelings of sin and *samskaras*, influences, in the mind, which may have been suppressed since childhood. When a reaction starts in the body, the mind is influenced more than the body, and mental disturbance, unrest and excitement develop. There may also be loss of appetite, and thirst.

Vajroni mudra is practised to control this. It is said that it is the greatest or most beneficial of all yogic practices, *ayam yoge yoga-shreshtho*, and provides mastery to yogis. With due precaution and effort in this practice bindu siddhi is achieved, and for a person who attains control or mastery over bindu, nothing on this earth is impossible.

Yogis have added another line of thinking. Besides making the senses and self-control strong and powerful, when semen is conserved in the body, the life force hidden in the chromosomes is also preserved and this life force influences the *chakras*, the psychic centres in the subtle body. That is why it is said, *siddhe bindau mahaayatne kim na sidhyati bhootale*, a human being can achieve victory over the earth element by means of bindu siddhi.

This principle is very simple. Mooladhara chakra is the centre of reproduction and the centre of the earth element, *bhuh* or *prithvi tattwa*. In normal life, the energy of mooladhara chakra takes the form of external energy and is discharged. That is why the asana linked to vajroni mudra is called brahmacharyasana, that state of body, or *asana* which helps a human being to attain celibacy. When this energy is conserved and preserved, then the same energy, taking the form of vital force or *prana* in the subtle body, is helpful in the awakening of kundalini.

It has also been written, *bhogena mahataa yukto yadi mudraam samacharet, tathaapi sakalaa siddhir-bhavati tasya nishchitam*, despite excessive craving and running after sensorial pleasures, all kinds of siddhis can be attained by the practice of this mudra.

ASHWINI MUDRA: HORSE GESTURE

What is ashwini mudra?

Swami Satyananda: The word *ashwini* means 'horse' and in this context the word *mudra* means 'attitude'. Therefore, this practice can be literally translated as 'the attitude of the horse'. The practice resembles the movement a horse makes with its sphincter immediately after evacuation of the bowels. If one watches the anus of a horse, the rhythmic contraction and relaxation of the anal muscles will be noticed. In this way, the horse often does the yogic practice of ashwini mudra.

Why is ashwini mudra categorized as a mudra?
Swami Satyananda: Ashwini mudra prevents the escape of pranic energy and redirects it upward for spiritual purposes.

Is it essential that only the anal muscles are contracted in ashwini mudra?
Swami Satyananda: It is impossible to confine the muscular contraction only to the small area of the anus. Other pelvic muscles and muscles associated with the sexual organs will also contract. But one should try as much as possible to concentrate on the contraction at the anus. At first this is difficult, but with practice it becomes easier and easier.

What is the best posture for practising ashwini mudra?
Swami Satyananda: Ashwini mudra can be done in almost any asana, including any of the meditation asanas. It can be integrated with any asana performed in one's asana program. For example, it can be performed while holding paschimottanasana or sarvangasana. This means that two practices can be done at the same time, bringing additional benefits.

What are the physical benefits of ashwini mudra?
Swami Niranjanananda: Ashwini mudra strengthens the anal muscles and alleviates disorders of the rectum and reproductive organs such as constipation, haemorrhoids and prolapse of the uterus or rectum. In such cases, this mudra is most effective performed daily, preferably in an inverted asana. The squeezing action removes accumulated blood from the vicinity of the rectum, considered to be a contributing factor in haemorrhoids. It removes indigestion by stimulating intestinal activity, and enhances the functioning of the intestines, helping remove constipation.

What is the most effective way to practise ashwini mudra for the relief of piles?

Swami Satyananda: Piles are characterized by an accumulation of blood in the region of the anus. The practice of ashwini mudra helps to squeeze this stagnant blood away from the anus. This process is intensified if the mudra is combined with an inverted asana such as sarvangasana. Ashwini mudra physically draws the blood away from the anus and sarvangasana allows the blood to drain downwards, back to the heart. Every sufferer of piles should definitely practise this combination daily.

How can ashwini mudra be combined with pranayama?

Swami Satyananda: Ashwini mudra can be integrated with nadi shodhana pranayama by holding the anal contraction during retention of the breath.

Why is ashwini mudra used as preparation for moola bandha?

Swami Satyananda: To practise moola bandha correctly one must have sensitivity in the region of the anus and the perineum (the area between the anus and the sexual organs). Ashwini mudra is an excellent technique for developing this sensitivity. Without mastering ashwini mudra it is very difficult for most people to practise moola bandha correctly.

Why is ashwini mudra an important practice?

Swami Niranjanananda: Ashwini is an important mudra. It allows the energy to flow through the body so that the practitioner always remains healthy by acquiring strength and vitality, and lives a long life. Ashwini mudra is described in *Gheranda Samhita* (3:82–83):

> *Aakunchayed gudadvaaram prakaashayet punah punah;*
> *Saa bhavedashvineemudraa shaktiprabodhakaarinee.*
>
> *Aashvinee paramaa mudraa guhyarogavinaashinee;*
> *Balapushtikaree chaiva akaalamaranam haret.*

Contracting and expanding the anal region repeatedly is called ashwini mudra. It awakens kundalini. (82)

This mudra is the destroyer of diseases pertaining to the anus and reproductive system, the provider or enhancer of physical energy, and the saviour from untimely death. (83)

As a result of practising ashwini mudra, control over the anal muscles is achieved. One can expand and contract them, just like a horse, *ashwini*, does. It is such a simple mudra that no difficulty is encountered while doing it.

VAJROLI MUDRA (FOR MEN): THUNDERBOLT ATTITUDE
SAHAJOLI MUDRA (FOR WOMEN): SPONTANEOUS PSYCHIC ATTITUDE

What is vajroli mudra according to the traditional texts?
Swami Satyananda: There are two types of vajroli – one is concerned with *maithuna* (sexual intercourse under prescribed conditions) and the other is a simple raja yoga form in which the urethra is contracted upward. It is the latter that is commonly taught and that is used in kriya yoga.

The full practice involves years of preparation which commences with the simple contraction of the urogenital muscles and later the sucking up of liquids. Only after the sixth practice is perfected can the seventh be successfully attempted by the yogi – that is, the practice included in *maithuna*, yogic intercourse. Through this practice of vajroli, the sexual energy, hormones and secretions are reassimilated into the body. Its outcome is the union of the negative and positive poles of energy within one's body. It is stated in *Hatha Yoga Pradipika* (3:83):

Svechchhayaa vartamaano'pi yogoktairniyamairvinaa;
Vajroleem yo vijaanaati sa yogee siddhibhaajanam.

Even one living a free lifestyle without the formal rules of yoga, if he practises vajroli well, that yogi becomes a recipient of siddhis (perfections).

According to this sloka, sexual life can be elevated from the sensual to the spiritual plane if it is practised in a particular way: for this, vajroli has been described.

What is the meaning and significance of vajroli and sahajoli mudras?

Swami Satyananda: The word *vajroli* is derived from the Sanskrit root *vajra*, meaning 'thunderbolt' or 'lightning' and it has various meanings and implications. It is the weapon of Lord Indra and also means 'mighty one'.

Vajra in this context refers to *vajra nadi* which governs the urogenital system. It is the second innermost layer of sushumna nadi. Vajra nadi is the energy flow within the spine which governs the sexual systems of the body. This pathway is directly connected with the unleashing of powerful psychic forces. In mundane life it is responsible for the sexual behaviour, or libido. In tantric sadhana this energy is not suppressed, it is awakened and redirected. Vajroli, sahajoli and amaroli are mudras which specifically sublimate sexual energy into *ojas*, vitality, and kundalini shakti.

Sahajoli is from the root *sahaj*, meaning 'spontaneous'. *Vajroli* is therefore the force which moves upward with the power of lightning, and *sahajoli* is the psychic attitude of spontaneous arousing.

What is sahajoli mudra?

Swami Satyananda: Sahaj means 'spontaneous'. Sahajoli is an important part of vajroli, just as jalandhara is part and parcel of uddiyana. In tantra, vajroli is done by men and the same practice when done by a woman is sahajoli: just as a man should practise gradual contractions of the urogenital muscles so should the woman. The entire vaginal passage has to be contracted. Sahajoli is performed in siddha yoni asana.

Once siddha yoni asana is perfected, the practice of sahajoli should be developed gradually.

What are the benefits of the simple form of vajroli and sahajoli mudras?

Swami Satyananda: Vajroli and sahajoli mudras regulate and tone the entire urogenital system. They help overcome psycho-sexual conflicts and unwanted sexual thoughts. They also conserve and redirect energy, enhancing meditative states.

By their practice swadhisthana chakra is awakened: during the practice, awareness is held on swadhisthana.

How are hatha yoga and tantra related?

Swami Satyananda: The system of hatha yoga consists of a substratum of tantric practices. Only the ritualistic aspects have been omitted: it is not coincidence that the system was handed down from a tantric guru. In hatha yoga the basic techniques for uniting the positive and negative energies within the individual have been maintained.

Vajroli, sahajoli and amaroli have been secretly preserved because of social beliefs which consider them to be 'immoral behaviour'. Initiation into the practice is only given to ardent and dedicated yogis, not to the common person or the casual enquirer.

What is the role of vajroli and sahajoli mudras in hatha yoga and tantra?

Swami Satyananda: Celibacy has its own merits, but it is not good for all. It is opposing the realities and processes of nature. So what to do? Hatha yoga came up with a suggestion. It is called the principle of preservation. One who masters the technology of preservation is a *brahmachari*.

Even one who is married and a householder can be a brahmachari if the technology of preservation can be mastered. Preservation is important, the act is not important. If a negative experience occurs, that is due to loss, not due to the act. For this purpose, sahajoli has been prescribed for women and vajroli for men. In *Hatha Yoga Pradipika* (3:85) it is written:

Mehanena shanaih samyagoordhvaakunchanamabhyaset.
Purusho'pyathavaa naaree vajroleesiddhimaapnuyaat.

By practising gradual upward contractions during the emission in intercourse, any man or woman achieves perfection of vajroli.

In the tantric system it is said that the husband and wife should practise tantra together and for that purpose they must master certain techniques. The man has to master vajroli and the woman has to master sahajoli, in combination with moola bandha and uddiyana bandha (not as bandha but as mudra).

Perfection of vajroli means being able to withdraw the seminal fluid during the height of climax. This involves the practice of contracting and controlling the muscles of the urogenital complex. It should be practised daily in siddhasana or siddha yoni asana in progressive stages. Initially the muscles of the genital, excretory and urinary organs tend to contract simultaneously. The muscular contractions have to be isolated in three distinct areas. Eventually contractions become so forceful that upward suction is created. In the female body the labia minora should move upwards with complete contraction. Practice of uddiyana bandha before vajroli creates greater suction and tighter contraction.

The yogini practises sahajoli to regulate the hormones secreted from the ovaries. This is the principle of preservation, and hatha yoga believes this to be the important point. Man must preserve his *veerya*, semen, and the female must preserve her secretions, *rajas*. Abstention from sexual life is not advocated. This is one of the most important points which must be clearly understood, because it is a scientific point.

What is the place of vajroli mudra in the modern world?
Swami Satyananda: Vajroli mudra is an important practice today in the Kali Yuga when the ability and need to

179

express oneself in the material and sensual world is predominating. There is a need to act in the external world and simultaneously develop inner awareness. The purpose of life should be to attain a deeper and more fulfilling experience beyond the empirical sensory experience alone.

Who is qualified to practise vajroli and sahajoli mudras?

Swami Satyananda: Vajroli and maithuna were never meant for the general public because most people are victims of their emotions and passions. The first requirement for the practice is a passionless state of mind. Maybe one or two people today can fit into this category. Only those who have entered the highest states of samadhi know what a passionless state is.

These practices result in greater personal power and if used by selfish people they will incur catastrophe upon themselves and others. The purpose of liberating the energy through vajroli is to go beyond personal identity and the limitations of the ego. If yoga is practised only to gain psychic power, or if vajroli is an excuse for any lesser fulfillment, the practices are being misused. Therefore, in *Hatha Yoga Pradipika* (3:95) it says:

Ayam yogah punyavataam dheeraanaam tattvadarshinaam.
Nirmatsaraanaam vai sidhyenna tu matsarashaalinaam.

Verily this yoga is perfected by virtuous and well conducted men who have seen the truth and not those who are selfish.

To whom will a guru impart the knowledge of vajroli mudra?

Swami Satyananda: A novice will not be able to find a guru to teach him the traditional method of this practice. Nor will a guru teach any person who is untrustworthy or cannot understand the purpose of the practices. Likewise one has to be careful when reading about these practices as interpreted by non-yogis because incorrect descriptions have surely

180

been given. Precisely for this reason many people have a misconception concerning vajroli. Only those who can comprehend the subtle laws of tantra, kundalini, energy and consciousness can appreciate its significance and necessity. Preparation for vajroli, therefore, must specifically be done under the guidance of a guru and not just any teacher. In reality this form of vajroli is rarely taught. The *Hatharatnavali* (2:74–75) says:

Vajroleem kathayishyaami gopitaam sarvayogibhih;
Atee tadrahasyam hi na deyaa yasya kasyachit.

Svapraanaistu samo yasmaat tasyaiva kathayedghruvam;
Putrasyaapi na daatavyaa gurushishyakramam vinaa.

Now I will talk about vajroli which is kept secret by all yogis. The secret process of this should not be revealed to an unsuitable person. (74)

The person whom the guru feels to be like his own prana, verily it should be told to him. It should not be given even to one's own son without the guru-disciple tradition. (75)

Hatharatnavali (2:103–104) further states:

Ajnaata yogashaastrena vajroleem stree to naabhyaset;
Ayam yogah punyavataam dhanyanaam tattvashaalinaam.

Nirbhatsaraanaam sidhyeta na tu matsarashaalinaam;
Sarveshaameva yogaanaam ayam yogah shubhankarah.

The lady who does not know the science of yoga should not practise vajroli. This yoga is successful to the courageous and the pious yogis who have an insight into reality. (103)

Success in yoga can be achieved only by those who are in no way selfish. It cannot be achieved by self-seeking ones. This yoga is auspicious among all the yogas. (104)

181

Therefore, even though instructions and techniques are given it should not be attempted out of curiosity.

How can sensual involvement lead to higher awareness?

Swami Satyananda: According to tantra, *bhoga*, or sensual involvement, can be the means to yoga. Sense interaction can lead to higher awareness. The very idea that the ultimate experience can unfold through sensual experience is not one that many people in the last few centuries, and even earlier, have been able to accept. Some commentaries on the hatha yoga texts refuse to accept this as a part of the science of yoga and completely omit the slokas from the original text pertaining to vajroli and maithuna, yogic intercourse, stating that they are obscure and repugnant practices only followed by those yogis who lack the willpower to reach their goal otherwise. It is, however, stated in *Hatha Yoga Pradipika* (3:103):

> *Dehasiddhim cha labhate vajrolyabhyaasayogatah.*
> *Ayam punyakaro yogo bhoge bhukte'pi muktidah.*

By the yoga of vajroli practice, perfection of the body fructifies. This auspicious yoga even brings liberation alongside with sensual involvement (bhoga).

This important sloka states a basic concept of tantra that contradicts and shatters puritanical ideas: we have a physical body and cannot deny its existence. Until one knows the experiences of the senses how can deeper and subtle awareness evolve? Experience is of the mind and not the physical body. First we have to know what the physical experience is. Then by increasing the subtle perception, the experience can be reawakened in the mind without involving the physical senses.

During the day we see with our eyes but what happens at night when we dream? We are not seeing through the eyes but nevertheless, the mind is experiencing. We are re-experiencing what has been perceived. In tantra, therefore, the physical body is the means to delve more deeply into the mind and the reality of existence.

What instructions are given for women in the traditional practice of vajroli mudra?
Swami Satyananda: Just as a man should be adept in the practice, the woman also has to be well practised and adept. There are few references in the hatha yoga texts specifying practices meant for women but in *Hatha Yoga Pradipika* (3:99) it is clearly stated:

> *Pumso bindum samaakunchya samyagabhyaasapaatavaat;*
> *Yadi naaree rajo rakshedvajrolyaa saapi yoginee.*

If a woman practises vajroli and saves her rajas and the man's bindu by thorough contraction, she is a yogini.

Just as a man should practise gradual contractions of the urogenital muscles so should the woman. According to tantra that is sahajoli. *Hatharatnavali* (2:93, 101–102) states:

> *Sindoorasadrisham yonau streenaamaasthaayikam rajah.*
> *Ritumatyaa rajo'pyeva rajo bindum cha rakshayet.*

> *Tatah param samarthahsyaadoordhvam aakunchayedrajah.*
> *Tasyaah shareere naadastu bindutaameva gachchhati.*

> *Sabindustadrajashchaiva ekeekritya svadehajau;*
> *Vajrolyabhyaasayogena yogasiddhih kare sthitaa.*

Rajas is permanent, like red lead, in the reproductive organ of a woman. The rajas should be saved during menstruation like bindu is to be saved. The woman should practise vajroli. (93)

After that she should draw up the rajas if possible. The nada in her body moves like bindu. (101)

Bindu and rajas produced in the body should be mixed through the vajroli practice of yoga. Then success is at hand. (102)

What is the purpose of vajroli and sahajoli mudras?

Swami Satyananda: The purpose of these mudras is to convert *retas*, sexual energy, into *ojas*, highly refined pranic or psychic energy. This process is called *urdhvaretas* – the sublimation of sexual energy. Prana is the essence of both retas and ojas; vajroli and sahajoli help to bring about sublimation of the grosser retas into the more refined ojas.

Sexual energy should give one vitality and strength, it cannot just be denied and refused. It should make one confident, brilliant, full of vigour and vitality. Vajroli achieves this by controlling the production of semen. With vajroli, the energy level is raised. Vajroli gives its practitioner absolute control over the influx of energy and the processes going on in the testicles.

What are the pranic effects of the perineal mudras?

Swami Satyananda: In the region of the perineum where there are many nerve endings, there is a main nadi known as the vajra nadi which corresponds to the sciatic nerve. There is another nadi, brahma nadi, which runs through the centre of sushumna. These nadis are specifically stimulated or acted upon when vajroli, sahajoli or ashwini mudra is practised.

Brahma represents the creative aspect, the sexual urge, desire. With the practice of vajroli, sahajoli and ashwini mudras the flow of apana within brahma nadi is reversed, and all the psychological, physical, mental and emotional desires are transcended. Apana is reversed and begins to move in brahma nadi in the other direction.

How can the full practice of vajroli be developed?

Swami Satyananda: The complete technique of vajroli can be developed by the following steps:
1. Sit in siddhasana and practise uddiyana, increasing gradually until it can be held for one and a half minutes.
2. Eliminate acidity of urine by means of i) diet, ii) water, and iii) seeds of dry coriander.

3. Practise interrupted urination while performing namaskara. Time needed: six months.
4. Suck the urine back up. Time needed: one or two years.
5. Hold back the ejaculation up to one minute.
6. Progressively increase the period of holding back until permanent retention is achieved.
7. Direct the concentration to the chakras.

How are liquids sucked into the urethra in vajroli mudra?

Swami Satyananda: In the hatha yoga tradition a tube or catheter is inserted into the penis for practising this stage of vajroli mudra. First air is drawn into the bladder, then water, later oil, honey and finally liquid mercury. According to some authorities, it is neither essential nor advisable to use any liquid other than water. Instead of drawing further viscous liquids into the bladder, pure water may be used while varying the suction exerted by increasing the height to which the liquid is raised. This is briefly described in *Hatha Yoga Pradipika* (3:86):

> *Yatnatah shastanaalena phootkaaram vajrakandare;*
> *Shanaih shanaih prakurveeta vaayusanchaarakaaranaat.*

By slowly drawing in air through a prescribed tube inserted into the urethra of the penis, gradually air and prana traverse into the vajra kanda.

The *Hatharatnavali* states that vajroli/sahajoli should be done by men and women. However, this particular practice is specifically for men. The complete method of practice is not given in *Hatha Yoga Pradipika,* but in *Hatharatnavali* (2:80–85), there are detailed descriptions.

How can a woman perfect sahajoli mudra?

Swami Satyananda: Just as a man prepares for vajroli by practising contractions and then drawing up air and water through a catheter via the urethra, so a woman can practise in a similar way. Instead of inserting a catheter into the urethra, however, a tube is inserted into the vagina so that a portion of it extends outside. She then sits on a bucket of water and practises uddiyana bandha. If water is not sucked into the vagina through this process, then nauli is practised. When this has been perfected, the water is retained inside for as long as possible and nauli is performed. This cleanses the vagina of old secretions.

When these practices are perfected, the tube is discarded and water is taken in directly. When the water can be retained inside only by the practice of moola bandha and without uddiyana, the perineal muscles associated with moola bandha and vajroli/sahajoli have become strong.

How rare is perfection of vajroli mudra?

Swami Sivananda: Vajroli mudra is an important yogic kriya in hatha yoga. One has to work hard to get full success in this kriya. There are very few people who are experts in this act. This kriya is of immense help in the establishment of brahmacharya. It must be gradually practised until twelve inches of the catheter can be drawn into the urethra. Raja Bhartrihari could do this kriya very dexterously.

Not even a drop of semen comes out of the yogi who practises this mudra. Even if it is discharged, he can draw it back. The yogi who draws his semen up and preserves it conquers death. A good smell emanates from his body. Lord Krishna was a skilled expert in this mudra. That is the reason why he was called a *nitya*, constant, brahmachari although he was amidst several gopis.

How can the sexual act be sublimated for spiritual purposes?

Swami Satyananda: It is a difficult question and the answer is unpalatable to many, because religious people are very puritan. They don't even want to hear impure words, but I don't consider anything impure. Everything is a part of nature.

At the end of the sexual act there is an experience. Where does this experience take place? It takes place in the higher centres, but where is it experienced? At the lower centre. If one can have that experience at the higher centre, then both the act and the experience have been sublimated. But how can it be sublimated? By the practice of vajroli mudra.

By the practise of vajroli and sahajoli, an experience that originally takes place in the higher centre, but is experienced at a gross centre, is sublimated. When delicious sweets are eaten, where does the experience take place? In the tongue? No, the tongue has no mind. The experience takes place at a higher centre, but we are not capable of experiencing it there because our experiential faculty is too gross, so it is experienced in the tongue or mouth. If the capacity of experience can be sublimated, then the sweetness will be experienced straight away in the brain, and that experience will be everlasting.

How is sexual energy transformed into spiritual energy through vajroli mudra?

Swami Satyananda: In mundane life, the climax of sexual experience is the one time when the mind becomes completely void of its own accord and consciousness beyond the body can be glimpsed. However, that experience is short-lived because the energy is expressed through the lower energy centres. This energy which is normally lost can be used to awaken the dormant power of kundalini in mooladhara. If the sperm can be withheld, the energy can be channelled through sushumna nadi and the central nervous system, to the dormant areas of the brain and to the sleeping consciousness.

The sexual act is the one means to totally concentrate and captivate the mind, but in tantra it should not be the ordinary experience. The experience has to be more than the gross or sensual one. Awareness and control have to be developed. The senses have to be used, but only as the means of awakening the higher consciousness, not the animal consciousness, and for this vajroli mudra and various tantric rituals must be perfected.

Why does yoga transform the sexual act into a spiritual practice when other traditions condemn the sensuality of sex?

Swami Satyananda: Man has four basic desires known as *purushartha* or *chaturvarga*, the first of which is *kama* or 'sensual gratification'. This needs to be fulfilled to a certain extent, but it should not pull the consciousness down. It should be a means to accomplish a greater result. Every action, including the sex act, should be directed towards realizing the truth of existence. Then one is living a spiritual life. Spiritual life does not depend on living up to puritanical morality.

If one can follow puritanical ideals and attain enlightenment, then practise them, but do not condemn others who cannot. The moment rigid ideals are created stating that the spiritual path has to be like 'this' and cannot be like 'that' one's ability to have a total experience becomes limited.

Why are vajroli and sahajoli practised during sexual intercourse?

Swami Satyananda: During maithuna the bindu or semen is not supposed to be released but if this occurs then it must be drawn up through the generative organ by vajroli. The flow of bindu can be reversed at various stages, for example, through the practices of vipareeta karani mudra and khechari mudra.

The classical hatha yogic texts state that so long as bindu falls into the 'sun', decay and death are the end result, as it is consumed by the fire during the lifespan. The sun represents rajas in manipura, but rajas also refers to vaginal secretions. Therefore, if the bindu falls into the rajas, the practice of vajroli has not been successful. When bindu falls to manipura, what is actually consumed by the fire are its sattwic, nectarine qualities which enlighten the

188

body and bestow immortality. Below manipura the chakras are concerned with instinctive animal functions and tamasic qualities, and if the bindu is spilled here it becomes a poison, causing suffering and death. It is stated in *Hatha Yoga Pradipika* (3:87):

Naareebhage patadbindumabhyaasenordhvamaaharet;
Chalitam cha nijam bindumoordhvamaakrishya rakshayet.

The bindu (semen) that is about to fall into the woman's vagina should be made to move upwards with practice. And if it falls, the semen and the woman's fluid should be conserved by drawing it up.

Therefore, during the practice of maithuna a sattwic state of mind has to be maintained at all costs, even though the lower chakras are activated; the rajasic and tamasic tendencies of those centres are to be recognized and controlled.

How does vajroli mudra lead to the union of Shiva and Shakti?

Swami Satyananda: It is not just a matter of control during maithuna which can awaken the higher centres. It is the appropriate combination of the opposite elements and energies. When hydrogen gas and oxygen combine there is an instant explosion. Similarly in the physical body when the positive and negative elements combine there is an explosion. When the union takes place in the nucleus of mooladhara chakra, kundalini shakti is released. It is stated in *Hatha Yoga Pradipika* (3:91):

Ritumatyaa rajo'pyevam nijam bindum cha rakshayet;
Mendhrenaakarshayedoordhvam samyagabhyaasayogavit.

The knower of yoga, perfect in the practice, conserves his bindu and the woman's rajas by drawing it up through the generative organ.

At that time, if vajroli is practised, the energy rises up sushumna and the central nervous system to ajna chakra in the brain. The purpose of the practice is neither indulgence nor birth control but specifically to expand the consciousness. The experience has an impact that can last for hours, days or weeks. When vajroli has been perfected, the expanded state of consciousness becomes a permanent experience. The *Shiva Samhita* (4:86–87) states:

Bindurvidhumayo jneyo rajah sooryamayastathaa;
Ubhayormelanam kaaryam svashareere prayatnatah.

Aham binduh rajah shaktirubhayormelanam yadaa;
Yoginaam saadhanavataam bhaveddivyam vapustadaa.

Know that the seminal fluid is the moon and the ovarian fluid is the sun. It is necessary to coalesce the two within one's own body. (86)

In fact I (Shiva) am the seminal fluid and the ovarian fluid is Shakti. When the two are united in the body of the yogi, he attains a divine body. (87)

There are two processes: one is the process of uniting the sun and the moon through vajroli and maithuna. Secondly, that process has to take place within one's own body. Only the guru can further illumine this to the disciple.

Why is preservation of semen believed to be so important?
Swami Satyananda: Nature has provided the mechanism of seminal release, but although it is generally not known, nature has also provided a means to control this mechanism through various practices of hatha yoga. If the release of semen and ova can be controlled, a new range of experience dawns. Those experiences are also endowed by nature, even if only a few people have gained them. Therefore, the techniques should not be considered to be against the natural order.

Tantra does not denounce the normal sexual relation-ships but it definitely says no ejaculation. For that one has to practise vajroli and the women have to learn sahajoli. When the energy which is produced at the lower centre is retained, one must then be able to direct it to the higher centre through shambhavi mudra, so that the experience does not become a physical experience but it just remains an experience.

A person who has perfect control of body and mind, is a yogi in every situation. A person who gorges himself on food, for example, is just as 'obscene' as a person who indulges in uncontrollable sexual acts. According to *Hatha Yoga Pradipika*, if vajroli is well practised, even in an otherwise free lifestyle, that yogi's attainments in life will be greater, and a greater source of vital and mental power will become available to him. A few great yogis and masters had these experiences and consequently instructed their disciples in the oli mudras and other hatha yoga techniques.

Why is the preservation of semen associated with long life?
Swami Satyananda: In *Hatha Yoga Pradipika* (3:88) Yogi Swatmarama has written:

Evam sanrakshayed bindum mrityum jayati yogavit.
Maranam bindupaatena jeevanam bindudhaaranaat.

Therefore, the knower of yoga conquers death by preserving the bindu (semen). Release of the bindu means death; conservation of semen is life.

This sloka demands detailed discussion. The word *bindu* means point or nucleus. The nucleus of every cell is this same bindu. It contains the chromosomes which encode the entire memory and evolutionary potential of the species. Of course, it is not only loss of semen which causes death. Cell degeneration, death and replacement is continually occurring at a certain rate in all the tissues of the body (except in the central nervous system where the neurons are not replaced). Semen and menses are specifically referred to because their rate of formation and turnover exceeds by far

191

the turnover rate of other cells, and therefore has the most metabolic significance.

How is the connection between semen and immortality to be understood? It is twofold. In common life, union of these cells creates another bindu, another individual and another universe. This is the glimpse of immortality through one's progeny. Additionally, according to Yogi Swatmarama, if seminal release from the body can be quelled a man has tapped within his own body that same primal source of life. Both medical science and modern psychology have dismissed the ancient belief in the value of retaining the semen as an old wives' tale. However, from the yogic experience, this myth contains more essential truth than all the medical and psychological tomes ever published.

There have always been 'experts' who have nevertheless remained ignorant about the purpose of existence. The modern age is no exception. There may be intellectual giants, there may be compassionate and even heroic men, there may be dedicated humanists, but this is not enough if they have failed to grasp transcendental experience. Their endeavours and achievements remain within the realm of empirical consciousness and the lower mind.

Why has Yogi Swatmarama made a claim that loss of semen is the cause of death? The semen contains an enormous force in molecular or potential form. It can be compared to the potential contained within an atomic bomb. The seminal fluid discharged in a single emission contains an average of 400 million spermatozoa. Each of these minute sperm possesses enough energy to swim 3,000 times its own length. In relative terms that is the same amount of energy used up by a six-foot man swimming one and a half miles. That is the proportional amount of the body's vital energy packed into a single sperm cell expelled from the body in a single seminal emission.

When the shedding and ejaculation of semen is habitual, frequent and uncontrolled, that individual is being constantly drained of a quantum of highly potent living essence which the body has no option but to continually replace using a constant supply of metabolic energy. Where has this energy which is lost in the semen come from? From the nutritional viewpoint, it is derived from the dietary nutrients, broken down in digestion, assimilated into the blood and constituted into the nucleic acids and the fatty protein structure of the spermatozoa. Metabolic energy is consumed every step of the way. Constant replacement of discharged semen demands that a diet rich in fats and proteins be consumed. This imposes a heavy working burden on the digestive organs and glands, such as liver and pancreas, as well as on the heart, circulatory and eliminative systems.

As a result, the cells and tissues of the bodily systems demand replacement more rapidly, and the higher overall cell turnover leads to greater expenditure of metabolic energy, accelerates the metabolic rate and elevates the basal body temperature. According to gerontologists, who investigate the ageing and degenerative process, elevation and acceleration of these factors are the major cause of rapid physical degeneration and early death of the human body.

According to Yogi Swatmarama, preservation of the semen in the body conserves energy and bestows upon the yogi a power and experience not known to a man accustomed to losing semen throughout his life. He declares that semen which is withheld is the very nectar of immortality.

Could it be that seminal retention sustains a greater conscious power in the body, mind and will of a yogi? Does seminal retention create an indwelling fountain of joy, power and bliss which enlightens the human brain? These are the questions which modern scientists have to ask. It is not sufficient to dismiss the claims and experiences of yogis as unscientific myths.

Why control the semen? Certainly not for any moralistic reason. Note well that Yogi Swatmarama is not recommending celibacy, only the retention of semen. It is

193

because if a man can escape from the slavish compulsion to expel the semen, he can realize within himself the source of freedom, immortality and bliss.

Hatha Yoga Pradipika in its entirety sets out a method to preserve the body and mind. Let those who would realize the truth seek a guru and practise according to initiation and instructions.

How can preservation of semen remove the fear of death?
Swami Satyananda: Fear of death is one of the most fundamental motivating forces governing human personality and behaviour. It has been identified as one of the *kleshas*, or afflictions, by Sage Patanjali, as it is a root cause of suffering. Fear of death stems from identification of the self with the physical body. Release of semen strongly reinforces this identification. When a yogi can control the bindu, preventing its release from the body even in maithuna, identification with the body ceases, and consciousness is freed from physical identification. Then the fear of death dissolves. In *Hatha Yoga Pradipka* (3:89) it says:

> *Sugandho yogino dehe jaayate bindudhaaranaat;*
> *Yaavad binduh sthiro dehe taavat kaalabhayam kutah.*

As long as the bindu (semen) is steady in the body, then where is the fear of death? The yogi's body smells pleasant by conserving the bindu.

Even though a person may say that he does not fear death, nevertheless his body's reactions and responses betray that he is still governed by this fear. It remains a subconscious determinant of his behaviour. To convince the conscious mind that 'I am fearless in the face of death' is not difficult. It is only a psychological matter. How can we convince the deeper mind and overcome the physiological responses of fear which are subconsciously determined? For that, tantric and yogic sadhana are necessary and a competent guru should be sought.

How does vajroli mudra help develop a one-pointed mind?

Swami Satyananda: Yogis have always claimed that autonomic body functions can be consciously controlled, but it takes time and effort. It is only recently that science is proving this true. According to *Hatha Yoga Pradipika* (3:90) control of semen by the mind is possible:

> *Chittaayattam nrinaam shukraam shukraayattam cha jeevitam.*
> *Tasmaachchhukram manashchaiva rakshaneeyam prayatnatah.*

> A man's semen can be controlled by the mind and control of semen is life-giving. Therefore, his semen and mind should be controlled and conserved.

The easiest functions to control are those associated with the voluntary nervous system: the practice of asanas develops this ability. For more subtle control, pranayama is used, as the rate and depth of the breath influences the physiological systems of the body, the brainwave patterns and modes of thinking. In this way, the functions of the reproductive organs can also be influenced and eventually controlled by yoga practices such as vajroli mudra, over a sustained period of time.

Release of reproductive secretions is not only a physiological process, the mind is also involved. Without mental involvement the release cannot occur. In vajroli, the role of sensory pathways, *jnanendriya*, and mental imagery in initiating sexual responses must be witnessed. Control of mind begins by becoming aware of the process. By isolating awareness, the mind remains unexcited in the midst of sensory perception. When the mind can be witnessed in this way, excitation of the motor responses, *karmendriya*, can be controlled, and semen can be withheld. Control of mind means control of the whole process.

By the practice of vajroli one can learn to control the physical mechanism, but side by side with this, mental control must be developed. When the mind wanders in useless fantasy, energy is dissipated. When the mind is totally concentrated on a specific object, symbol or point, pranic movements are channelled and the bindu is maintained. In hatha yoga the mind has to be kept on the aim of the practices in order to induce total one-pointedness.

How do the esoteric and exoteric interact in the transcendence achieved by vajroli?

Swami Satyananda: How and where is the bindu which has been withdrawn from the rajas to be experienced? It has to be traced to its origin through vajroli. It is a point in consciousness. It is not in the body, nor in the mind, but it is experienced through the body and the mind.

When mooladhara chakra awakens in maithuna, the bindu of consciousness must be raised by vajroli, away from the sensual experiences. How to control the manifestation of this bindu? How to sustain and prolong this experience and realize its source? The bindu or semen is the interface between matter, energy and consciousness. If one tries to focus one's awareness on that experience in mooladhara, is it the semen, the material, one is trying to isolate, or the consciousness, or is it an experience of energy which one is undergoing? Or is it the point of one's own consciousness that is being located? It is the bindu, that is all: that bindu must be withheld, withdrawn and redirected upwards by vajroli.

Where does the point of consciousness go when vajroli is performed? Try to remember or re-experience it. Where is it experienced? Does it retreat upward towards its source? Or was its source in mooladhara and by vajroli it is being enticed to rise? By vajroli, this bindu rises to ajna chakra. It manifests at the eyebrow centre and can be experienced there in ajna. It is stated in *Hatha Yoga Pradipika* (3:100):

Tasyaah kinchidrajo naasham na gachchhati na samshayah;
Tasyaah shareere naadashcha bindutaameva gachchhati.

Without doubt, not even a little rajas is wasted – through vajroli, the nada and bindu in the body become one.

Ajna is not the source of bindu, but through vajroli its form will manifest there. By sustaining vajroli that bindu goes beyond ajna, where it becomes subtler than audible sound or *nada* in the consciousness, i.e. it becomes *ashabda*. The sound, or nada, released from the chakras below ajna, is traced back to its source where the bindu and nada are one. It is somewhere in the totality of consciousness – above, beyond and within – where the mind has dissolved, time and body do not exist, but only consciousness in the form of soundless sound.

To conclude, the practice of vajroli brings equilibrium in the mind and body. It revitalizes the body, activates all the energy centres and awakens sushumna nadi. The higher faculties of the brain are activated: it is perhaps the most powerful practice in the awakening of kundalini and higher consciousness. However, unless the practitioner maintains a sattwic state of awareness, it is useless.

What are the attainments of the yogini who perfects sahajoli mudra?

Swami Satyananda: All the attainments which a man gains by perfection of vajroli, a woman can also achieve. A woman is normally compelled to experience the mental and physical fluctuations of the menstrual cycle. The loss of energy which accompanies the shedding of menses is obligatory. However, if the ovum is withdrawn by the practice of vajroli, this continuing loss of energy is averted and the menstrual loss diminishes. In *Hatha Yoga Pradipika* (3:102) it is written:

Rakshodaakunchanaadoordhvam yaa rajah saa hi yoginee.
Ateetaanaagatam vetti khecharee cha bhaved dhruvam.

She is verily a yogini who conserves her rajas by contracting and raising it. She knows past, present and future and becomes fixed in khechari (i.e. consciousness moves into the higher realm).

197

A yogini who has perfected vajroli and withdrawn the bindu becomes very powerful. She experiences the awakening of a higher energy force within her body and her consciousness effortlessly expands into transpersonal awareness. This readily occurs because a woman can intuit the nature of higher consciousness and understands the hidden power underlying acceptance and surrender, whereas for a man, the barrier of personal ego often proves insurmountable.

Siddhis manifest more easily to a woman because her intuitive faculties are by nature more highly evolved. She has actually always been aware of them in a rudimentary, dormant form. A woman is more aware of her own subconscious mind and that of others and if she can withdraw the bindu by vajroli, the individual consciousness easily moves into the universal mind space, *chidakasha*, and the attitude of khechari mudra spontaneously occurs. As the tongue moves back into the upper palate, becoming fixed there without support, so the mind moves from the centres below vishuddhi and enters the total space of consciousness where the barrier of time dissolves and the past, present and future become known.

How is the uniting of consciousness and energy achieved by vajroli mudra?

Swami Satyananda: In the classical texts of hatha yoga it is repeatedly advocated that the reproductive secretions must be drawn up into the body through the practice of vajroli, so that bindu and rajas, i.e. consciousness and energy, remain within the body. This enables the sexual impulses to travel up through the central nervous system to the higher centres of the brain. In *Hatharatnavali* (2:92) it says:

Tasmaachchhukram manshchaiva rakshaneeyam prayatnatah;
Evam yo bhajate naareem taameva manasaa ramet.

Therefore, semen as well as chitta (consciousness) should be preserved with effort. The person should love mentally that lady only, with whom he practises vajroli.

This form of vajroli has nothing to do with 'obscene conduct or ritual'. Vajroli, amaroli, sahajoli and maithuna are scientific practices to unite the negative and positive poles of energy within the nucleus of consciousness. If the potential of the bindu can be exploded, a greater awakening unfolds. In the practice of vajroli in maithuna, man is the positive pole of energy. He represents the factor of time, while woman is the negative pole and represents space, for these two polarities also exist within each individual. For this reason *Hatharatnavali* (2:98) says, "Only through this can a person become a raja yogi and by no other means."

Mooladhara chakra is the seat of Shakti and sahasrara is the abode of consciousness, Shiva. During maithuna, mooladhara is directly stimulated so that the kundalini shakti can rise to sahasrara. Even if it fails to reach sahasrara it will still awaken dormant centres of perception because each of the ascending chakras is directly connected to specific centres of experience in the brain. This is one path leading to the expansion of consciousness.

The other is on the basis of connecting the two poles within one's being. Awakening of kundalini is a process of the higher mind which is triggered in the human nervous system. It is the experience of the greater mind and intelligence which is lying beyond the fence surrounding one's mind and personality.

In the course of evolution the kundalini has to become known; it is inevitable because it already exists, suppressed within. It is physiological unfoldment and a scientific destiny. Ultimately the fusion of the two poles within the seat of one's own consciousness has to take place in order to realize reality.

How does perfection of vajroli in maithuna bestow siddhis?

Swami Satyananda: Perfection of vajroli is the union within one body of the two opposite forces, prana and mind, which results in the ascent of kundalini. As kundalini travels up to sahasrara through the various energy and psychic centres, specific perfections of mind and body, known as *siddhis*, become apparent. This is stated in *Hatha Yoga Pradipika* (3:101):

Sa bindustadrajashchaiva ekeebhooya svadehagau;
Vajrolyabhyaasayogena sarvasiddhim prayachchhatah.

The bindu and the rajas in one's own body unite through the union by practise of vajroli, thus bestowing all perfections or siddhis.

Now the union of the opposite poles to awaken mooladhara is to be accomplished within the body of the yogi by a more subtle process. In this context, the terms rajas and bindu are redefined. In this stage of vajroli, the union is to be established between consciousness, Shiva, and energy, Shakti, within the yogi's body.

The *Goraksha Satark* (v. 74, 76) states that:

Bindu is Shiva (consciousness), rajas is Shakti (energy). Bindu is the moon (ida) and rajas is the sun (pingala). From the mingling of these two, one obtains the highest state. Shukra bindu is joined with bindu (the brain centre), and rajas is joined with the sun (manipura). One who knows how to unite the two is an adept.

Therefore, when vajroli in maithuna is accomplished, the further perfection of vajroli within the adept is then to be accomplished in three stages.

Whereas in maithuna the rajas of the female practitioner is the manifest Shakti, now Shakti becomes the mind. Shiva remains the male body, as in maithuna, and mooladhara is now awakened by concentrating the mind upon the trigger point of mooladhara in the perineum. For this purpose, various specific yantras, forms and mantras are concentrated upon there, as in kriya yoga. Secondly, when mooladhara awakens, *ida nadi*, the mind, and *pingala nadi*, the vitality or prana, are drawn together at each successive chakra by vajroli mudra so that the bindu rises through the sushumna nadi in the spinal passage to bindu visarga, manifesting there as eternal nada.

Shiva – pure consciousness – now resides in the brain as nada while the total Shakti – energy or rajas – is awakened in the sun, manipura. The awakening within the adept's body is stabilized at this level. Consciousness remains elevated within the spine of the adept. Mind at ajna is raised to Shiva (pure consciousness) issuing from bindu as nada. Rajas (Shakti) is raised from mooladhara and established in manipura and the bindu has been withdrawn from the two lower chakras.

In the final stage, union of the pure consciousness (Shiva) at bindu and the total energy (Shakti) at manipura is to be accomplished. Accomplishment of the first two stages involves the withdrawal of the bindu from the mooladhara and swadhisthana chakras. Shakti, which formerly manifested in these centres as sense gratification, instinctual desire and passion, now manifests through manipura chakra as will, *ichchha shakti*, and through anahata chakra as compassion. Will is transcended sensuality, compassion is transcended passion, and enlightenment is transcended mind. Will, universal love and higher awareness become the basic instinct, desire and mind of the adept.

Perfection of vajroli is not accomplished until final union between the Shakti at manipura and the Shiva at bindu is accomplished. Yogi Gorakhnath states clearly that this union is the highest state. This is the final union of yoga, because it means that the yogi's will, intuition, intellect and emotions become conscious manifestations of the cosmic or divine intelligence: such a person is a medium of divine power. Personal desires have been sacrificed in the ascent of kundalini to become the willpower of Shakti. Having surrendered the mind at ajna in that ascent, it has been superseded by the cosmic intelligence (Shiva). Paradoxically, this surrender allows an enormous cosmic power to manifest. The body and mind of the adept have become the possession and expression of Shakti, while individual consciousness has merged with pure consciousness (Shiva).

201

According to Yogi Gorakhnath, it is possible for a sadhaka to accomplish successive stages by ardent practice of vajroli, with guru's blessings and guidance. No yogic text can be more explicit than this in describing the higher stages of tantric sadhana, because the role of the guru in these attainments can never be adequately revealed.

In hatha yoga and tantra, the satguru is worshipped both internally and externally as Lord Shiva because he has attained that status. Such a guru leads, guides and cajoles his disciple every step of the way. In attaining the higher states, it is not that the disciple is only following the guru's instructions and receiving his best wishes: a transmission of the guru's consciousness and energy into the disciple is occurring. The guru is revealing, sharing and bequeathing something which he has attained.

A light can only be kindled from one which is already burning. This is why, in the yogic tradition, no adequate repayment can ever be made to that illumined one who kindles the divine light in his disciples.

7

The Bandhas

WHAT ARE BANDHAS?

What is the meaning and significance of the word bandha?
Swami Satyananda: *Bandha* means lock. The Sanskrit word literally means 'to bind', 'to hold captive' or 'to tighten and contract'. These definitions precisely describe the physical action involved in the bandha practices and their effect on the pranic body. Bandha is a technique through which the opposite poles of energy, or *shakti*, are bound together. Specific parts of the body are gently yet powerfully contracted and tightened, locking and accumulating the pranas in particular areas, then redirecting their flow into sushumna nadi for the purpose of spiritual awakening.

Bandha may also be defined analogously, being likened to the 'damming of a river', 'building a bridge' or 'building over the sea'. This can be interpreted as meaning that a *bandha* is a vehicle to traverse the ocean of *samsara*, worldly existence, and to reach the other shore, of enlightenment.

What is the traditional place of bandhas within hatha yoga?
Swami Satyananda: Bandhas are a small but important group of yogic practices. Traditionally, bandhas were classified as part of mudras, and were handed down by word of mouth from guru to disciple. *Hatha Yoga Pradipika* and *Gheranda Samhita* deal with bandhas and mudras together, and the

ancient tantric texts also make no distinction between the two. Bandhas are extensively incorporated in mudra as well as pranayama techniques. Their locking action, however, reveals them as a fundamentally important group of practices in their own right

Bandhas should first be practised and mastered individually. Only then can they be beneficially incorporated with mudra and pranayama practices. When combined in this way, they awaken the psychic faculties and form an adjunct to higher yogic practices.

What are the bandhas?

Swami Niranjanananda: Looking at the group of mudras as defined in hatha yoga, one finds a subgroup called bandhas. Bandhas or locks are a group of four practices which coordinate the flow of prana shakti throughout the body. These bandhas are very specific in their application and effect. The fourth bandha, maha bandha, is a combination of the other three.

The first is known as *moola bandha*, the perineal lock or contraction. The practice of moola bandha helps reverse the flow of *apana shakti*, the downward moving energy. Moola bandha also activates mooladhara and swadhisthana chakras.

The purpose of *uddiyana bandha*, the abdominal lock or contraction, is to activate and prepare manipura chakra as the centre for the fusion or union between prana, apana and samana shakti.

The third bandha is *jalandhara bandha*, the throat lock. With jalandhara bandha a negative pressure is created, forcing the natural upward flow of *prana shakti* to flow downwards.

With the practice of moola bandha apana flows upwards, with the practice of jalandhara bandha prana flows downwards, and with the practice of uddiyana bandha prana and apana will merge with *samana*, the sideways moving energy flow between the navel and diaphragm. This is the purpose of the bandhas.

How do the bandhas work?

Swami Niranjanananda: The bandhas are physical and psychic locks which disrupt the sensations being created in the nerves inside the body and brain, and awaken other specific kinds of sensations. Any process of contraction or expansion in the internal organs, whether in the neck, throat, perineum or anal region, changes the reactions, emotions, and the quantum of energy in the internal organs. It brings the body to a stimulated or peaceful state, resulting in the experience of inner stability.

How do bandhas interact with prana?

Swami Sivananda: Bandhas pertain to the pranas: that which binds prana is bandha. They do not allow the prana to move upwards or the apana to move downwards. They bind and unite the prana with the apana and send the united prana-apana along the sushumna nadi.

Why are the bandhas important in hatha yoga?

Swami Satyananda: How is it that a group of only four practices is considered equal to or of greater importance than the hundreds of asana, pranayama and mudra practices and their variations? Traditionally, the fact that the spiritual aspirant was introduced to bandhas secretly and only after he had mastered the execution of many, often complex, asanas, pranayamas and mudras shows that the practice of bandhas was highly respected by yogic practitioners.

There are innumerable techniques which can be practised in the path of self-realization but many involve either forced mental concentration or sensual restrictions. Therefore, it is difficult for the average person to apply himself to accomplish the task. However, it can be achieved by learning to control the body without mental conflicts, as in the practice of bandhas.

Tantra approaches the problem of higher experience by being a friend of the mind and not an enemy. Therefore, no matter what a yogi's personal philosophy may be, the three bandhas are considered as important as eating and sleeping.

How do bandhas unlock energy?

Swami Satyananda: Bandha is a technique through which the opposite poles of energy or shakti are bound together. Through contraction of muscles and organs in the physical body, the shakti is accumulated in a particular centre.

The true meaning of *bandha*, therefore, is essentially paradoxical, for it is said that by locking or contracting certain muscles on the physical level a subtle process of 'unlocking' goes on simultaneously on mental and pranic levels.

Modern muscle relaxation therapies advocate that by the systematic contraction and relaxation of muscles, one gains complete physical and mental relaxation. The underlying rationale is that in order to remove physical and mental tension it is more effective to first exaggerate the tension already existing in the body by willfully contracting the tense muscle group.

Bandhas work in a similar way, but simultaneously affect the physical, pranic, mental, psychic and causal bodies. They have far reaching effects as they are associated with powerful energy centres in the spine and brain. Therefore, bandhas are dynamic, explosive and immediate in their effect.

What are the mechanics of the bandhas?

Swami Satyananda: Bandhas involve the contraction or squeezing of muscles. As there are three bandhas, there are three main muscle groups involved: perineal muscles, abdominal muscles and cervical (neck) muscles. The perineum is in between the excretory and urinary organs. Contraction of the perineum is moola bandha, contraction of the abdomen is uddiyana bandha and contraction of the throat is jalandhara bandha.

Contraction of these muscle groups affects the nervous, circulatory, respiratory, endocrine and energy systems. When a muscle is contracted a nerve impulse is relayed to the

206

brain, triggering other neuronal circuits and nervous centres. This in turn affects the state of consciousness. In response to this stimulation, the brain adjusts its firing patterns.

MOOLA BANDHA: THE PERINEAL LOCK

What is moola bandha?

Swami Sivananda: Sit in siddhasana. Press the perineum with the left heel. Contract the perineum. Put the right heel on the organ of generation. Practising kumbhaka, forcibly draw apana vayu slowly upwards. This requires much practice. This is called *moola bandha*, destroyer of decay and death. It is described in *Shiva Samhita* (4:41):

> *Paadamoolena sampeeda gudamaargam suyantritam;*
> *Balaadapaanamaakrishya kramaadoordhavm suchaarayet;*
> *Kalpito'yam moolabandho jaraamarananaashanah.*

Pressing well the perineum with the heel, forcibly draw upwards the apana vayu slowly by practice. This is described as moola bandha – the destroyer of decay and death.

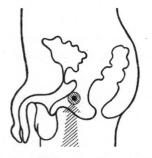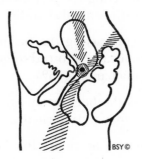

What is the meaning of moola bandha?

Swami Satyananda: The Sanskrit word *moola* means 'root', 'firmly fixed', 'source' or 'cause'. In this context it refers to the root of the spine or the perineum where *mooladhara chakra*, the seat of *kundalini*, the primal energy, is located. Moola bandha is effective for locating and awakening

207

mooladhara chakra. Therefore, moola bandha is generally known as the perineal lock.

How is moola bandha described in the hatha yoga scriptures?

Swami Satyananda: Moola bandha is an important yoga-tantra practice which is widely mentioned in the scriptures. One of the fullest descriptions is given in the *Hatha Yoga Pradipika* (3:61–64):

Paarshnibhaagena sampeedya yonimaakunchayedgudam;
Apaanamoordhvamaakrishya moolabandho'bhidheeyate.

Adhogatimapaanam vaa oordhvagam kurute balaat;
Aakunchanena tam praahurmoolabandham hi yoginah.

Gudam paarshnyaa to sampeedya vaayumaakunchayed balaat;
Vaaraamvaaram yathaa chordhvam smaayaati sameeranah.

Praanaapaanau naadabindoo moolabandhena chaikataam;
Gatvaa yogasya samsiddhim yachchhato naatra samshayah.

Pressing the perineum/vagina with the heel and contracting the rectum so that the apana vayu moves upward is moola bandha. (61)

By contracting the perineum the downward moving apana vayu is forced to go upward. The yogis call this moola bandha. (62)

Press the heel firmly against the rectum and contract forcefully and repeatedly, so that the vital energy rises. (63)

There is no doubt that by practising moola bandha, prana and apana, and nada and bindu are united, and total perfection attained. (64)

Here, the word *apana* refers to the function of the body, at all levels, gross and subtle, which expels energy and waste materials. In the context of pranayama, apana refers to exhalation. *Prana* refers to the specific functions of the body which supply energy to maintain the body. This prana is contained in food and air that is breathed, as well as subtle prana in the environment. In the context of pranayama, prana refers to inhalation.

Balance of prana and apana implies that there is equilibrium between the incoming and outgoing energies of the body. In the case of pranayama, balance of inhalation and exhalation signifies *kumbhaka*, the retention of breath.

By performing moola bandha and thereby influencing the release of sex hormones and the sexual impulses, a constant flow of nectar is induced from bindu visarga. This is experienced as *nada*, transcendental sound. By controlling bindu visarga, one controls creation within the microcosmos.

Moola bandha is also clearly described in the *Yoga Chudamani Upanishad*, *Hatharatnavali* and *Gheranda Samhita*.

What is the purpose of moola bandha?

Swami Niranjanananda: Moola bandha is effective in releasing brahma granthi and for locating and awakening mooladhara chakra. At the physiological level, it is the contraction of certain muscles in the pelvic floor. At the subtle level, however, it is the contraction of mooladhara chakra itself. At the pranic level, moola bandha is responsible for redirecting the downward flow of apana. By steady contraction of the perineum, the apana force is drawn upward and merged with the agni mandala in the region of samana in order to facilitate the awakening of kundalini.

Which part of the pelvic floor is contracted in moola bandha?

Swami Satyananda: Moola bandha is the contraction of specific muscles in the pelvic floor, not the whole perineum. In the male body, the area of contraction is between the anus and the testes. In the female body, the point of contraction is behind the cervix, where the uterus projects into the vagina.

On the subtle level, it is the energizing of mooladhara chakra. The perineal body, which is the convergence of many muscles in the groin, acts as a trigger point for the location of mooladhara chakra. Initially, this area is difficult to isolate, so it is recommended that ashwini and vajroli mudras are practised in preparation for moola bandha.

How can one prepare for moola bandha?

Swami Niranjanananda: In order to understand moola bandha, one must first perfect two other associated practices: ashwini mudra and vajroli/sahajoli mudra. *Ashwini mudra* is contraction of the anal sphincter. *Vajroli/sahajoli mudra* is contraction of the urinary passage. These two contractions must be performed independently in order to perfect them. There must be awareness of the internal pressure point which is being affected by each contraction.

At first, when practising moola bandha, both contractions take place. When this happens, one becomes aware of a third point slightly inside the body, which is very sensitive. It tickles a bit when this point is contracted. Maintaining the contraction at this exact point is the practice of moola bandha. When this exact point is discovered, the practice of moola bandha begins. Then ashwini and vajroli are left, and moola bandha is concentrated on.

Should moola bandha be repeatedly contracted, or retained?

Swami Niranjanananda: Generally speaking, in the practice of a bandha a state of pressure or focusing is continuously maintained. Contracting and releasing is more indicative of a mudra, while the meaning of *bandha*, is to hold that focus, lock it and maintain that lock as long as possible.

What rules are given for the practice of moola bandha?

Swami Niranjanananda: The rules given by Sage Gheranda for the practice of moola bandha in *Gheranda Samhita* (3:8–9) are to practise in solitude, observe silence and practise with effort:

Sugupto viralo bhootvaa mudraametaam samabhyaset.

Abhyaasaadbandhanasyaasya marutsiddhirbhaveddhruvam;
Saadhayedyatnatastarhi maunee tu vijitaalasah.

Aspirants who wish to move beyond *samsara,* the materialistic world, should practise this mudra in a hidden place. With the practice, marut siddhi is certain. Therefore, it should be practised with effort, silently and without laziness. (8–9)

Why solitude? When one is removed from worldly attractions, mental stability is possible. The instruction to be alone is given to help the practitioner remain unaffected by the external world

Observing *mouna,* silence, conserves prana shakti. Constant talking leads to internal restlessness, scattering and lack of balance. Speech and sight are activities of the senses which dissipate inner energy. According to medical science sixty percent of stimulating sensations originate from vision. The eyes look here and there, taking a constant stream of information to the brain. A great deal of inner energy is used to perceive, categorize and analyze all this information. There is only awareness of visual information directly related to the present situation, but much more is actually being perceived. This process continues for sixteen hours a day. Only during sleep, when the eyes remain closed, are the sensations reduced.

It is the same with speech. Speech does not only mean talking. The mind also speaks through the medium of thoughts. Many types of speech are recognized in the yogic tradition. Yoga considers all kinds of internal manifestations as part of speech, including the expression of feelings. The practice of mouna is advocated for the simple reason that during mouna the expressions over which the individual has no control and which manage the personality are kept quiet.

The third instruction given is to practise moola bandha with effort, which means maintaining the state of concentration that is attained. In the beginning it may be held for only half a minute before the lock is released, but eventually one should have the capacity to maintain the bandha for fifteen to twenty minutes. Yogis have the capacity to maintain a position for hours at a time. Of course, the bandha will have an effect even if it is only maintained for a minute or two, but the energy needed to awaken the brain and kundalini will not be generated by one or two minutes of practice. In order to enhance, activate and focus the energy it is necessary to practise for as long as possible.

In addition to these three instructions, a fourth instruction needs to be added. Moola bandha should not be practised without the guidance of a guru. Negative changes in the personality begin to take place if the experience of energy comes from an incorrect method. Instead of progressing on the proper path, there can be a downfall. Therefore, such practices, which awaken the subtle energies within, should not be performed without the instructions and guidance of the guru.

What are the general physiological effects of moola bandha?

Swami Niranjanananda: Moola bandha is useful for digestive problems, especially in the colon and for treating haemorrhoids. Moola bandha also tones and strengthens the pelvic organs. In the female it strengthens the ligaments, preventing prolapse of the uterus, and releases blood congestion, which helps to regulate menstruation. In the male it helps deal with prostate problems, premature ejaculation and impotency. It also sublimates the instinctive drive and the sexual drive, with the raising of consciousness from the level of brahma granthi to the area of vishnu granthi.

What are the effects of moola bandha on the brain?

Swami Niranjanananda: Mooladhara chakra lies in close proximity to a point called the perineal body, which is a small area where all the many muscles and ligaments of the

212

perineum converge. It is around this area that the sensation of mooladhara chakra stimulation is felt. By practising vajroli/sahajoli and ashwini mudras, and trying to separate the two muscle groups, mooladhara chakra is automatically stimulated. Then, by isolating that contraction the point of mooladhara can be pulled up. Normally there is no awareness of this area, and it may be quite contracted a lot of the time due to various psychological and environmental stresses: these muscles are highly reactive to stress as well as to psychological tension.

Through the practice of moola bandha, control is gained over the muscles of the perineal body. The base of the brain, especially the reticular activating system, is also stimulated. This part functions like a filter, allowing only so much energy to go through to the brain. It is this part of the brain which keeps the rest of the brain awake, conscious and alert. Regular stimulation of this perineal area has the effect of stimulating the reticular activating system, thereby creating a greater sense of whole body awareness, taking us out of our heads and into the whole body.

The spinal cord can be thought of as an extension of the base of the brain, descending down the back of the body. It is really a part of the brain. If the base of the brain is stimulated with moola bandha, the spinal cord is also made more conscious, which revitalizes all the other organs as the energy passes through them.

What are the mental and spiritual benefits of moola bandha?

Swami Satyananda: Moola bandha bestows many physical, mental and spiritual benefits. It stimulates the pelvic nerves and tones the urogenital and excretory systems. It is helpful in psychosomatic and degenerative illnesses. It relieves depression and promotes good health. It helps to realign the physical, mental and psychic bodies in preparation for spiritual awakening. Moola bandha is a means to attain sexual control. It may be used for *brahmacharya*, the sublimation of sexual energy for spiritual development, or for enhancement of marital relations.

What is the effect of moola bandha on the nadis?

Swami Niranjanananda: Several nadis emanate from the lower spine and many nadis terminate there. Some nadis emanate from the lower spine and rise up to the brain. Mooladhara, as the base, is highly sensitive. When the contraction is continuously maintained, creating an unfamiliar internal sensation, the nadis related to the autonomic nervous system are stimulated. The effect of this stimulation is reflected in the brain via its connection with the spine. There are also centres inside the brain linked with the chakras.

Mooladhara chakra is considered to be located just below the spinal column. It follows that there is a related centre in the brain. It is this centre which is awakened as a result of vibrations at mooladhara. The sensation travels through the nadis up to the brain and awakens that sleeping region of the brain associated with mooladhara.

There is also the direct influence on the mooladhara region. Another effect of this influence is to change the direction of the flow of apana vayu in the lower body. When the direction of apana vayu changes, victory over old age is achieved. This is recognized as a siddhi in yoga.

Why do yogis try to reverse the downward flow of apana?

Swami Sivananda: The apana vayu has a natural tendency to move downwards. Through the practice of moola bandha, the apana vayu is made to move upwards by contracting the perineum and by forcibly drawing it upwards. The prana vayu is united with the apana and the united prana-apana is made to enter the sushmnna nadi or brahma nadi. Then the yogi attains perfection in yoga. This is a secret in yoga. Then the yogi is dead to the world. He drinks the nectar of immortality. He attains all divine glories and powers. In *Hatharatnavali* (2:59–61) it is written:

214

Adhogatimapaanam vai oordhvagam kurute balaat;
Aakunchanena tam praahurmoolabandhom hi yoginah.

Praanaapaanau naadabindu moolabandhena chaikataam;
Tato yogasya samsiddhim yachchhataam naatra samshayah.

Apaanapraanayoraikyam kshayo mootra pureeshayoh;
Yuvaa bhavati vriddho'pi satatam moolabandhanaat.

By contraction (of the perineum) the apana vayu, of which the natural course is downwards, is forcefully (though cautiously) directed upwards. The yogis proclaim this action to be moola bandha. (59)

Prana and apana, nada and bindu, having attained union through moola bandha, the yogi attains perfection in yoga. There is no doubt about it. (60)

Urine and ordure diminish because of the union of apana and prana. By constant practise of moola bandha even old persons become young. (61)

When the apana is united with prana, the anahata sounds or different kinds of *nadas,* mystical inner sounds, are distinctly heard by the yogi, as the outside sounds are shut out. He has deep concentration. Prana, apana, nada and bindu unite now. The yogi reaches perfection in yoga.

Does moola bandha help awaken kundalini?

Swami Niranjanananda: Moola bandha is helpful in awakening kundalini. Kundalini shakti can be understood in many forms. One form is awakening the element of energy hidden inside mooladhara. The second form is awakening the brain centres related to mooladhara. The expansion or development of consciousness that then takes place on awakening mooladhara is regarded as a kundalini experience, because that state takes consciousness to a new *loka,* or dimension, which changes the thinking, conduct and karma.

The importance of moola bandha in kundalini awakening is also clearly stated in *Hatharatnavali* (2:62–63):

Apaano chordhvagam jaate prayaate vahnimandale;
Tathaanalashikhaadeeptaa vaayunaa preritaa yathaa.

Dadaahataa bhujangeeva nishvasya rijutaam vrajet;
Bilam pravishya tatraiva bhujangee naantaram vrajet.

When the apana rises up and reaches the sphere of
the fire (the navel region) the flames of the fire blaze,
fanned by the vayu. (62)

Just as a female serpent (straightens up) with a hiss when
beaten by a stick, such a female serpent (kundalini)
entering into the hole (sushumna) does not move
anywhere. (63)

What is the effect of moola bandha on the metabolism?

Swami Satyananda: All the practices which unite the two
opposite forces, prana and apana, generate and release
immense heat in the body. This increases the metabolic
rate for a short period, and as a result, elimination and
degeneration are decreased; absorption and assimilation
improved, and the nervous system, blood circulation
and brain functions are greatly stimulated. The mind
becomes alert, sensual desires and the need for sleep
decrease, and even during the dream state, there is greater
awareness. When moola bandha is practised regularly
the physiological need for food decreases, and the same
symptoms which appear due to perfection of pranayama
and uddiyana bandha, manifest. This is described in *Hatha
Yoga Pradipika* (3:65):

Apaanapraanayoraikyam kshayo mootrapureeshayoh;
Yuvaa bhavati vriddho'pi satatam moolabandhanaat.

With constant practise of moola bandha, prana and
apana unite, urine and stool are decreased and even
an old person becomes young.

Why does moola bandha produce heat in the body?

Swami Satyananda: When the perineal body is constantly contracted, the prana shakti which normally escapes through this passage is redirected to the navel centre, which is the seat of the fire element or *agni tattwa*. When any chakra is activated heat will be produced, but manipura becomes excessively hot because of the fire element. This centre is responsible for maintaining the body temperature and regulating the digestive fire. The nervous impulses sent from the coccygeal plexus are said to 'fan the fire'. Moola bandha and uddiyana bandha are techniques which redistribute and rechannel pranic heat and nervous impulses from the lower to the higher centres, or from the grosser to the subtler centres. These effects are described in *Hatha Yoga Pradipika* (3:66–67):

Apaana oordhvage jaate prayaate vahnimandalam;
Tadaanalashikhaa deerghaa jaayate vaayunaahataa.

Tato yaato vahnyapaanau praanamushnasvaroopakam;
Tenaatyantapradeeptastu jvalano dehajastathaa.

Apana moves up into the region of fire (manipura chakra, the navel centre), then the flames of the fire grow, being fanned by apana vayu. (66)

Then, when apana and the fire meet with prana, which is itself hot, the heat in the body is intensified. (67)

What happens when moola bandha awakens kundalini?

Swami Satyananda: When kundalini is awakened the whole central nervous system becomes active and charged with energy. Energy passes from the firing of one neuron to the next and the chains of nerve fibres straighten with the force of the energy. Thus, in *Hatha Yoga Pradipika* (3:68–69) it says:

Tena kundalinee suptaa santaptaa samprabudhyate;
Dandaahataa bhunjageeva nishvasya rijutaam vrajet.

Bilam pravishteva tato brahmanaadyantanram vrajet;
Tasmaannityam moolabandhah kartavyo yogibhih sadaa.

Through this (meeting of apana and prana), the sleeping kundalini is aroused by the extreme heat and it straightens itself just as a serpent beaten with a stick straightens and hisses. (68)

Just as a snake enters its hole, so kundalini goes into brahma nadi. Therefore the yogi must always perform moola bandha. (69)

The normal amount of energy which passes through the central nervous system is of a low frequency compared to that of kundalini. In the average person, the energy which flows through the central nervous system is of such a low voltage that it is only sufficient to power the instinctive consciousness and body functions. Most of one's energy flows out through the sense organs. By practising moola bandha, that same energy can be redirected up to the higher brain centres, which normally do not receive much of a charge.

To manifest the so-called 'super human' qualities, the entire pranic capacity has to be increased and the central nervous system and brain have to be charged with the high voltage energy of kundalini shakti. In order to purify and strengthen the chakras, moola bandha, jalandhara bandha, uddiyana bandha and kumbhaka are practised. Then, when kundalini rises, it will pass through *brahma nadi*, the innermost layer of sushumna.

JALANDHARA BANDHA: THE THROAT LOCK

What is jalandhara bandha?

Swami Sivananda: Contract the throat. Press the chin firmly on the chest. This bandha is practised at the end of *pooraka*, inhalation and beginning of *kumbhaka*, retention. By the practice of this bandha the prana moves in the right path. It is united with apana. Ida and pingala nadis are shut out. The gastric fire which is situated in the region of the navel consumes the nectar which exudes out of the sahasrara through the hole in the palate. The yoga student should

218

practise this bandha in order to prevent the nectar being thus consumed. The yogi drinks the nectar and attains immortality. Jalandhara bandha is described in the *Yoga Chudamani Upanishad* (v. 40):

> *Kritvaa samputitou karou dridhataram badhvaatha padmaasanam;*
> *Gaadham vakshasi sannidhaaya chubukam dhyaanam cha tachcheshtitam;*
> *Vaaramvaaram apaanam oordhvam anilam prochchaarayet pooritam;*
> *Munchanpraanamupaiti bodhamatulam shakti prabhaavaan narah.*

Sit in padmasana, crossing the legs with the hands pressed firmly on the knees. Press the chin firmly against the chest and meditate on That (Brahman). Again and again breathe in and out, and raise the apana force to the region of prana, filling it fully. In this way, with the help of Shakti the practitioner acquires infinite knowledge.

What is the meaning of jalandhara bandha?

Swami Satyananda: The Sanskrit word *jalan* means 'net'. The word *dhara* means 'stream', 'mass of flowing fluid'. This leaves the meaning of the word jalandhara open to various interpretations. The most likely is that it means 'net' or 'cluster of nadis' or 'pathways'. Therefore, *jalandhara* is the practice or physical lock that controls the net or network of nadis in the neck. These *nadis* can be taken to mean blood vessels, nerves or pranic passages. The 'fluid' or stream can cover all these different levels of subtlety, for jalandhara bandha will influence all of them.

An alternative definition is that *jal* means 'water'. *Jalandhara bandha* is therefore the throat lock which holds the nectar or fluid flowing down to vishuddhi from bindu, and prevents it from falling into the digestive fire. In this way, prana is conserved.

There is another explanation of the meaning. There are sixteen specific centres in the body called *adharas*. This word means 'base' or 'substratum'. They refer to chakras which are located in the following sixteen regions of the body: toes, ankles, knees, thighs, perineum, coccyx, navel, heart, neck, tonsils, tongue, nose, eyebrow centre, eyes, back of the head and crown of the head. In various practices one's awareness is rotated through these centres. Prana flows through these regions within the pranic body. Therefore, *jalandhara bandha* can also be defined as the practice that locks the pranic network in the neck. This prevents the flow of prana between these centres and directs prana into sushumna nadi.

Why is jalandhara bandha important?

Swami Niranjanananda: Jalandhara bandha is a technique that frees the blockages of rudra granthi. Jalandhara bandha is thus the physical contraction or lock which controls the network of nadis, nerves and blood vessels flowing through the neck to the brain. Jalandhara bandha is the most important bandha associated with pranayama as it accompanies all practices of *kumbhaka*, prolonged breath retention.

How is jalandhara bandha practised in kriya yoga?

Swami Satyananda: In kriya yoga a simpler, more subtle form of jalandhara bandha is practised where the head is simply bent forward so that the chin presses the neck. The shoulders and the arms do not move. This variation is often used during pranayama to minimize external movement and avoid disruption of the pranayama mudra, such as nasagra.

What type of breathing is used during jalandhara bandha?

Swami Satyananda: The breath is retained during jalandhara bandha. The retention can be with *antar kumbhaka*, inner retention or *bahir kumbhaka*, outer retention, depending on the practice and integration with other techniques. That is, one can either breathe in deeply, fully inflating the lungs and then do jalandhara bandha, or one can exhale deeply, and then do jalandhara bandha. Both methods have their use in association with various practices.

It must be emphasized that the duration of kumbhaka should never be more than is comfortable. There should be no straining under any circumstances. The duration of breath retention can be increased over a period of weeks and months.

What are the physical effects of jalandhara bandha?

Swami Niranjanananda: Holding the breath for a period of time with jalandhara bandha creates a strong nervous stimulus, which distracts the attention from the need to breathe. At the same time, contracting the throat affects the trachea and the blood vessels going to the brain. The blood supply to the brain is slowed down as pressure is placed on these blood vessels in the neck, especially the carotid sinus. Therefore, the breath can be held longer than normal with this technique.

When the head is bent forward the spine is pulled up and elongated, gently stretching the meninges around the brain. This subtle pressure opens up the knots in the physical structure around the brain and spine. Stimulus at the throat level also helps to balance thyroid function, which regulates metabolism. With regular practice, there is a gentle, repetitive stimulus to the thyroid, not a major stimulus as in sarvangasana, for example.

In discussing the physiological effects, it should be kept in mind that yoga is absolutely holistic in theory and practice. It cannot be said that any one practice directly influences any particular organ or gland. All yogic practices simply stretch and squeeze, contract and expand. This is seen in jalandhara bandha: the neck is placed in one posture and then in another. Each vertebra, muscle, nerve channel, gland, etc., creates a self contraction. In the course of time, this gentle compression and expansion alters the total functioning of an organ, in the same way as when a sponge is filled with water and repeatedly squeezed dry.

There are certain practices which are said to affect a particular organ directly, such as the liver, kidneys or stomach. This is an indication of the organ on which the asana is supposed to work and improve the function. So it is not a question of whether thyroid and parathyroid functioning can be improved by practising jalandhara bandha, although it has been known to happen. In physiology, one person will practise a bandha and it will affect a particular part of the body. Another person will practise the same bandha and it will affect a different part of the body.

Research and experiments average out the results obtained from a number of people. The physiological and psychophysiological explanations are mechanical. They provide a deeper understanding of which structures are involved and which energies may be involved, but how the practices work is not really known, just as respiratory physiologists do not really understand how the respiratory muscles work. We do not understand simple functions, let alone extremely complicated processes and manoeuvres.

Yogic explanations and physiological explanations try to complement each other, but it is important not to oversimplify mechanical research results. Yoga allows direct and deep access to the nervous system with controls that allow self-regulation. If yoga practices, such as bandhas or kumbhaka, are added to other existing methods and techniques, then the core of the system is somehow strengthened and stabilized with long-lasting effects.

Why is the neck an important region physically and pranically?
Swami Niranjanananda: Many nadis, nerves and blood capillaries pass through the neck, which is a relatively small passage, into the head. Therefore, jalandhara bandha exerts

an influence on the many nadis concentrated in the region of the neck, throat, head and shoulders. When this practice is performed correctly, the pressure is divided, so that energy goes towards the head as well as travelling down the back.

The body has sixteen adharas, bases or receptacles, and jalandhara bandha influences these bases. These sixteen bases can be understood in different ways. For example, they refer to major organs and parts of the body through which the various bodily activities are conducted and managed. They are: toes, ankles, knees, thighs, perineum, genitals, navel region, heart, base of the neck, throat, root of the tongue, nosetip, eyebrow centre, forehead, *brahmarandhra* (top back of the head) and crown. The throat region is locked by jalandhara bandha along with all the nadis and nerves that must pass through the throat to enter the head. Thus jalandhara bandha influences the entire body. This is mentioned in *Gheranda Samhita* (3:10):

Kanthasankochanam kritvaa chibukam hridaye nyaset;
Jaalandharekrite bandhe shodashaadhaarabandhanam.

Contract the throat and place the chin on the chest. This becomes jalandhara bandha. It gives control over the sixteen bases.

Vishuddhi is sometimes referred to as the middle chakra because it is the transition region between the manifest and unmanifest dimensions, as can be understood when meditating on its element, *akasha* or space. Vishuddhi chakra's sixteen petals relate directly to the adharas. Sage Gheranda's description relates to the essential function of jalandhara bandha in awakening vishuddhi chakra and is close to the subtle kriya yoga variation.

How does jalandhara bandha affect the thyroid gland?
Swami Niranjanananda: This bandha closes the windpipe and compresses various organs in the throat. In particular, the stimulus to the throat helps to balance thyroid function

and regulate the metabolism. The whole body depends on the thyroid gland for perfect development and maintenance. Jalandhara bandha massages and tones the thyroid gland, enhancing its efficacy. The thyroid and parathyroid glands are master glands located in the throat, and when they are regulated the whole metabolism is affected, influencing health and longevity.

What is the purpose of putting pressure on the carotid sinuses by practising jalandhara bandha?
Swami Satyananda: The full form of jalandhara bandha used in hatha yoga compresses the carotid sinuses, which are located on the carotid arteries, the main arteries in the neck supplying blood to the brain. The simple variation used in kriya yoga exerts a subtler pressure. These sinuses help to regulate the circulatory and respiratory systems. Normally, a decrease in oxygen and increase in carbon dioxide in the body leads to an increased heart rate and heavier breathing. This process is initiated by the carotid sinuses. By exerting pressure on these sinuses, this tendency is prevented, allowing for decreased heart rate and increased breath retention. This encourages introversion – one tends to become oblivious to the outside world. The whole nervous system and brain become sedated, and there is a tendency to become more one-pointed.

Jalandhara bandha allows one to hold the breath for longer periods of time. Normally, decrease of oxygen and increase of carbon dioxide in the system lead to an increase of the heart rate and harder breathing to compensate. This is initiated through the carotid sinuses. The pressure on these sinuses during jalandhara bandha prevents this tendency. Therefore, one is able to hold the breath for much longer periods. These effects are a great help in meditation practices.

What effect does jalandhara bandha have on the pranas and chakras?
Swami Niranjanananda: The throat is the region of vishuddhi chakra. When control over vishuddhi is achieved

or vishuddhi chakra is awakened, according to kundalini yoga a state of immortality is attained, that is, victory over death. Here death does not mean physical death, which comes at the end of life. In this context death means control over the changes which take place in the body. Sometimes during the course of sadhana, after the awakening of the chakras, a state is attained in which the physical body does not decline; this is called immortality. This state is attained only by *siddhas*, perfected persons. In *Gheranda Samhita* (3:11) it is written:

Jaalandharamahaamudraamrityoshcha kshayakaarinee;
Siddho jaalandharo bandho yoginaam siddhidaayakah;
Shanmaasamabhyasedyo hi sa siddho naatra samshayah.

This great mudra by the name of jalandhara bandha gives victory over death. Mastery over jalandhara bandha provides siddhis to yogis and by practising it for just six months a yogi definitely becomes a perfected being.

In the context of sadhana this mantra says that jalandhara bandha can be perfected after six months continuous practice, and that if this is done, there is no doubt about attaining *siddhi*, perfection. The question arises, what sort of siddhi, mastery or state is achieved by the mere pressing of the neck and lowering of the chin?

It has been observed that if jalandhara bandha is done correctly, the physical feeling of a lock in the throat region or pressure created inside the brain and chest is not the only experience. This pressure influences the prana shakti. According to yoga, prana is energy which continuously flows upwards in the chest. The pressure created in the neck and chest during the practice of jalandhara bandha reverses the flow of prana shakti, making it flow downwards.

When prana shakti starts flowing downward and apana shakti starts flowing upward through the practice of another bandha, such as moola bandha, both these energies meet at manipura chakra, resulting in a state of awakening in the chakra system of the body. This same kind of stimulus occurs in the brain, and an alert state dawns.

Even in normal practice, pressure or heaviness in the head is felt and this pressure activates ajna chakra and the dormant centre in the middle of the brain. Kriya shakti begins to flow in them and awakening occurs. In kundalini yoga the practice of jalandhara bandha is used specifically to change the speed of prana and to awaken vishuddhi, ajna, bindu and sahasrara chakras.

Why is it said that jalandhara bandha bestows immortality?
Swami Niranjanananda: In *Gheranda Samhita* (3:11) it says, *Jaalandhara-mahaa-mudraa-mrityoshcha kshayakaarinee*, the practice of jalandhara bandha brings victory over death. *Mrit* indicates death or mortality, *amrita* means not-death or immortality. Kundalini yoga says that *amrita*, a nectar of immortality, is produced in the region of bindu visarga. Normally this travels through the throat into the body, but when this secretion is burned up and digested by the life processes, the body ages. The yogis, however, do not let this hormone go to manipura and it is not burned up in the digestive fire in the abdominal region. This prevents ageing, and gives victory over death.

This principle may appear a bit unnatural or imaginary, but according to medical science there is a gland in the bindu region which is equivalent to a pea in size and its role in the overall functioning of the body is yet to be established. Once scientists thought that the brain was mapped and that after early childhood, and definitely after adolescence, its tasks and capacities were established and there was just a slow deterioration taking place from then on. However, along with stem cell research, the concepts and studies of neuroplasticity in the brain show that the body and brain can regenerate themselves in previously unthought of ways. At this stage there are still many differences of opinion regarding regeneration of brain cells and their interconnecting dendrites, but the claims of yoga are becoming more highly regarded. Perhaps one day research will 'discover' this mysterious nectar of immortality related to the ageing and regeneration of the physical body, thus proving the experience of the yogis to be true.

UDDIYANA BANDHA: THE ABDOMINAL LOCK

BSY©

What is uddiyana bandha?

Swami Sivananda: Empty the lungs by a strong and forceful exhalation. Now contract and forcibly draw up the intestines and also the navel towards the back, so that the abdomen rests against the back of the body high up in the thoracic cavity. This is uddiyana bandha.

When this bandha is practised, the diaphragm, the muscular portion between the thoracic cavity and abdomen, is raised up and the abdominal wall is drawn backwards. The trunk is bent forward when doing uddiyana. Uddiyana can be done in sitting and standing postures. It is described in *Hatha Yoga Pradipika* (3:57):

> *Udare pashchimam taanam naabheroordhvam cha kaarayet;*
> *Uddiyaano hyasau bandho mrityumaatangakesaree.*

> Pulling the abdomen back in and making the navel rise is uddiyana bandha. It is the lion which conquers the elephant, death.

What is the meaning of uddiyana bandha?

Swami Satyananda: The Sanskrit word *uddiyana* means 'to rise up' or 'to fly upward'. This practice is so called because the physical lock applied to the body causes the diaphragm to rise towards the chest, creating a natural upward flow of energy. Uddiyana is therefore often translated as the stomach lift. Another interpretation is that the physical lock helps to direct prana into sushumna nadi so that it flows upward to sahasrara chakra. This is mentioned in *Hatha Yoga Pradipika* (3:55–56):

Baddho yena sushumnaayaam praanastooddeeyate yatah;
Tasmaaduddeeyanaakhyo'yam yogibhih samudaahritah.

Uddeenam kurute yasmaadavishrantam mahaakhagah;
Uddeeyaanam tadeva syaattatra bandho'bhidheeyate.

Uddiyana bandha is so-called by the yogis because through its practise the prana (is concentrated at one point and) rises through sushumna. (55)

The bandha described is called the rising or flying bandha, because through its practice, the great bird (shakti) flies upward with ease. (56)

Movement of shakti in the body is described as a bird. In the Upanishads, alternating activities of ida and pingala nadis are said to ensnare the consciousness like a bird which is tied to its perch. It tries to fly away time and time again, but is constantly pulled down. In the *Varaha Upanishad* it says, "The breath follows life in the same way that a shadow follows an object. Uddiyana is the practice that makes the ever-restless breath fly upwards." However, if the shakti of ida and pingala can be brought together and released through sushumna, it will ascend and ultimately be freed in sahasrara chakra, the highest heaven.

Why is uddiyana bandha practised?

Swami Sivananda: Uddiyana is a blessing to humanity. It imparts beautiful health, strength, vigour and vitality to the practitioner. When it is combined with *nauli kriya*, which consists of churning the contents of the abdomen, it serves as a powerful gastro-intestinal tonic. These are two potent

228

weapons of the yogi to combat constipation, weak peristalsis of the intestines and gastro-intestinal disorders of the alimentary system. The effect of uddiyana on the digestive region is described in *Shiva Samhita* (49–50):

Nityam yah kurute yogee chaturvaaram dine dine;
Tasya naabhestu shuddhih syaadyena siddho bhavenmarut.

Shanmaasamabhyasanyogee mrityum jayati nishchitam;
Tasyodaraagnirjvalati rasavriddhih prajaayate.

The yogi who always practises it four times a day, purifies thereby his navel, through which the winds (pranas) are purified. (49)

By practising for six months, the yogi certainly conquers death; the gastric fire is kindled and there takes place an increase in the fluids of the body. (50)

Those who want to practise nauli should practise uddiyana first. Uddiyana reduces fat in the belly. For abdominal exercises nothing can compare with uddiyana and nauli. They stand unique, unrivalled and unprecedented amongst all systems of physical exercises in the East and West.

He who practises uddiyana bandha, conquers death and becomes young. It is very helpful in keeping up brahmacharya. All bandhas awaken the kundalini.

What is the correct way to practise uddiyana bandha?
Swami Niranjanananda: In uddiyana bandha, a negative pressure is created inside the body by exhaling fully. Then, by flexing the spine, there is an automatic inward contraction of the abdominal wall. Of the two segments of the abdominal wall, the upper segment is easier to contract than the lower one. One of the mistakes many people make is to work the upper abdomen and not the lower one. It is necessary to work around the navel as a central point, which entails working the lower abdomen as well. Sometimes one needs to put more force on the lower abdomen. This in turn puts pressure

229

onto the nerve plexuses, the celiac plexus (the solar plexus) and the sacral plexus. When uddiyana is performed, there is an automatic suction of the throat inwards and a pulling up of mooladhara, owing to the negative pressure. This makes jalandhara and moola bandhas much easier to perform.

What is the best sequence of practice for uddiyana bandha?

Swami Satyananda: Uddiyana bandha is an advanced technique and should be attempted only under the guidance of a competent teacher. It should be practised after attaining proficiency in external breath retention, and jalandhara and moola bandhas. Jalandhara must always be done with uddiyana. Agnisara kriya is an excellent preparatory practice.

Uddiyana bandha must be practised on an empty stomach. The bowels should also be empty. Uddiyana bandha is easier to perform if preceded by an inverted asana. It is ideally performed in conjunction with mudras, bandhas and pranayamas. If practised on its own, it should be performed after asanas and pranayamas and before meditation.

What are the physical benefits of uddiyana bandha?

Swami Satyananda: With regular practise of uddiyana the effects become visibly apparent. Vitality increases as uddiyana has a powerful toning effect on the visceral organs, muscles, nerves and glands. The suction created stimulates blood circulation and absorption. The heart is squeezed and gently massaged by the upward pressure of the diaphragm. The suction or negative pressure in the thorax draws venous blood up from the abdomen into the heart and at the same time, arterial blood is drawn into the internal organs. The autonomic nerves comprising the solar plexus are strengthened. The processes of digestion, assimilation and elimination are directly affected.

Improper functioning in the alimentary canal is the most basic cause of disease. Uddiyana effects optimal functioning in this area, thereby overcoming many related diseases. Uddiyana bandha also strengthens the diaphragm and other respiratory muscles and renders them more mobile. Improper respiration and gas exchange is the other major cause of disease and degeneration. The lungs are tightly squeezed during uddiyana and this induces a greater efficiency of gas exchange, i.e. absorption of oxygen and expulsion of carbon dioxide. Because the brain is deprived of oxygen for a short period during retention, its capacity to absorb oxygen is also increased.

In *Hatha Yoga Pradipika* (3:59) it says:

Naabheroordhvarvamadhashchaapi taanam kuryaatprayatnatah;
Shanmaasamabhyasenmrityum jayatyeva na samshayah.

The region above and below the navel should be drawn backward with effort. There is no doubt that after six months of practise, death is conquered.

With so many wonderful benefits, it is not surprising that uddiyana can slow down the natural process of degeneration and ageing and make even an old person look young: according to the sloka, after six months of practise, death can be averted.

First uddiyana has to be perfected, and it is not perfect until the breath can be retained for more than three or four minutes. Then it has to be practised regularly for months and months in combination with other practices and a conducive diet. In *Varaha Upanishad* it says, "To practise uddiyana seriously, the diet should be good and taken in small quanitities." Even if the degenerative process is not completely reversed, at least there will be noticeable physiological and psychological benefits and the ageing process is definitely slowed down.

However, old age and death are natural processes and today there are few adept yogis who have perfected themselves to the extent of reversing the ageing process and overcoming death. Also, those who have done so,

231

nevertheless usually submit themselves to the natural laws of the body.

Why is uddiyana bandha useful for stress management?

Swami Niranjanananda: Uddiyana bandha works strongly on the adrenal glands. Therefore, it helps one to handle stress. In fact, all the bandhas work on the glands: jalandhara affects the thyroid and pituitary glands, and moola bandha affects the urogenital system.

How can uddiyana bandha be perfected?

Swami Satyananda: If bandhas are to be practised perfectly they must be learned from a guru or qualified teacher. In the yoga texts, full details are always omitted, and if one tries to practise according to instructions given in books, one will never know if it is actually practised correctly and according to individual needs and capacity. For perfection of all yogic practices there are two basic requirements: the guru and regular practice. This is said in *Hatha Yoga Pradipika* (3:58):

> *Uddeeyaanam tu sahajam gurunaa kathitam yadaa;*
> *Abhyasetsatatam yastu vriddho'pi tarunaayate.*

> Uddiyana is easy when practised as told by the guru. Even an old person can become young when it is done regularly.

What is the effect of uddiyana bandha on the pranic body?

Swami Satyananda: On a pranic level, uddiyana pulls the apana vayu up from the abdominal and reproductive organs towards the chest. Through uddiyana and jalandhara the prana is carefully locked into the navel region where union of prana and apana with samana can occur and induce the awakening and ascent of kundalini. Powered by udana vayu, it is taken up to the higher centres. Of course, this is a major event in the course of one's sadhana and it does not take place with one or two rounds of practice. It requires patient and ardent performance in combination with other techniques.

Why is the awakening of manipura by uddiyana so important?

Swami Niranjanananda: This can be understood by turning to kundalini yoga. Briefly, it is said that when kundalini awakens and rises, the possibility remains that it will return to a dormant state, but once kundalini crosses manipura chakra there will be no return, no fall. Therefore, to cross manipura chakra is to open the door to liberation and remove obstacles in the journey towards liberation. With the practice of uddiyana bandha, manipura chakra is awakened and one crosses the threshold, leaving behind the possibility of kundalini falling back down. For this reason, in *Gheranda Samhita* (3:13) Sage Gheranda says that uddiyana bandha is the best of all the bandhas, enabling one to naturally attain *mukti*, liberation:

Samagraad bandhanaaddhyetaduddeeyaanam vishishyate;
Uddeeyaane samabhyaste muktih svaabhaavikee bhavet.

Uddiyana bandha is the foremost bandha. One attains liberation easily by its practice.

How does uddiyana bring liberation?

Swami Satyananda: Uddiyana is said to be the most powerful of all the bandhas because it can draw apana upward within a short time and bring about the awakening of kundalini. Due to its suction force, the shakti can be pushed through sushumna to ajna chakra, the great door to liberation. This is written in *Hatha Yoga Pradipika* (3:60):

Sarveshaameva bandhaanaamuttamo hyuddiyaanakah;
Uddiyaane dridhe bandhe muktih svaabhaavikee bhavet.

Of all the bandhas, uddiyana is the best; once it is mastered, mukti or liberation occurs spontaneously.

MAHA BANDHA: THE GREAT LOCK

What is the meaning of maha bandha?

Swami Satyananda: The Sanskrit word *maha* means 'great'. *Maha bandha* is called the great lock as it combines all the three bandhas in one practice. It is described in *Hatha Yoga Pradipika* (3:74):

Moolasthaanam samaakunchya uddiyaanam tu kaarayet; Idaam cha pingalaam baddhvaa vaahayetpashchime pathi.

By contracting the perineum, performing uddiyana and locking ida and pingala with jalandhara, sushumna becomes active.

What is the effect of maha bandha on external breath retention?

Swami Niranjanananda: Maha bandha manipulates and refines external kumbhaka. If external kumbhaka is performed well, then as one goes into jalandhara bandha, uddiyana should begin to occur automatically. Once uddiyana occurs, then isolation of moola bandha is easy because there is an automatic lifting up of the perineum through suction.

What are the effects of maha bandha?

Swami Satyananda: Maha bandha gives enhanced benefits of all three bandhas. It affects the hormonal secretions of the pineal gland and regulates the entire endocrine system. The degenerative and ageing processes are checked and every cell of the body is rejuvenated. It introverts the mind prior to meditation. When perfected, it can fully awaken prana in the main chakras. Maha bandha leads to the merger of prana, apana and samana in manipura chakra, which is the culmination of all pranayamas.

What is the effect of maha bandha on the pancha pranas?

Swami Niranjanananda: The three bandhas act upon three of the five pranas. Moola bandha raises the apana energy. Jalandhara reverses the flow of prana and sends it downward to the navel region. When these two forms of energy meet samana in the navel, manipura is activated. The activation of manipura then stimulates sushumna.

With the practice of uddiyana bandha, a vacuum is created in the lower abdominal region. The Upanishads mention that when practising uddiyana bandha the heart should be held at the throat region. This means that the force of the contraction should create a total vacuum. Once the vacuum is released, the air fills it up with force. The same kind of principle is applied here with prana. When we create a vacuum in the region of samana, for a short time only, the pranas fill up that empty space. This kind of contraction also has a deep influence on the nervous system.

Maha bandha is described in *Shiva Samhita* (4:21):

Tatah prasaaritah paado vinyasya tamuroopari;
Gudayonim samaakunchya kritvaa chaapaanamoordhvagam;
Yojayitvaa samaanena kritvaa praanamaghomukham;
Bandhayedoordhvagatyartham praanaapaanena yah sudheeh;
Kathito'yam mahaabandhah siddhimaargapradaayakah;
Naadeejaalaadrasavyooho moordhaanam yaati yoginah.
Ubhaabhyaam saadhayetpadbhyaamekai suprayatnatah.

Then (after mahamudra), having extended the (right) foot, place it on the (left) thigh; contract the perineum, and draw the apana vayu upwards and join it with the samana vayu; bend the prana vayu downwards, and then let the wise yogi bind them in trinity in the navel. I have told you now the maha bandha, which shows the way to emancipation. By this, all the fluids in the vessels of the body of the yogi are propelled towards the head. This should be practised with great care, alternately with both feet.

Why is it important to still the pranas and breath?

Swami Satyananda: Prana is in a constant state of flux in the body, sometimes being directed through the external senses, sometimes towards the internal organs. Sometimes prana shakti in pingala predominates and sometimes chitta shakti in ida, and this creates various biorhythms and states of mind. The yogic practices moderate these fluctuations between the extremes of ida and pingala.

It is most important to remain aware of these extremes. It means developing the state of balanced awareness where mind is neither extrovert nor introvert, no matter whether you are working, thinking, eating or practising asana or meditation. If a state of conscious awareness cannot be maintained while awake, then in deeper states also, the awareness will be lost. When sushumna awakens or when the breath stops, it should be a conscious experience, only then can the experience of death be altered. This effect of maha bandha is stated in *Hatha Yoga Pradipika* (3:75):

> *Anenaiva vidhaanena prayaati pavano layam.*
> *Tato na jaayate mrityurjaraarogaadikam tathaa.*

> By this means (maha bandha) the prana and breath become still. Thus death, old age and sickness are conquered.

What other practices can be combined with maha bandha?

Swami Sivananda: Generally the yogi does maha mudra, maha bandha and maha vedha mudra together. This is a good combination. Then only are maximum benefits derived. The yogi achieves all his desires and obtains siddhis. In *Hatharatnavali* (2:48) it is written:

> *Roopalaavanyasampannaa yathaa stree purusham vina;*
> *Mahaamudraa mahaabandho nishphalau vedhavarjitau.*

> Just as the beauty and charm of a wife serve no purpose in the absence of the husband, similarly maha mudra and maha bandha unaccompanied by vedha, are futile.

236

In *Shiva Samhita* (4:27) it says:

Mahaamudraamahaabandhau nishphalau vedhavarjitau;
Tasmaadyogee prayatnena karoti tritayam kramaat.

The maha mudra and maha bandha become fruitless if they are not followed by maha vedha; therefore, the yogi should practise all these three successively with great care.

What is the attainment when maha bandha is perfected?

Swami Satyananda: Though there are many techniques for establishing a state of equilibrium and union between mind and body, the most effective is said to be the combination of these three bandhas. Maha bandha is the culmination of asana, pranayama, mudra and bandha. Perfection in it induces a state of perfect equanimity which unfolds into pratyahara or even spontaneous dhyana. In *Hatha Yoga Pradipika* (3:76) it states:

Bandhatrayamidam shreshtham mahaasiddhaishcha sevitam.
Sarveshaam hathatantraanaam saadhanam yogino viduh.

The great siddhas practise these three best bandhas. Of all the sadhanas in hatha yoga and tantra, the yogis know this practice (maha bandha).

There are innumerable techniques which can be practised in the path of self-realization but many involve either forced mental concentration or sensual restrictions. Therefore, it is difficult for the average person to apply himself to accomplish the task. However, it can be achieved by learning to control the body in such a way as maha bandha, without mental conflicts.

Tantra approaches the problem of higher experience by being a friend of the mind and not an enemy. Therefore, no matter what a yogi's personal philosophy may be, the three bandhas are considered as important as eating and sleeping, and are as well known as ABC. In *Shiva Samhita* (4:22) it is written:

Bhavedabhyaasato vaayuh sushumnaam madhyasangatah;
Anena vapushah pushtirdridhabandho'sthipanjare;
Sampoornahridayo yogee bhavatnyetaani yoginah.
Bandhenaanena yogindhrah saadhayetsarvameepsitam.

Through this practice, the wind (prana) enters the middle channel of the sushumna, the body is invigorated by it, the bones are firmly knitted, the heart of the yogi becomes full (of cheerfulness). By this bandha, the great yogi accomplishes all his desires.

PRACTISING BANDHAS

Why is it said that practising bandhas can be dangerous?

Swami Niranjanananda: It is dangerous to sit behind the wheel of a car if one hasn't learned to drive. It is dangerous to walk if one hasn't learned how and where to walk. It is dangerous to eat food if one doesn't really know what is being eaten. There is danger in everything if one has not been taught. If one is careful in other things, why not be careful when practising yoga? Some yogic practices require study. They require a qualified teacher who can guide the student.

What is the best sequence of practice for bandhas?

Swami Niranjanananda: First practise asana: asana is preparation for bandha. Initially, it may be necessary to practise the bandhas individually and independently in order to perfect them, but once mastery is attained, they are practised in conjunction with pranayama and mudra techniques, making them even more powerful. Bandha, mudra and pranayama are to be practised together: bandha forms part of the pranayama experience, not the asana experience.

Why do yogis practise bandhas with pranayama?

Swami Sivananda: Yoga teaches the methods to control prana and attain blissful union with the Lord through such control. Through the practice of pranayama and bandhas, the prana

238

is brought under control. *Siddhi* or perfection in the practice of pranayama is attained through the help of bandhas.

Should bandhas be practised individually or only with pranayama and mudra?

Swami Satyananda: Bandhas should first be practised and mastered individually. Only then can they be beneficially incorporated into mudra and pranayama practices. When combined in this way, they awaken the psychic faculties and form an adjunct to higher yogic practices.

What is the purpose of practising bandhas?

Swami Niranjanananda: Bandhas aim, firstly, at eliminating the three psychic blocks, or *granthis*, which hamper the awakening of prana at the pranamaya kosha level; secondly, at eliminating boundaries which are created in the consciousness by the world of the senses; and thirdly, at allowing the consciousness to become more free flowing rather than a limited perception.

8

Effects of the Bandhas

BANDHAS AND THE PRANIC BODY

How do bandhas effect the pranic body?

Swami Satyananda: The physical contraction or lock has an extensive influence on the pranic body. When the bandhas are practised, the flow of prana that continuously streams through the subtle body is redirected and even stopped, directly influencing the mind. The whole body and mind are tranquillized and become receptive to higher states of awareness. Such is the power of the bandhas when they are perfected.

The physical, endocrinological and neurological aspects of bandhas can be better understood when it is appreciated that the body is a complex, yet well organized, field of various energy systems based on one fundamental energy principle called *prana*. Though the bandhas have major positive physical effects, their main effect and purpose is at the pranic level.

When do bandhas occur spontaneously?

Swami Satyananda: Moolabandha, uddiyana bandha and jalandhara bandha are specific techniques for accumulating the available supply of prana. Whether they are known about or not, they occur spontaneously when one is established in siddhasana. When prana is awakened, the body is naturally

240

guided into various mudras, bandhas and pranayama techniques which may not even have been known to the practitioner. In *Hatha Yoga Pradipika* (1:42) it states:

Tathaikasminneva dridhe siddhe siddhaasane sati;
Bandhatrayamanaasaatsvayamevopajaayate.

Thus, through securing siddhasana, the three bandhas occur by themselves.

Why are bandhas combined with pranayama?

Swami Satyananda: When pranayama is practised the pranas in the lower body are stimulated, but a means of forcing this pranic energy up is needed. Somehow, a negative force which will push the pranic energy up through the spinal cord needs to be created. For this reason pranayama should be practised in coordination with specific bandhas.

When bandhas are performed with pranayama they create a negative force like the ejecting force used to extract water from a well. There are two forces used for pumping water: the sucking force and the ejecting force. When pranayama is practised with the bandhas, an ejecting force is put into action.

Pranayama generates prana in the lower body. Next, to conduct the prana up to the brain, moola bandha, then uddiyana bandha and finally jalandhara bandha must be performed. In this way, prana is conducted to the brain with the help of the subtle circulatory system.

The network of vessels through which the blood circulates is not just an arrangement of hollow tubes. It is a generator and distributor of prana as well. These vessels become charged and polarized as the blood circulates around the body. It is as though the whole arterial and venous circulation becomes magnetized. The flow of blood through the vessels generates a biomagnetic force just as a forceful flow of water is used to generate hydroelectricity. This is how prana shakti is able to permeate and enliven even the most distant cells and tissues of the body.

When are bandhas used with pranayama?

Swami Niranjananda: Maximum benefit is gained from pranayama when retention is practised with the bandhas. When one practises internal retention in prayanama, two bandhas should be used: jalandhara and moola. When one practises external retention, three bandhas should be used: jalandhara, moola and uddiyana.

What is the purpose of using bandhas to redirect consciousness upwards?

Swami Satyananda: According to many esoteric philosophies the downward flow of prana, *apana*, represents the part which leads man's consciousness to the lower, more earthy elements: satisfaction of instinctive desire, over indulgence, lethargy, apathy, laziness and so on. According to these philosophies, it is believed that an individual's essential nature is godlike and that in order to reunite or realize this, one's consciousness must be redirected. In relation to this, the role of bandhas, and especially moola bandha, is to block the descending movement of consciousness and redirect it upwards.

A useful analogy is to liken bandhas to the locking, stopping, obstructing and redirecting power of a dam wall. Water is contained so that it can be redirected for useful work as desired by the controller. Just so, bandhas hold and centralize energy (physical, mental and psychic), focusing it at the site of contraction so that it can be redirected for useful work as desired by the controller. These areas are infused with a fresh, vital force capable of checking imbalances in the body systems.

Through the perfection of bandhas the yogi is able to lock himself into the 'eternal now', devoid of the dualities of existence, motion and change. His consciousness, unfettered by the modifications of thought, is able to merge into the field of unified consciousness. As such, the bandhas induce *pratyahara*, sense withdrawal, and are preliminary techniques for meditation.

What yogic practises are used to reverse the flow of prana?

Swami Satyananda: There are two methods for reversing the direction of energy flow. It can be done physiologically or with the mind.

In hatha yoga, the practise of bandhas creates a negative pressure. When this negative pressure is created, the energy begins to be reversed. When uddiyana bandha, moola bandha or vajroli mudra are practised, the negative pressure begins, because with these bandhas, those doorways, those portals through which the energy flows downwards, are being blocked. To make this negative pressure more active and efficient, vipareeta karani mudra is performed.

The mudras and bandhas are physiological techniques. An example of a mental method is the directing of the breath during ujjayi pranayama so that it feels as if it is ascending and descending in the spine. This also reverses the direction of energy.

How do bandhas expand the pranic field?

Swami Niranjanananda: A bandha is also a means to expand the pranic or ionoplasmic field which is concentrated around the chakras. This can be understood if ida and pingala are considered as three dimensional rotating coils.

When jalandhara bandha is performed, by lowering the head so that the chin presses the hollow at the base of the neck, raising the shoulders and holding the breath, the field around vishuddhi chakra is expanded. This has the effect of increasing the strength of the pranic field in this area. The amplitude of the wave form and its range of activity are increased. The ionoplasmic field now extends in a greater density from anahata to ajna.

Likewise, the influence of uddiyana bandha – performed by breathing out, holding the breath externally and sucking in the abdominal area – expands the field around manipura chakra. When practised by itself, this bandha extends the ionoplasmic field in greater density from swadhisthana to

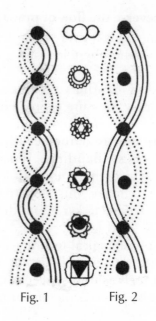

Fig. 1

Fig. 2

Fig. 1: Modified wave forms when moola bandha is practised by itself.

Fig. 2: Wave forms when the three bandhas are performed together.

anahata and when combined with jalandhara bandha, the field is expanded from swadhisthana to ajna.

The third bandha, moola bandha, is practised by contracting the area of the perineum. When practised by itself, the field around mooladhara is expanded and when practised in conjunction with uddiyana and jalandhara bandhas, the ionoplasmic field from mooladhara to ajna is expanded. When jalandhara, uddiyana and moola bandhas are practised simultaneously in maha bandha, one of the most important techniques in many advanced yogic sadhanas, it increases the ionoplasmic and pranic energies throughout the body and develops and activates many dormant brain cells.

BANDHAS AND THE CHAKRAS

How do the granthis interact with the chakras?

Swami Niranjanananda: As long as the granthis continue to exist, one's experience of the chakras is totally material, physical and gross.

When a person is physically bashed by somebody, intense fear is created: mooladhara and swadisthana become active in their negative aspects of fear and insecurity. There is a desire to run away, a desire to hide. There is no feeling of safety and comfort. This negative expression of the chakras

244

is further intensified by the presence of the brahma granthi, the knot.

Similarly, if one has a fight with one's companion the fight creates a feeling of mental and emotional disturbance which is intensified because of the vishnu granthi, or knot. It tightens the whole area more and more, and that person is literally in the grip of the crisis.

How do the bandhas affect the chakras?

Swami Satyananda: Moola bandha and uddiyana bandha are techniques which redistribute and rechannel pranic heat and nervous impulses from the lower to the higher centres, or from the grosser to the subtler centres. When the perineal body is constantly contracted, the prana shakti which normally escapes through this passage is redirected to the navel centre, which is the seat of the fire element or *agni tattwa*. When any chakra is activated, heat will be produced, but manipura becomes excessively hot, as it is ruled by the fire element. In *Hatha Yoga Pradipika* (3:65–67) it is stated:

> *Apaanapraanayoraikyam kshayo mootrapureeshayoh;*
> *Yuvaa bhavati vriddho'pi satatam moolabandhanaat.*
>
> *Apaana oordhvage jaate prayaate vahnimandalam;*
> *Tadaanalashikhaa deerghaa jaayate vaayunaahataa.*
>
> *Tato yaato vahnyapaanau praanamushnasvaroopakam;*
> *Tenaatyantapradeeptastu jvalano dehajastathaa.*

With constant practice of moola bandha, prana and apana unite, urine and stool are decreased and even an old person becomes young. (65)

Apana moves up into the region of fire (manipura chakra), then the flames of the fire grow, being fanned by apana vayu. (66)

Then, when apana and the fire meet with prana, which is itself hot, the heat in the body is intensified. (67)

This centre is responsible for maintaining the body temperature and regulating the digestive fire. The nervous impulses sent from the coccygeal plexus are said to 'fan the fire'.

How do the bandhas help to raise the kundalini beyond the level of manipura?

Swami Satyananda: Practise of uddiyana bandha awakens the sushumna passage at manipura chakra by creating a convergence of the vital and mental energies at the solar plexus: then kundalini can rise beyond this centre. In *Hatha Yoga Pradipika* (3:116) it says:

> *Bhaanoraakunchanam kuryaatkundaleem chaalayet tatah;*
> *Mrityuvaktragatasyaapi tasya mrityubhayam kutah.*

> Contracting the sun in manipura, kundalini should be moved. Even if such a person should be on the verge of death, where is the need to fear death?

Various practices which purify manipura chakra, such as uddiyana and nauli, are prescribed in hatha yoga. These strengthen the solar plexus and increase vitality and longevity. They give strength and resilience to the body and radiance to the personality. There is no doubt that the dominating and shining qualities of the sun manifest in the individual who performs these practices daily.

What is the process of awakening prana in the different chakras?

Swami Niranjanananda: The purpose of the bandhas is to awaken the chakras that are responsible for the awakening of the pranas and the ascent of kundalini.

In moola bandha, mooladhara chakra is stimulated and the pressure of the mooladhara contraction also spreads into the area of swadhisthana. In the practice of uddiyana bandha, manipura is directly stimulated, but at the same time the pressure is directed towards anahata by pulling up the diaphragm. In jalandhara bandha, vishuddhi is directly affected, but there is also pressure created in the head region to stimulate ajna, bindu and sahasrara chakras. The purpose of these three bandhas is to provide the experience of *pranotthana*, or awakening of the pranas, in the different chakras.

What effect do the bandhas have on the chakras?

Swami Niranjanananda: The role of bandhas is very specific in hatha yoga. With moola bandha, the perineal lock, pressures are created in the perineal region of mooladhara and swadhisthana chakras and there is also releasing of that pressure: creating and releasing, creating and releasing, creating and releasing, thereby causing the muscles and nerves to repeatedly relax and expand.

Gradually this works through brahma granthi which is the knot in that particular centre. As soon as that knot is removed the positive expressions of the chakra can govern the personality. As long as the knots are there, chakras will always give negative results. The negative power of the chakra will manifest with the knots. When the knots are gone, the positive power of the chakras manifests.

EFFECT OF THE BANDHAS ON THE BODY

What is the effect of bandhas on the endocrine system?

Swami Satyananda: The performance of bandhas with pranayama affects the whole body: the organs, muscles, nerves and various physical processes are massaged, stimulated and controlled through the will of the practitioner.

The bandhas bring harmony and efficient functioning to the endocrine system. Jalandhara bandha directly influences the pituitary, pineal, thyroid, parathyroid and thymus glands; uddiyana bandha directly influences the adrenal glands and pancreas; moola bandha directly influences the gonads and the perineal body/cervix (which are said to be vestigial endocrine glands). All bandhas have an indirect effect on the pituitary, pineal and brain.

247

The performance of bandhas has been experimentally shown to activate all parasympathetic activities in the body which includes a decrease in heart rate, respiration and blood pressure (only in an individual with normal blood pressure), and a general sense of rest and relaxation. Sympathetic activity in the body is decreased, a further sign of relaxation.

What is the effect of the bandhas on the nervous system?

Swami Satyananda: Parasympathetic fibres emerge from the neck and pelvic areas, while sympathetic fibres emerge from the upper back and lower back areas. The parasympathetic and sympathetic nervous systems are both rebalanced by the stimulation of the bandhas. This has a direct effect on the hypothalamus, (responsible for the endocrine system), which relays its information to the limbic (emotional) system and the cerebral cortex (outer layer of the brain).

Additionally, alpha brainwaves increase, a sign of deep relaxation indicating a slowing of nervous system activity. Confused and/or crossed neuronal circuits in the brain are reordered, in effect retraining the brain.

What is the effect of the bandhas on the digestive and excretory systems?

Swami Satyananda: The digestive system is toned, massaged and revitalized due to the pressure exerted on the internal organs; harmony in the activity of the urogenital system occurs as a result of reflex action via the nervous system.

EFFECT OF THE BANDHAS ON THE MIND

What are the effects of bandhas on the mind?

Swami Satyananda: The conscious contraction and tightening of specific parts of the body has vast repercussions. The physical contraction or lock has an extensive influence on the pranic body, as the flow of prana that continuously streams through the subtle body is redirected and even stopped. This has direct influences on the mind, as each of the physical and pranic locations associated with the bandhas is related neurologically to a specific area in the spinal cord and brain, and therefore the psyche.

Contraction at the physical level activates and awakens dormant faculties in the brain and mind. The whole body and mind is tranquillized and made receptive to higher states of awareness. Mastery of the bandhas leads to the fullest realization of one's potential. Such is the power of bandhas when they are perfected.

How do bandhas affect the mind?

Swami Niranjanananda: Bandhas have a different and definite function. Bandhas lock the flow of energy and concentrate it at one point, at one psychic centre. It is said that with the use of bandhas, apart from awakening and channelling the pranic energy, it is also possible to block the flow of the *chitta vrittis*, the modifications of the mind.

Bandhas are used to alter the flow of prana in order to affect, influence and alter the experiences of the mind. This makes sense, as the mind is composed of consciousness and energy. In the practices of pratyahara and dharana one tries to expand the horizons of consciousness, to become aware of the different activities that take place in one's consciousness. This energy is not actually experienced in the same way as thoughts are experienced. Even though thoughts are also energy, the main body and structure of thought is controlled by consciousness. Desire, love and compassion, hatred and anger, are all forms of energy, but consciousness controls them.

The other aspect of mind, the energy aspect, is controlled by prana. So when the pranas are balanced and channelled, the mind also becomes still and balanced. Therefore, the practice of bandhas has been prescribed separately. Bandhas are as important as the practice of asana and pranayama: while pranayama awakens the prana, bandhas concentrate it. Bandhas stop the dissipation of prana and channel the pranic forces for the awakening of kundalini.

What is the effect of bandhas on a hyperactive mind?

Swami Niranjanananda: One of the subjective experiences which applies to everyone with the practice of bandhas, is that when a bandha is held for a long period, its effect is noticed on the activity of the mind. If moola bandha is practised at a time when the mind is highly active, it will calm down. If jalandhara bandha is practised when the mind is hyperactive, the mind calms down. So, the locks, or bandhas, stop mental dissipation and assist the mind to achieve a point of concentration, internal harmony and balance.

How do bandhas help release emotions which become stuck in the body as tension?

Swami Niranjanananda: Bandhas are locks: there are three areas of the body which become blocked or locked when under stress or tension. Many people notice that when they are under pressure the stomach, perineum or neck becomes tight. Secondary effects, such as indigestion or tension headaches, may then occur. These three areas reflect the stresses of the body.

This is unconscious tensing, while bandhas are con-scious tensing. Unconscious tensing creates stress, however, conscious tensing releases stress, as the process and move-ment are being controlled. This means tension is not being created, rather it is being controlled and guided.

There is another important factor in relation to this, an example of which can be seen in soldiers. They tend to be very tight in the stomach region, which means that manipura is activated and tensed; so soldiers have a lot of aggression, they are extremely dynamic because this whole area is in a state of fight or flight. Similarly, when there is contraction in the perineal region, that person is much more afraid, fearful and insecure, because mooladhara and swadhisthana chakras have been tightened.

Yet when mooladhara and swadhisthana are consciously blocked at the time of practising moola bandha, psychological and mental tensions and stresses can be released. By practising uddiyana bandha the energy of manipura can be released. Similarly, when the neck is tight at the end of an intense day of work, it is natural to move the neck up and down to release the pressure. Therefore, yogis have prescribed jalandhara bandha for softening tensions held in the neck.

What is the effect of the bandhas on consciousness?
Swami Satyananda: The bandhas induce five different kinds of retention, or immobility: retention of muscles, breath, senses, thought and consciousness. Once retention of consciousness is achieved, the yogi is prepared for the next stage of his spiritual rebirth, the awakening of kundalini. The bandhas act as triggering mechanisms for the activation of this powerful force residing at the base of the spine.

What type of mental and emotional transformation do the bandhas bring?
Swami Niranjanananda: *Jalandhara bandha* is the neck contraction and when tensions are released from this region one can learn to live in a space other than that of the head. Jalandhara bandha, therefore, influences the rational and the feeling aspects of the personality.

Uddiyana bandha is the contraction of the diaphragm and the navel area, which is regarded as one area in yoga. The function of uddiyana bandha is to ground feelings on an earthly plane. Emotions are represented by the air element, associated with the upper body, while solidity or stability in life is represented by earth, linked with the lower body.

Moola bandha relates to awareness of the instinctive level, the aspect of reaction: when mooladhara is blocked there is a lack of awareness of one's reactions, blow-ups and explosions of things that happen instantaneously, without rational knowledge.

What happens when moolabandha and jalandhara are practised at the same time?

Swami Satyananda: Moola and jalandhara are important bandhas to perfect. By performing moola bandha and jalandhara bandha together, the sushumna passage between mooladhara and vishuddhi is isolated. Jalandhara bandha prevents prana vayu from passing upward beyond vishuddhi. Moola bandha prevents apana from escaping downwards below mooladhara. These two vayus are forced together and their union in manipura is gradually accomplished.

The awakening of manipura chakra is a definite milestone in the spiritual life of a yogic aspirant. With this, kundalini is considered to have risen from mooladhara and become established in manipura. This affects the source in the brain where the nectar flows from bindu visarga. In physiological terms, this flow of nectar is associated with the release of hormones from the pituitary gland into the bloodstream.

THE GRANTHIS

What are granthis?

Swami Niranjanananda: *Granthis* are knots. Just as a knot can be tied in a rope, similarly in the body there are three granthis, three knots. The granthi, the knot which controls mooladhara and swadisthana is the *brahma granthi*; the granthi which controls manipura and anahata is *vishnu granthi* and the granthi which controls vishuddhi and ajna is *rudra granthi*. There are only three bandhas and they assist in releasing the three psychic knots, or granthis, in the personality which are the main blockages or attachments that confront the sadhaka.

1. *Brahma granthi* is the first knot, or psychic block, where energy and consciousness interact and manifest in a certain way. It is supposed to be the lowest knot, covering the areas of mooladhara and swadhisthana chakras. It

creates fear and insecurity, attachments to material objects, sensual pleasures and selfishness. It is also known as the perineal knot and is awakened and stimulated by the practice of moola bandha.

2. *Vishnu granthi* is the second knot and covers the areas of manipura and anahata chakras. It creates bondage to other people, emotional relationships and attachment to emotional situations. Also known as the navel knot, it is activated by the practice of uddiyana bandha.

3. *Rudra granthi* is the third knot and covers the areas of vishuddhi, ajna and sahasrara chakras. Rudra granthi represents the obstacles created by the power of the intellect, along with attachment to siddhis and other higher psychic experiences. It is also known as the neck knot and is activated by the practice of jalandhara bandha.

As long as the knots exist, the negative power of the chakras manifest, but when they are released, the positive power of the chakras manifest. The build-up of prana during the practice of bandhas releases these knots of bondage, so that the sadhaka is free to attain what lies beyond all attachment.

Why are the bandhas associated with the granthis?

Swami Satyananda: To further understand bandhas they must be seen not only as locks, but also as removers of blocks or blockages, in the form of physical and mental impurities. Traditional yogic texts speak of three granthis or psychic knots, located at mooladhara, anahata and ajna chakras. These three are called the brahma, vishnu and rudra granthis.

The granthis prevent the free flow of prana along sushumna nadi and thus impede the awakening of the chakras and the rising of kundalini. They represent psychic blocks and mental problems that prevent an individual soaring into the realms of meditation. These blocks or knots have to be removed if one wants to know the experience of higher awareness. They can be removed either permanently or temporarily.

Bandhas are particularly effective in breaking open or removing these blocks, at least for a short period of time, as they act directly on the three granthis. Temporary removal helps to gradually eliminate the blocks permanently. In yogic language, these granthis prevent the flow of prana into the main pranic passage of the body, the *sushumna*. When they are released, prana immediately begins to flow through sushumna nadi, which leads to increased receptivity of the mind and in turn higher experiences.

How can physical practices such as the bandhas remove the granthis, which are psychic?

Swami Satyananda: These so-called knots are in the psychic body, not in the physical body, but physical manipulations such as bandhas can unlock them. Each level of manifestation has repercussions on other levels. It is not realistic to rigidly separate the physical body, pranic body and the mind body. They are all interrelated and part of a whole. They are only divided or categorized for convenience of explanation.

Therefore, the physical body influences the mind and pranic body. The pranic body influences the mind and physical body. And the mind influences the pranic and physical body. Anyone who doubts this should read the book entitled *Psychic Discoveries Behind the Iron Curtain* by Sheila Ostrander and Lynn Schroeder, where scientific evidence is given. Better still, one should practise yoga, develop sensitivity and find out from personal experience.

Bandhas, like all other yogic practices, act on and influence different levels of individual being. They have profound effects on the physical, pranic and mental levels.

What is brahma granthi?

Swami Satyananda: Brahma granthi is the first knot and it is associated with mooladhara and swadhisthana chakras. It is linked with the survival instinct, the urge to procreate and with deep, instinctive knowledge, awareness and desire.

When brahma granthi is transcended, the *kundalini* or primal energy is able to rise beyond mooladhara and swadhisthana without being pulled back down by the attractions and instinctual patterns of the personality.

What is vishnu granthi?

Swami Satyananda: The second knot is vishnu granthi, associated with manipura and anahata chakras. These two chakras deal with the sustenance of the physical, emotional and mental aspects of human existence. Manipura sustains *pranamaya kosha*, the energy body, governing the digestion and metabolism of food. Anahata sustains *manomaya kosha*, the mental body, and they both affect *annamaya kosha*, the physical body.

Once vishnu granthi is transcended, one is no longer bound by physical, mental and emotional attachments. Relationships and energy become more universal, rather than being limited by personal preferences or aversions.

What is rudra granthi?

Swami Satyananda: The final knot is rudra granthi, which is associated with vishuddhi and ajna chakras. Vishuddhi and ajna sustain *vijnanamaya kosha*, the intuitive or higher mental body, and represent the transformation of an existing form, idea or concept into its universal aspect.

When rudra granthi is pierced, individuality is dropped. The old ego identification is left behind and the experience of unmanifest consciousness, beyond the phenomenal universe, emerges at ajna and sahasrara chakras.

What type of energy is blocked in each of the granthis?

Swami Niranjanananda: The three bandhas are tools for the opening of three blocks. In kundalini yoga we call these blocks granthis. The knot of brahma is where the energy manifestation of the creative process is blocked. The knot of vishnu is where the energy manifestation of sustenance, maintenance and preservation is blocked. The knot of Shiva, or rudra granthi, is where the energy process which helps in transcendance is blocked.

How does maha bandha loosen the granthis?

Swami Satyananda: The force generated from the bandhas may be likened to that of increased pressure in a tube. Imagine a piece of tubing rising vertically from the ground. This tube represents sushumna nadi, the main pranic energy channel which runs up the spine.

1. Moola bandha seals off the lowest portion of the tube, thus preventing apana, the downward flow of prana, from escaping below mooladhara. It stimulates energy in mooladhara, awakening kundalini shakti.
2. Jalandhara bandha seals off the top portion of the tube, preventing prana vayu from passing upward, beyond vishuddhi. Prana is now locked within this tube.
3. Uddiyana bandha completes maha bandha. It further increases pranic pressure by stimulating manipura chakra, filling and expanding the closed tube.

Thus, when maha bandha is performed, prana is compressed in sushumna. The locks prevent its downward and upward movement, at the same time stimulating energy. Release of the bandhas flushes prana through the whole body, and as prana is by nature vital, life-giving energy, the body is relaxed, toned and rejuvenated. The granthis can then be pierced and untied, expanding consciousness.

How does the brahma granthi reflect one's state of consciousness?

Swami Niranjanananda: Brahma granthi is the knot of Brahma. Brahma is the manifest force of life and creation. In relation to the world in which we live or, according to tantra, in the world of yonis or different life forms, Brahma controls the energies of mooladhara and swadhisthana. It is linked with the urge to procreate and with deep instinctive knowledge, awareness and desire.

256

This experience is known as the blockage of Brahma because it holds our consciousness at a level related to desires of the physical dimension, sensuality, procreation and the instinctive urge to survive, which we generally cannot transcend. Once this blockage is removed from the realm of consciousness and energy, instincts of the so-called deep-rooted karmas, samskaras or desires do not affect or alter the other patterns of consciousness and energy. The kundalini or primal energy is able to rise beyond mooladhara and swadhisthana without being pulled down by the other attractions to which our consciousness is attached.

How does vishnu granthi reflect the sustaining energy of Vishnu?

Swami Niranjanananda: Vishnu granthi is the area where the personality and the body are sustained. Manipura sustains the physical body in a practical way. The food one consumes is converted to energy and distributed throughout the body. The process of conversion of matter into energy in a form which can be used for maintenance and growth of the body is a function of manipura.

In the same way, anahata sustains the mental structure in the form of emotions, which are raw, unrefined, intense expressions of subtle energy, which can manifest as anger, compassion and so on. This pure unadulterated energy is the force which sustains manomaya kosha and pranamaya kosha. Vishuddhi, the all-pervading space, is the subtle energy which sustains vijnanamaya and anandamaya koshas.

The sustenance aspect of all human dimensions is governed by these three chakras which vitalize, feed, balance and nurture the subtle bodies. This is the function of vishnu granthi. Once the vishnu granthi blockage is removed, one begins to sustain oneself from energy drawn from the universe and not from a localized centre. The energies of the body become harmonious with the energy of the cosmos. The interaction between the human personality and the cosmos happens naturally and spontaneously.

What happens when rudra granthi is released?

Swami Niranjanananda: Rudra granthi, or the knot of rudra, governs ajna and sahasrara chakras. It represents the transformation of an existing form, idea or concept into its universal aspect. Therefore, the dropping of individuality happens when rudra granthi is pierced.

The word *rudra* means 'howling energy'. It is derived from the root *rud*, which means 'to cry', and also the word *roodan* meaning 'the cry'. The process of detaching from our deeply fused attachment to the whole of life and to our individuality is a process of breaking apart or tearing asunder – the howling which takes place here is the piercing of rudra granthi.

To leave the known, manifest consciousness and enter unmanifest consciousness, where vijnanamaya and anandamaya become active, is the tearing of rudra granthi. Here there is a breaking away of the old, the ego awareness, the mental awareness, the physical awareness, and an evolving of the sixth sense or the eye of intuition, the third eye.

This sixth sense and beyond is a state where the omniscient nature of consciousness is experienced, where past, present and future become known. With that omniscient awareness one moves on to sahasrara, where the final merger of the individual soul and the universal cosmic soul occurs.

What is the psychophysiological understanding of the granthis?

Swami Niranjanananda: *Granthis* are 'ways of being' which somehow limit our energy. They are physical, pranic and mental contractions which create individuality and prevent understanding of our real cosmic form. Psychophysiologically, all physical and mental experiences arise out of the granthis, tying us to the world.

The three granthis correspond to the three major connecting areas of the body. Brahma granthi is the lowest part of the body where both the legs and digestive tract connect to the pelvis. Vishnu granthi is the area of the diaphragm where the chest and abdomen connect. These connecting areas also overlap. The manifestation of rudra granthi will affect other chakras and granthis; for example, a problem at the level of ajna chakra comes down to vishuddhi chakra and interferes with expression, such as speech. A problem at the vishnu granthi level can also manifest in speech. The voice can be used to express the intellect and also to express the heart. In singing, the flow of energy is upwards from the heart through the throat. To express ideas and concepts, energy moves from the area of rudra granthi down into the throat. These flows are interrupted by physical, mental, emotional and pranic contractions at various levels.

At a muscular level, contraction at brahma granthi may result in unconscious, prolonged contractions of parts of the perineum, especially when one is tense or involved in a relationship with someone. These psychophysiological contractions maintain a limited state.

Similarly, for vishnu granthi, with the diaphragm; in this area one protects the heart, withholding expression of power. Psychophysiological problems at manipura arise when one diminishes one's own strength, tightening the stomach, contracting the energy and creating illness and weakness. This may be due to a fear of expressing power and strength.

In the area of rudra granthi, blockages are expressed in contractions of the jaw and the back of the neck. At a psychophysical level, there is a lot of interconnection between the three granthis. All illnesses arise from these contractions. For example, with rudra granthi, contractions at the base of the skull will affect the ears and jaw muscles and perhaps create sinus problems. The bandhas help to energize, straighten and reconnect the flow between various levels of our being.

What happens if sushumna awakens before the granthis have been released?

Swami Niranjanananda: The granthis prevent the free flow of prana along sushumna nadi and, therefore, hamper the awakening of the chakras and the rising of kundalini. It has been the experience of advanced practitioners in the higher techniques that, with the awakening of prana and sushumna, certain spinal contractions can be experienced at these three points. There is a tightening of the nadi, where the body adopts different postures such as bending backwards and losing the sense of balance. This occurs because at the time of pranic awakening, the blockage is being experienced in either brahma granthi, vishnu granthi or rudra granthi.

How can the granthis, the knots, be untied?

Swami Niranjanananda: Untying is not the physical process of tying and untying. The concept of granthis is about the content in that region which has been kept there for so many years, for so much time, in the form of archetypes and impressions.

Untying the knots means these archetypes and impressions are released. It is like wiping the blackboard clear of everything that was written on it, and then having the freedom to create one's own knots again but this time, create them with more wisdom.

9

The Pancha Dharana:
Five Concentration Practices

According to the teachings of Swami Niranjanananda

THE HATHA YOGA DHARANAS

Why does *Gheranda Samhita* include five dharana practices in the category of mudra?

The term *mudra* is explained as a physical and psychic gesture with far reaching effects on mind, body, emotions and prana; in fact, on the whole psyche. When practised regularly, mudras influence the attitudes deeply and are tools for spiritual awakening. Within the broad category of mudras, Sage Gheranda includes bandhas and dharanas: these are listed in *Gheranda Samhita* (3:1–3):

Gheranda uvacha:
Mahaamudraa nabhomudraa uddeeyaanam jalandharam;
Moolabandho mahaabandho mahaabedhashcha khecharee.

Vipareetakaree yonirvajronee shaktichalanee;
Taadaagee maandukee mudraa shaambhavee panchadhaaranaa.

Ashvinee paashinee kaakee maatangee cha bhujanginee;
Panchavimshatimudraashcha siddhidaa iha yoginaam.

Sage Gheranda said: maha mudra, nabho mudra, uddiyana bandha, jalandhara bandha, moola bandha, maha bandha, maha bheda mudra, khechari mudra; (1)

261

Vipareeta karani mudra, yoni mudra, vajroni mudra, shakti chalini mudra, tadagi mudra, manduki mudra, shambhavi mudra, the five dharanas or concentrations; (2)

Ashwini, pashinee, kaki, matangi and bhujangini are the twenty-five mudras. These enable yogis to attain siddhi, perfection or mastery. (3)

Sixteen mudras, four bandhas and five *dharanas*, concentration practices, are described in these verses. The dharanas are: prithvi dharana, ambhasi dharana, agneyi dharana, vayviye dharana and akashi dharana. While *bandhas* are mudras with a specific 'locking' function, the five dharanas focus and lock the prana and awareness on a specific point or quality using psychic rather than physical tools.

Sage Gheranda described these five concentration practices, *pancha dharana*, under the category of mudra, but actually he is explaining one of the basic principles of kundalini yoga. The dharanas are advanced practices. From the basic 'mechanical' point of view they require some knowledge of the use of mantras and yantras according to the kundalini yoga tradition. For progress to be made, however, one also has to prepare one's consciousness. Traditionally, these techniques can only be used after some success in the practice of shambhavi mudra.

From the pancha dharana, energy from the five elements of the universe – earth, water, fire, air and space – is acquired. Mastery over the five elements of nature is the culmination of the pancha dharana. An adept can go to heaven and return while still embodied; the ability to direct the consciousness to travel in any direction desired is attained.

Why is mastery of pranayama necessary for practise of the pancha dharanas?
Any kind of dharana practice is incomplete until mastery over pranayama is achieved. These dharanas are practised with *pooraka*, breathing in, and holding the breath inside. This should be developed naturally without strain by

first being aware of the natural pause at the end of each inhalation, and letting it gradually lengthen.

Initially ujjayi breathing is used, observing the breath moving up and down the spine between mooladhara and the throat. In the beginning the only aim is to gradually achieve control over the breath. After three or four months, holding the breath for up to one minute is practised. Thus the capacity of the body is increased little by little. In this way, the goal can finally be achieved.

With expert guidance moorcha pranayama can be incorporated. The breath is retained for up to three or four minutes during part of the practice. Advanced practitioners just relax and watch the spontaneous flow or stoppage of the breath. The prana is to be retained inside.

One begins with short practices of five or twenty minutes – however long the practice can be maintained with an alert awareness and a witnessing attitude. Eventually the practice of *dharana*, concentration, can be done for approximately two hours.

It must be remembered that these practices are not perfected in a day. It is not possible to inhale deeply and retain the prana inside on the very first day. In order to retain the prana inside for up to two hours, it is imperative to have mastered pranayama prior to the practice. Yogis keep doing a practice continuously for years; only then is mastery or perfection of the practice attained.

PARTHIVI DHARANA: CONCENTRATION ON EARTH

What is the purpose of practising concentration on the earth element?

The practice of concentrating on the earth element, *parthivi dharana*, more commonly called *prithvi dharana*, is an attempt to awaken mooladhara chakra through meditation and concentration. It is said in this mantra that the *ishta devata*, the chosen deity, of mooladhara chakra is Lord Brahma, whose function is to create.

Mooladhara chakra

The process of creation commences with the earth element. Whether it is vegetation, a mountain, a stone, an animal, a bird or a human being, everything is created out of *prithvi tattwa*, the earth element. There is also the goddess of the skin, of the sense of touch, whose name is Dakini. Brahma and Dakini are the controllers of mooladhara chakra.

How is the energy of the earth element invoked in prithvi dharana?

Instructions are given to imagine or concentrate on the earth element in the heart, *hridisthaapitam*, during the practice. Here *hrid* does not mean the physical heart; rather it means focusing the *antahkarana*, inner tools of consciousness, on the yantra. In *Gheranda Samhita* (3:17–18) it is written:

Yattatvam haritaaladesharachitam bhaumam lakaaraanvitam,
Vedaasram kamalaasanenasahitam kritvaa hridisthaapitam;
Praanam tatra vileeya panchaghatikaashchittaanvitam dhaarayet;
Aishaa stambhakaree sadaa kshitijayam kuryaadadhodhaaranaa.

Paarthiveedhaaranaamudraam yah karoti tu nityashah;
Mrityunjayah svayam so'pi sa siddho vicharedbhuvi.

The colour of the earth element is yellow like orpiment (a yellow mineral used as a pigment), the bija or seed mantra is *Lam*, it is square in shape and Brahma is the God. Manifest it with the yogic power, retain it in the heart and hold the prana there up to five ghati (about two hours). It is known as prithvi mudra or adhodharana mudra. After mastering it, a practitioner becomes the conqueror of the earth. (17)

One who practises prithvi dharana wins over death and wanders over the earth as a siddha, a perfected person. (18)

In this first verse the *yantra,* or geometrical blueprint, of earth is referred to. He refers to the earth element as yellow. The yantra, symbol or diagram of the earth element is square in shape, and it is to be retained in the heart, which means deep inside, and the practitioner has to be aware of its bija mantra, *Lam* लं. The sadhaka must also be aware of the other characteristics of earth and feel them as part of his own nature. The feeling is of the essential unity of oneself and all beings with the mother earth, and of the benevolence of the earth element.

The sloka says that a person who masters this practice achieves victory over the earth element, its merits and demerits. It is believed in yoga that one lifetime is probably not adequate to perfect a *sadhana* or practice. These techniques should be practised slowly and only under the guidance of a competent teacher. If force is applied, the responsibility is not that of yoga, or of the teacher.

AMBHASI DHARANA: CONCENTRATION ON WATER

What is the symbolism of ambhasi dharana, concentration on the water element?

It is said that swadhisthana chakra is the symbol of the unconscious state. According to kundalini yoga, swadhisthana chakra is related to *jala tattwa,* the water element. The vehicle of this chakra is a crocodile, which is considered to be the vehicle of Varuna, the water god. Yoga regards the unconscious mind as extensive, large and deep like an ocean, the depth and limit of which no one has been able to gauge. In the symbol of swadhisthana, a small crescent moon and stars are shown in the night sky.

Swadhisthana chakra

The light of the night sky over the ocean is not the light of knowledge or the ray of discrimination or wisdom or feeling. This moon, with the stars in the sky, is considered to be a symbol of mental energy. This mental energy, *manas shakti* or *chitta shakti*, illuminates the unconscious state itself. Above the crescent moon the mantra *Vam* is inscribed. Retaining both yantra and mantra in the heart, the innermost centre, the prana is held inside for about two hours.

How is the energy of the water element invoked during ambhasi dharana?

Sitting in a meditative posture, one becomes still and aware of the breath. The mind is then focused on a crescent moon, the yantra of *apas tattwa*, the water element. The bright silver-white crescent moon is visualized, and the awareness is moved around its curved outline. The transparent fluidity of water is felt, its pure refreshing taste is recalled. One's own connection with water, and attraction to the bright crescent moon of its yantra, must be felt.

One then begins to feel or hear or repeat mentally the mantra of apas tattwa, which is *Vam* वं. The mantra *Vam* is seen shining in the light of the centre of the crescent moon. There is awareness of the seed mantra of the yantra of apas tattwa, *Vam*, like a pulse beat. The yantra and mantra are retained in the centre of awareness. One is also aware of the other characteristics of water, and feels them as part of one's own nature. The essential unity of oneself and all beings with the life-giving water element, and the benevolence of the water element, are felt.

Awareness of the *laya*, the rhythm of the breath, is like the waves of the ocean as one dissolves in the water element.

There is awareness of the natural pause at the end of each inhalation, and it gradually lengthens. Prana is retained inside. Mastery of the breath must develop naturally, as in prithvi dharana.

266

To end the practice, the mind must be disengaged from the mantra *Vam* and from the yantra of the water element. One must again be aware of the earth element which is part of one's own nature. One must be aware of the solidity and shape of the physical body and become conscious of the outside world.

In *Gheranda Samhita* (3:19–20), ambhasi dharana is described:

Shankhendupratimam cha kundadhavalam tattvam kilaalam shubham;
Tatpeeyooshavakaarabeejasahitam yuktam sadaa vishnunaa;
Praanam tatra vileeya pancha ghatikaashchittaanvitaam dhaarayet;
Eshaa duhsahataapapaapaharineesyaadaambhasee dhaaranaa.

Aambhaseem paramaam mudraam yo jaanaati sa yogavit;
Jale cha ghore gambheere maranam tasyanobhavet.

The colour of water is bright white like that of a conch, moon or lotus. Its bija mantra is *Vam* and its god is Lord Vishnu. Retaining the focus on this element in the heart, become one-pointed and hold the prana by kumbhaka up to five ghati (about two hours). This mudra is known by the name of ambhasi dharana. Leaving aside all worries, breathe in deeply, retain the breath up to five ghati and meditate on the water element. Meditate on the merits, demerits, yantra and symbol of the water element. By this dharana all the pains, heat and sins of a human being are destroyed, i.e. internal heat and excitement are finished. By doing this practice, no harm can come to a person, even in deep water.

How should one prepare for the practice of dharana on the water element?

Only once the attitude of witnessing the samskaras and karmas becomes an established part of the personality can the practice of dharana on swadhisthana chakra be beneficially undertaken for extended periods of time. Before practising this dharana, it is essential to understand and expand the awareness into the conscious and subconscious states of mind. Practising yoga nidra on a regular basis helps to purify the conscious and subconscious states, releasing samskaras that bubble to the surface of the mind as one relaxes. Gradually one comes to know the mental actions and reactions that take place in the subconscious state of mind.

According to yoga, samskaras and karmas manifest strongly in the unconscious mind, as it is their *karmakshetra*, or field of activity. It is their place of origin and storehouse. When the need for something is felt, it comes up into the conscious state. When karmas and samskaras manifest strongly inside, tumbling and disrupting the life of a sadhaka so that one becomes scattered and can scarcely control one's life, this dharana is practised. It is not done all the time.

Prior to practising this dharana it is imperative to quieten the modifications of the mind in chitta. The first step is to understand and calm down the thoughts, feelings and modifications of mind which emerge in the conscious state and play out their roles. Next, one should try to understand the subconscious by getting to know the mental actions and reactions that take place in the subconscious mind. Only once the conscious and the subconscious are purified and are under control, when one can witness the samskaras and karmas that remain, is this practice of dharana on swadhisthana chakra undertaken.

There is also a hint about this dharana in the *Yoga Sutras* of Sage Patanjali. This dharana is practised in order to achieve *nirbija avastha*, the seedless state. This means that when one achieves control over the modifications of mind, intellect and chitta in the right manner, only samskaras remain. Then one also starts exhausting samskaras, making them rootless. It is at that time that *ambhasi dharana*, concentration on the water element, *jala* or *apas tattwa*, spontaneously takes place.

268

What precautions are given regarding the practice of dharana on the water element?

Gheranda Samhita (3:21) says that it is imperative to keep this practice secret:

> *Iyam tu paramaa mudraa gopaneeyaa prayatnatah;*
> *Prakaashaatsiddhihaanihsyaatsatyam vachmi cha tattvatah.*

> It is an important mudra and it is imperative to keep it secret. If a practitioner describes this practice to others or discloses this technique, his siddhi is destroyed. This is the truth.

Why is this said? It is an important practice that involves looking into the depths of the mind. If one forces oneself prematurely into the practice, the responsibility lies with the practitioner, not the technique. These techniques should be practised slowly and proper guidance should be followed. Without first mastering the technique, how can guidance be given to others with whom the technique may be shared? What is given here is an outline of the practice, a few words lashed together like a raft suitable for sailing in a serene lake. To cross the ocean a fully equipped vessel is needed and the instructions of the ship's captain have to be followed as the weather changes.

AGNEYI DHARANA: CONCENTRATION ON FIRE

What is the symbolism and action of agni, the fire element?

According to kundalini yoga, manipura chakra is related to *agni tattwa*, the fire element. The yantra of agni tattwa is an inverted red triangle and the mandala of manipura chakra contains an inverted red triangle with a picture of *Surya*, the sun god, in the centre. Its vehicle is a ram. Manipura chakra is considered to be a centre of prana shakti.

Even in the gross form when food is eaten, digestion takes place in the manipura region. In the subtle state, too, awakening or purification of prana takes place with

the awakening of manipura chakra. This chakra is responsible for the activity of the personality, the life force and dynamism. Along with their opposite characteristics, such as laziness, depression and sluggishness, these are the merits and demerits of manipura chakra.

Manipura chakra

How is the energy of agni invoked during agneyi dharana?
Fire is called *agni* or *vahni*. In *Gheranda Samhita*, Sage Gheranda refers to this concentration practice as *vaishvani dharana*.

Sitting in a meditative posture, one becomes still and aware of the breath and the energy flowing with the breath. The mind is focused on the yantra of agni tattwa. A bright red inverted triangle is visualized. Looking closely one sees three short *bhopura*, walls like fire-guards, that protect each side of the triangle. The awareness is moved around the three sides and the mantra of agni tattwa, which is *Ram* र is mentally repeated, or heard. The mantra *Ram* is seen shining in the centre of the fiery red light of the inverted triangle.

The beauty of the fire and its characteristic heat is seen. The pure bright light of fire flames giving light and warmth are recalled, they are seen calmly with a witnessing attitude, scorching anything attached. One's own connection with fire is felt, and attraction to the bright light of its yantra is experienced.

There is awareness of the seed mantra of the yantra of agni tattwa, *Ram*, like the beat of the dancing flames. This yantra and mantra are retained in the centre of one's awareness. There is also awareness of the other characteristics of fire, and they are felt as part of one's own nature, transforming one's nature and anything it comes

270

in contact with. Awareness of the power of transformation, the essential characteristic of the fire element, is felt. At the same time there is awareness of the rhythm of the breath, the natural pause at the end of each inhalation, the beginning, end and rebirth of each breath. The prana is retained inside.

Ending the practice, the mind is disengaged from the mantra *Ram* and from the yantra of the fire element. Again, there is awareness of the water element, which is also part of one's own nature. Again, there is awareness of the earth element, which is part of one's own nature, and of the solidity and shape of the physical body.

The practice of agneyi dharana is given in *Gheranda Samhita* (3:22–23):

Yannaabhisthitamindragopasadrisham beejam trikonaanvitam;
Tattvam vahnimayam pradeeptamarunam rudrena yatsiddhidam;
Praanam tatra vileeya panchaghatikaashchittaanvitam dhaarayet;
Eshaa kaalagabheerabheetiharinee vaishvaanaree dhaaranaa.

Pradeepte jvalite vahnau patito yadi saadhakah;
Etanmudraa prasaadena sa jeevati na mrityubhaak.

The region of fire is the navel region. Its colour is red. Its yantra is a triangle. Its mantra is *Ram* and its deity is Rudra. This fire element is full of streaming light, lustre, radiance and is the provider of siddhi, perfection. Manifesting it by yogic power, retain the prana with one-pointedness for five ghati (about two hours). By practising it, fear of death vanishes and no harm is done by fire. It is called vaishvanari dharana. If a sadhaka falls into a raging fire, he will not die due to the powerful effect of this mudra. (22–23)

How should the pranic awakening associated with agni tattwa be managed?

Manipura chakra is the storage centre of prana. The symbol of this energy or power is the sun god. The *ishta*, chosen deity, is Rudra, a form of Shiva – *rudra* 'means one who acquires a fierce form'. Until prana shakti is under control, it remains in a fierce form. When prana is awakened inside, it is possible for this shakti or energy to assume the form of a furious fire and burn the body and mind.

The point is that prana exists in the body in the form of fierce energy. When control is achieved over prana by means of consciousness, this prana grants all types of *siddhis*, powers, by coming under the control of the practitioner. However, if it is uncontrolled, the person becomes like *Bhasma-asura*, a demon, meaning that he becomes responsible for reducing himself to ashes. Therefore, do not practise these tattwa dharanas without a competent guide.

VAYVIYE DHARANA: CONCENTRATION ON AIR

What is the symbolism of vayu tattwa, the air element?

According to kundalini yoga, anahata chakra relates to *vayu tattwa*, the air element. The yantra of vayu tattwa is made up of two interlacing triangles. The apex of one triangle is pointing upward while the other one is inverted. At the centre the bija mantra of this yantra is *Yam*.

Anahata chakra has a jyoti like a candle flame burning in the centre of these interlaced triangles, and its light is spreading all around, up and down, right and left; four rays of light are emanating.

Anahata chakra

How is the energy of vayu tattwa invoked with the practice of vayviye dharana?

The same method is followed in this technique as for the previous tattwas. Ishwara is the ishta devata here. The three deities of the previous three tattwas: Brahma, Vishnu and Rudra, the trinity, are respectively the creator, sustainer and destroyer of the entire creation. In this practice, however, the deity is Ishwara, so the instruction is to practise vayviye

272

dharana, keeping that divine quality in mind. *Ishwara* represents that divine eternal existence or element which is indestructible and imperishable. It is that aspect which is contemplated for two hours along with the mantra and yantra of the air element.

Sitting in a meditative posture, one becomes still and aware of the breath and the energy flowing with the breath. The mind is focused on the yantra of vayu tattwa, the air element. The interlaced triangles of anahata chakra are visualized. Looking closely, the six points of the hexagonal shape that they form are visualized. These are like atoms of air, ready to fly apart yet constrained in the formation of the yantra. The awareness is moved to each point and the mantra of vayu tattwa, which is *Yam* यं, is mentally heard or repeated. The mantra *Yam* is shining in the centre of the six blue points of the interlaced triangles.

One becomes aware of the characteristics of air, aware of the touch of air against the skin, aware of the breath as it goes in and out, aware of the expansiveness and life-giving qualities of air. One becomes aware of the seed mantra *Yam* of vayu tattwa, whilst breathing in and out. The connection of all living creatures and oneself with the air element is witnessed. One merges with it, attracted to its yantra and mantra.

This yantra and mantra are retained in the centre of awareness. There is also awareness of the other characteristics of air and they are felt as part of one's own self. There is awareness of the rhythm of the breath, the natural pause at the end of each inhalation, the beginning, end and rebirth of each breath.

To end the practice, the mind is disengaged from the mantra *Yam* and from the yantra of the air element. There is awareness of the other elements which are part of one's nature, and of how one is feeling.

The practice of vayviye dharana is described in *Gheranda Samhita* (3:24–25):

Yadbhinnaanjanapunjasannibhamidam dhoomraavabhaasam
param;
Tattvam sattvamayam yakaarasahitam yatreshvaro devataa;
Praanam tatra vileeya panchaghatikaashchittaanvitam dhaarayet;
Eshaa khe gamanam karoti yaaminaam syaadvaayavee
dhaaranaa.

Iyam tu paramaa mudraa jaraamrityuvinaashinee;
Vaayunaabhriyate naapi khe cha gatipradaayinee.

The colour of *vayu*, air, is light black like that of collyrium or smoke. Its bija mantra is *Yam*. This tattwa has sattwic properties. Having manifested it by yogic power, retain the prana vayu up to two hours with one-pointedness. With the practice of this mudra, by the name of vayviye dharana, a sadhaka achieves the power to travel in space and cannot die due to air. This major mudra destroys old age and death and enables one to fly in space. (24–25)

Why is control over the feelings important when practising dharana on the air element?

According to kundalini yoga, anahata chakra relates to *vayu tattwa*, the air element. This chakra is related to feelings and experiences. Dual feelings manifest inside, love and compassion and also ill-feeling and anger. Anahata chakra has a link with the subconscious mental state in one's life. The reactions that originate in the subconscious mind influence anahata. The main thing in anahata chakra is to achieve control over the feelings, whether positive or negative. The need for harmony of feelings is expressed in *Gheranda Samhita* (3:26):

Shathaaya bhaktiheenaaya na deyam yasyakasyachit;
Datte cha siddhihaanih syaatsatyam vachmi cha chanda te.

This dharana should never be disclosed to an undevoted and wicked person. By doing so, siddhi is destroyed. My above statement is true.

When complete control over feeling, experience and behaviour is achieved, anahata chakra awakens. If internal feelings are even a little out of control, anahata chakra cannot be awakened. Therefore, it is imperative that the antahkarana is pure for the awakening of this chakra. Vayviye dharana should not be practised if one is emotionally unwell. It is not a therapeutic technique, rather it is to explore one's inner nature once relative balance and clarity have been achieved. Vayviye dharana leads to the awakening of anahata chakra and eventual freedom from emotional turmoil.

AKASHI DHARANA: CONCENTRATION ON SPACE

What is the symbolism of akasha tattwa, the space element?
The symbol of vishuddhi chakra is a circle and inside it is a drop of water. The colour of the circle is like the dark blue colour of the sea and in its centre is a drop of white. Its bija mantra is *Ham*. Its deity is Sadashiva. *Shiva* means benevolent one or auspicious one. That power by which one always achieves benevolence and auspiciousness, is *Sadashiva*. This practice is also known as *nabho dharana*.

Vishuddhi chakra

How is the energy of akasha tattwa invoked by akashi dharana?
Sitting in a meditative posture, one becomes still and aware of the breath and the energy flowing with the breath. The mind is focused on the yantra of *akasha tattwa*, the space element. A circle which has no beginning or end is visualized: this is the yantra of infinite space. As one looks closely, a multitude of multi-coloured points are seen, like atoms that can only exist within space. The mantra of akasha tattwa, which is *Ham* हं, is mentally heard or repeated. The

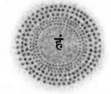

275

mantra *Ham* is seen shining in the centre of the dark circle composed of an infinite number of multi-coloured points.

One is aware of the characteristics of space, which is on the edge of manifestation and the unmanifest. One is aware of the expansiveness of space, and the seed mantra *Ham* of the space element, which contains the manifest universe. There is a feeling of merging with it, attracted to its yantra and mantra. This yantra and mantra are retained in the centre of awareness. There is also awareness of the other characteristics of space, and they are felt as part of one's own divine self.

Ending the practice, the mind is disengaged from the mantra *Ham* and from the yantra of the air element. Again there is awareness of the other elements which are part of one's nature, and of how one is feeling.

Akashi dharana is described in *Gheranda Samhita* (3:27–28):

Yatsinddhau varashuddhavaarisadrisham vyomaakhyamudbhaasate,
Tattvam devasadaashivena sahitam beejam hakaaraanvitam;
Praanam tatra vileeya panchaghatikaashchittaanvitam dhaarayet,
Eshaa mokshakapaatabhedanakaree kuryaannabhodhaaranaa.

Aakaasheedhaaranaam mudraam yo vetti sa yogavit;
Na mrityurjaayate tasya pralaye naavaseedati.

The colour of akasha tattwa, the ether element, is like the pure water of the ocean. Its bija mantra is *Ham* and its deity is Sadashiva. This nabhodharana mudra is perfected by retaining prana vayu for up to two hours, with a peaceful mind; it then opens the gate to liberation. A yogi who knows akashi dharana does not fall prey to death and does not perish even during pralaya (cosmic destruction).

Why is akashi dharana of particular importance for purifying the mind?

According to kundalini yoga, vishuddhi chakra is related to akasha tattwa, the ether or space element. It is also a symbol of the pure state of consciousness. In the four lower chakras one faces impure states of consciousness: disorders, feelings, uncontrolled energy, fear, insecurity, and so on. All these are impure states related to life. On reaching vishuddhi chakra, the barriers and borders of the antahkarana – whether it is mind, intellect, chitta or ahamkara – are crossed and a pure, conscious state of being is attained.

Practising this dharana helps one to awaken vishuddhi chakra, thereby attaining a pure state. It is also beneficial for one's ability to communicate. The sadhaka can open the gates of *moksha*, liberation, with the help of akashi dharana.

Appendices

Appendices

Index of Questions

1. Understanding Mudra

2. Hasta Mudras: Hand Mudras

4. Kaya Mudra: Postural Mudras

VIPAREETA KARANI MUDRA: INVERTED PSYCHIC ATTITUDE

PRANA MUDRA: INVOCATION OF ENERGY

5. Bandha Mudra: Lock Mudras

UNDERSTANDING LOCK MUDRAS

6. Adhara Mudra: Perineal Mudras

7. The Bandhas

WHAT ARE BANDHAS?

MOOLA BANDHA: THE PERINEAL LOCK

8. Effects of the Bandhas

9. The Pancha Dharana: Five Concentration Practices

Index of Scriptural Quotes

(3:98) The worries of old age and death disappear. A practitioner is neither touched by death nor old age, nor has any fear of water, air or fire. 35

(3:99) Twenty types of kapha problems such as asthma and colds are eliminated by practising the described mudras. There is no doubt about this. 35

(3:100) O Chanda! I have explained to you everything about mudras and there is nothing else to tell you. There is no other practice in the world like mudra which enables you to achieve success and completeness. 35

3. Mana Mudra: Head Mudras

(3:86): Inhale slowly through the mouth, shaping it like the beak of a crow. This is kaki mudra, the destroyer of all ailments. This great mudra should be kept secret by all means. 62

(3:87) By practising this mudra, relief from all disorders is achieved. Just like a crow, one becomes free from disease. 62

(3:88–89) Standing in water up to the throat, inhale deeply, drawing water up through the nostrils and expelling water out of the mouth. It should be practised repeatedly. This great mudra is known as matangini mudra. 62

(3:90) When it is perfected, there is no fear of old age and death, and a yogi becomes powerful like an elephant and always remains happy. 63

(3:91) It should be practised with concentration in a quiet, secluded place away from other people. This mudra should be perfected with sincere effort. 63

(3:92) Opening the mouth wide enough, suck air through the throat. This is known as bhujangini mudra. 64

(3:93) Once it is mastered, all abdominal disorders are removed; old age and death are eliminated. 64

(3:49) Sit in siddhasana and close the ears with both thumbs, both eyes with the index fingers, both nostrils with the middle fingers and the mouth with the ring fingers and little fingers. 68

(3:50–51) With the help of kaki mudra, pull the prana and join it with apana, and keeping the awareness at the

301

six chakras in the body, awaken kundalini shakti with the mantras *Hoom* and *Hamsa* and bring the jivatma (individual soul) along with it to sahasrara. 69

(3:52) There should be the silent feeling at that time that 'I am moving comfortably along with Shiva and enriched by Shakti. 69

(3:53) With the union of Shiva and Shakti I have become blissful Brahman too.' 69

(3:54) This is yoni mudra. By means of this mudra one becomes liberated from sins like killing a brahmin or a foetus, drinking alcohol or polluting the bed of the teacher. 70

(3:55) Yoni mudra is a top secret kriya. It is not easily accessible even to the gods. Those who achieve mastery over it by regular practice attain samadhi. 70

(3:56) All the major sins, minor sins, etc., of the universe are erased by yoni mudra. Thus it should be practised by people seeking salvation. 70

(7:12) Assuming yoni mudra, a yogi should create the feeling of shakti in himself and unite blissfully with paramatma. 74

(7:13) Thereafter, established in blissful oneness, one becomes one with Brahman and realizes 'I am Brahman'. This is non-dual samadhi (called laya siddhi yoga samadhi). 74

(3:76) Steady the gaze at the eyebrow centre, on one's self, the atma or soul, and meditate. This is shambhavi mudra. It is a very secret tantric practice. 84

(3:77) The Vedas, shastras and puranas are like an ordinary woman and shambhavi mudra is like a bride. 84

(3:78) Practitioners of this practice are themselves Adinath, Narayana and Brahma, the creator of this world. 85

(3:79) Take this saying as absolutely true, that a person knowing shambhavi mudra is Maheshwara, is Brahman in reality. 85

(3:32) Wherever one is and during all activities, a yogi should keep the tongue turned upward and retain the breath. Nabho mudra destroys all the disorders of a yogi. 91

302

(3:33) The nadi connecting the tongue and the root of the tongue, which is located underneath the tongue, is to be severed and the tip of the tongue is to be moved continuously. By applying butter and with the help of dohan kriya (the milking process) it is to be pulled with iron forceps.   97

(3:34) With daily practice the tongue becomes elongated. Its length should be so increased that it can reach the eyebrow centre. Khechari mudra is then accomplished.   97

(3:35) In this way the tongue should gradually be inserted into the root of the palate. By folding the tongue upward and backward, it should be taken right up to the nasal cavity. Keep the awareness fixed at the eyebrow centre at that time. This is khechari mudra.   97

(3:39–40) Therefore, strange types of juices keep being produced, day in and day out, through the tongue of the practitioner. New blissful experiences manifest. In the beginning salty, alkaline, bitter and astringent tastes and then the taste of butter, ghee (clarified butter), milk, curd, buttermilk, honey, grapes or raisins and then nectar are produced.   99

(3:36) The practitioner of khechari mudra is not troubled by unconsciousness, hunger, thirst, laziness, etc. Fear of any disorder or disease, old age and death vanishes as the body becomes divine.   101

(3:37) The physical body is neither burnt in fire nor dried up by wind. It can neither be made wet by water nor does poison have any effect as in the case of snake bite.   102

(3:38) The body becomes graceful and charming. Unshakeable samadhi is perfected. Various juices are produced as a result of the union between the forehead and the mouth through the tongue.   102

4. Kaya Mudra: Postural Mudras

(3:73) Sit in paschimottanasana and expand the abdomen as if it were full of water. This is an important mudra which removes the fear of old age and death.   126

5. Bandha Mudra: Lock Mudras

6. Adhara Mudra: Perineal Mudras

7. The Bandhas

9. The Pancha Dharanas: Five Concentration Practices

(3:3) Ashwini, pashinee, kaki, matangini and bhujangini are the twenty-five mudras. These enable yogis to attain siddhi, perfection or mastery. 262

(3:17) The colour of the earth element is yellow like orpiment (a yellow mineral used as a pigment), the bija or seed mantra is *Lam*, it is square in shape and Brahma is the God. Manifest it with the yogic power, retain it in the heart and hold the prana there up to five ghati (about two hours). It is known as prithvi mudra or adhodharana mudra. After mastering it, a practitioner becomes the conqueror of the earth. 264

(3:18) One who practises prithvi dharana wins over death and wanders over the earth as a siddha, a perfected person. 264

(3:19–20) The colour of water is bright white like that of a conch, moon or lotus. Its bija mantra is *Vam* and its god is Lord Vishnu. Retaining the focus on this element in the heart, become one-pointed and hold the prana by kumbhaka up to five ghati (about two hours). This mudra is known by the name of ambhasi dharana. Leaving aside all worries, breathe in deeply, retain the breath up to five ghati and meditate on the water element. Meditate on the merits, demerits, yantra and symbol of the water element. By this dharana all the pains, heat and sins of a human being are destroyed, i.e. internal heat and excitement are finished. By doing this practice, no harm can come to a person even in deep water. 267

(3:21) It is an important mudra and it is imperative to keep it secret. If a practitioner describes this practice to others or discloses this technique, his siddhi is destroyed. This is the truth. 269

(3:22–23) The region of fire is the navel region. Its colour is red. Its yantra is a triangle. Its mantra is *Ram* and its deity is Rudra. This fire element is full of streaming light, lustre, radiance and is the provider of siddhi, perfection. Manifesting it by yogic power, retain the prana with one-pointedness for five ghati (about two hours). By practising it, fear of death vanishes and no harm is done by fire. It is called vaishvanari dharana. If a sadhaka falls into a raging fire, he will not die due to the powerful effect of this mudra. 271

(3:24–25) The colour of *vayu*, air, is light black like that of collyrium or smoke. Its bija mantra is *Yam*. This tattwa has sattwic properties. Having manifested it by yogic power, retain the prana vayu up to two hours with one-pointedness. With the practice of this mudra, by the name of vayviye dharana, a sadhaka achieves the power to travel in space and cannot die due to air. This major mudra destroys old age and death and enables one to fly in space.   274

(3:26) This dharana should never be disclosed to an undevoted and wicked person. By doing so, siddhi is destroyed. My above statement is true.   274

(3:27–28) The colour of akasha tattwa, the ether element, is like the pure water of the ocean. Its bija mantra is *Ham* and its deity is Sadashiva. This nabhodharana mudra is perfected by retaining prana vayu for up to two hours, with a peaceful mind; it then opens the gate to liberation. A yogi who knows akashi dharana does not fall prey to death and does not perish even during pralaya (cosmic destruction). 276

GORAKSHA SATARK

6, Adhara Mudra: Perineal Mudras

(v. 74, 76) Bindu is Shiva (consciousness), rajas is Shakti (energy). Bindu is the moon (ida) and rajas is the sun (pingala). From the mingling of these two, one obtains the highest state. Shukra bindu is joined with bindu (the brain centre), and rajas is joined with the sun (manipura). One who knows how to unite the two is an adept.   200

HATHA YOGA PRADIPIKA OF YOGI SWATMARAMA

1. Understanding Mudra

(3:6) Maha mudra, maha bandha, maha vedha, khechari, uddiyana, moola bandha and jalandhara bandha.   17

(3:7) Vipareeta karani mudra, vajroli and shakti chalana, verily, these are the ten mudras which destroy old age and death.   17

(3:5) Therefore, the goddess sleeping at the entrance of Brahma's door should be constantly aroused with all effort by performing mudra thoroughly.   28

(3:8) Adinath said they are the bestowers of the eight divine powers. They are held in high esteem by all the siddhas and are difficult for even the gods to attain.   29

(3:9) These must remain secret just like precious stones, and not be talked about to anyone, just as one does not tell others about his intimate relations with his wife.   32

(3:128) Thus the ten mudras have been told by Adinath, Shambhu. Each one is the bestower of perfection to the self-restrained.   33

(3:130) By following explicitly his (guru's) words, and practising mudra, one obtains the qualities of anima, etc., and overcomes death/time.   36

(3:129) One who instructs mudra in the tradition of guru and disciple is the true guru and form of Ishwara.   36

3. Mana Mudra: Head Mudras

(4:41) Mind steady, eyes semi-open, gaze fixed on the nosetip, the moon (ida) and sun (pingala) suspended, without any movement (physical or mental), that one attains the form of light (jyoti) which is endless and is complete, radiant, the Supreme. What more can be said?   59

(4:36) Introverted, one-pointed awareness with an un-blinking external gaze, this is shambhavi mudra which is preserved in the Vedas.   79

(4:37) If the yogi remains with the awareness and energy absorbed in the internal object (for concentration) while the external gaze is motionless, though looking one is not looking, that indeed is shambhavi. When it is given with the guru's blessing, the state of shoonyashoonya arises. That is the real state of Shiva (i.e. consciousness).   79

(4:38) Shambhavi and khechari states, though there is a difference in the place of concentration or influence, both bring about ecstasy, absorption in void, in the experience of chit sukha (the pleasure of consciousness).   80

(4:39) With perfect concentration, the pupils fixed on the light by raising the eyebrows up a little, as from the previously described (shambhavi), mind is joined and instantly unmani occurs.   81

(3:125) For those who are alert and the mind one-pointed (disciplined) in samadhi, rudrani or shambhavi mudra is the greatest mudra for bestowing perfection. 82

(4:80) In my opinion, contemplation on the eyebrow centre leads to a mindless state immediately. It is a suitable method even for those with less intellect to attain the state of raja yoga. The laya attained through nada gives immediate experience. 86

(3:32) Khechari mudra is turning the tongue backwards into the cavity of the cranium and turning the eyes inwards towards the eyebrow centre. 95

(3:33) The tongue should be exercised and milked and the underneath part cut away in small degrees. Indeed khechari is perfected when the tongue touches the eyebrow centre. 95

(3:34) With a clean thin blade, gently cut away the membrane under the tongue. Cut it by a fine hair's breadth each time. 95

(3:35) Then rub in a mixture of powdered rock salt and turmeric. After seven days, again cut a hair's breadth. 95

(3:36) One should continue doing this regularly for six months, then the membrane at the root of the tongue will be completely severed. 95

(3:49) When the tongue enters the cavity, indeed heat is produced and the nectar flows from the moon. 104

(3:45) The yogi's body is forever full of the moon's nectar. Even if he is bitten by the king of snakes (Takshaka), he is not poisoned. 107

(3:44) With the tongue directed upwards, the knower of yoga drinks the fluid of the moon. Within fifteen days physical death is conquered. 107

(3:38) The yogi who remains with the tongue going upwards for even half a second is freed from toxins, disease, death, old age, etc. 109

(3:39) One who accomplishes this khechari mudra is neither troubled by diseases, nor death, lassitude, sleep, hunger, thirst or unconsciousness. 109

310

(3:42) When the upper cavity of the palate is sealed by khechari mudra, the bindu or semen cannot be lost even if one embraces a beautiful woman. 109

(3:43) Even when there is movement of the bindu and it enters the genitals, it is seized by closing the perineum and is taken upward. 109

(3:48) The word 'go' means tongue (and also means cow). When it enters into the upper palate, it is 'eating the flesh of the cow'. It (khechari) destroys the great sins. 110

(3:51) Fluid drips into the sixteen-petalled lotus when the tongue is inserted into the upper throat cavity; the paramshakti (kundalini) is released and one becomes concentrated in the experience which ensues. The yogi who drinks the pure stream of nectar is freed from disease, has longevity, and has a body as soft and as beautiful as a lotus stem. 112

(3:50) When the tongue constantly presses the cavity, the moon's nectar flows and has a saline, pungent and acidic flavour. It is like the consistency of milk, ghee, honey. Fatal diseases, old age and weapons are warded off. From that, immortality and the eight siddhis or perfections 114

(4:43) When the prana which is in the right and left nadis moves in the middle nadi (sushumna) that is the condition for khechari mudra. 114

(4:44) The fire (of shakti) being swallowed (suppressed) midway between, ida and pingala, in that shoonya (of sushumna), is in truth the condition for khechari mudra. 114

(4:45) The middle of the sun (pingala) and moon (ida) is the 'unsupported', in which is situated vyoma chakra or centre of ether (void). This mudra is called khechari. 115

(4:46) In the flow from the moon (bindu) is the beloved of Shiva (consciousness). The opening of the unequalled divine sushumna should be filled from behind (by the tongue). 115

(4:47) The sushumna being completely filled at the rear (upper palate) also is khechari. The practice of khechari mudra is followed by the state of unmani (consciousness devoid of mind). 115

(3:37) Having turned the tongue back, the three channels of ida, pingala and sushumna are controlled. This is khechari mudra and it is called the centre of ether. 116

(3:53) Five nadis convene in this cavity and it is the source of knowledge. Khechari should be established in that void, untainted (by ignorance). 117

(3:46) Just as fuel kindles fire and oil a lamp, so the indweller of the body does not vacate while the body is full of the moon's nectar. 117

(3:47) By constant swallowing of the tongue he can drink amaravaruni. I consider him of high lineage (heritage). Others destroy the heritage. 118

(3:40) One who knows khechari mudra is unafflicted by disease, unaffected by the laws of cause and effect (karma) and free from the bonds of time (death). 119

(3:41) Mind moves in Brahman (khe) because the tongue moves in space (khe). Therefore, the perfected ones have named this mudra khechari, moving in space, or Brahman. 119

(3:54) There is only one seed of creation and one mudra – khechari; one deva independent of everything, and one state – manonmani. 120

4. Kaya Mudra: Postural Mudras

(3:80) Digestion is strengthened by continual, regular practice and therefore, the practitioner should always have sufficient food. If one takes only a little food, the heat produced by the digestion will destroy the system. 138

(3:81)Therefore, on the first day, one should only stay a moment with the feet up and head down. The practice should be done daily, gradually increasing the duration. 138

(3:82) After six months of practise, grey hairs and wrinkles become inconspicuous. One who practises it for a yama (three hours) conquers death. 139

(3:78) There is a wonderful means by which the nectar is averted from falling into the opening of the sun. This is obtained by the guru's instructions and not from the hundreds of shastras (treatises). 139

312

(3:79) With the navel region above and the palate below, the sun is above and the moon below. It is called vipareeta karani, the reversing process. When given by the guru's instructions, it is fruitful.   140

5. Bandha Mudra: Lock Mudras

(3:30) These are the three great secrets which destroy old age and death, increase the digestive fire and bestow the siddhis of anima, etc.   147

(3:31) They should be done daily at every yama (three hour period). They bring out the virtues and destroy vices. Those who have perfect instructions should practise them gradually.   147

(3:10) Press the left heel into the perineum (or vagina), straighten the right leg, and with the hands, firmly take hold of the outstretched foot.   149

(3:11) By locking the throat and retaining the breath, the prana rises straight, just like a snake beaten with a stick becomes straight.   149

(3:12) So the kundalini shakti becomes straight at once. Then the two (ida and pingala) become lifeless as the shakti enters sushumna.   149

(3:13) Then exhale slowly and gradually, not quickly. Indeed this is described as maha mudra by the great siddhas.   149

(3:15) After practising on the left side, practise on the right side. When the number of rounds is even, discontinue and release the mudra.   149

(3:16) For one who practises maha mudra, there is nothing wholesome or unwholesome. Anything can be consumed, even the deadliest of poisons is digested like nectar.   150

(3:17) Abdominal disorders, constipation, indigestion and leprosy, etc., are alleviated by the practice of maha mudra. 150

(3:14) Maha mudra removes the worst afflictions (the five kleshas) and the cause of death. Therefore it is called 'the great attitude' by the ones of highest knowledge.   152

(3:18) Thus maha mudra has been described as the giver of great siddhis. It must be kept secret and not disclosed to anyone.   152

313

6. Adhara Mudra: Perineal Mudras

314

7. The Bandhas

(3:74) By contracting the perineum, performing uddiyana and locking ida and pingala with jalandhara, sushumna becomes active. 234

(3:75) By this means (maha bandha) the prana and breath become still. Thus death, old age and sickness are conquered. 236

(3:76) The great siddhas practise these three best bandhas. Of all the sadhanas in hatha yoga and tantra, the yogis know this practice (maha bandha). 237

8. Effects of the Bandhas

(1:42) Thus, through securing siddhasana, the three bandhas occur by themselves. 241

(3:65) With constant practice of moola bandha, prana and apana unite, urine and stool are decreased and even an old person becomes young. 245

(3:66) Apana moves up into the region of fire (manipura chakra, the navel centre), then the flames of the fire grow, being fanned by apana vayu. 245

(3:67) Then, when apana and the fire meet with prana, which is itself hot, the heat in the body is intensified. 245

(3:116) Contracting the sun in manipura, kundalini should be moved. Even if such a person should be on the verge of death, where is the need to fear death? 246

HATHARATNAVALI OF SRINIVASA BHATTA MAHAYOGINDRA

4. Kaya Mudras: Postural Mudras

(2:66) All the nectar that flows from the splendid moon (in the throat) is swallowed up by the sun (at the navel) and it is for this reason that the body gets old. 132

(2:67) There is a superb practice which binds the mouth of the sun in the navel. It can only be known from the instructions of a guru, not from millions of discussions. 132

(2:68) The practice in which the navel is above and the palate below, the sun above and the moon below, is known

as vipareeta karani. It can only be learnt from the words
uttered by the guru.   132

(2:69) This vipareeta karani destroys all sorts of diseases.
It increases the gastric heat of a regular practitioner.   139

(2:70) One who practises it (daily) should procure and eat
ample food. If he eats insufficient food, the increasing fire
soon consumes his body.   139

(2:71) On the first day one should remain for a very short
time with one's head below and feet above. The duration
of this practise should be increased day by day.   140

6. Adhara Mudra: Perineal Mudras

(2:74) Now I will talk about vajroli which is kept secret by
all yogis. The secret process of this should not be revealed
to an unsuitable person.   181

(2:75) The person whom the guru feels to be like his own
prana, verily it should be told to him. It should not be given
even to one's own son without the guru-disciple tradition. 181

(2:103) The lady who does not know the science of yoga
should not practise vajroli. This yoga is successful to the
courageous and the pious yogis who have an insight into
reality.   181

(2:104) Success in yoga can be achieved only by those who
are in no way selfish. It cannot be achieved by self-seeking
ones. This yoga is auspicious among all the yogas.   181

(2:93) Rajas is permanent, like red lead, in the reproductive
organ of a woman. The rajas should be saved during
menstruation like bindu is to be saved. The woman should
practise vajroli.   183

(2:101) After that she should draw up the rajas if possible.
The nada in her body moves like bindu.   183

(2:102) Bindu and rajas produced in the body should be
mixed through the vajroli practice of yoga. Then success
is at hand.   183

(2:92) Therefore, semen as well as chitta (consciousness)
should be preserved with effort. The person should love
mentally that lady only, with whom he practices vajroli.   198

7. The Bandhas

(2:59) By contraction (of the perineum) the apana vayu, of which the natural course is downwards, is forcefully (though cautiously) directed upwards. The yogis proclaim this action to be moola bandha. 215

(2:60) Prana and apana, nada and bindu, having attained union through moola bandha, the yogi attains perfection in yoga. There is no doubt about it. 215

(2:61) Urine and ordure diminish because of the union of apana and prana. By constant practise of moola bandha even old persons become young. 215

(2:62) When the apana rises up and reaches the sphere of the fire (the navel region) the flames of the fire blaze, fanned by the vayu. 215

(2:63) Just as a female serpent (straightens up) with a hiss when beaten by a stick, such a female serpent (kundalini) entering into the hole (sushumna) does not move anywhere. 216

(2:48) Just as the beauty and charm of a wife serve no purpose in the absence of the husband, similarly maha mudra and maha bandha unaccompanied by vedha, are futile. 236

JNANARNAVA TANTRA

6. Adhara Mudra: Perineal Mudras

(Ch 22) After realizing the exact knowledge of dharma and adharma (healthy and unhealthy lifestyle), every aspect of the (material) world becomes holy: stool, urine, nails, bone, all are holy aspects in the sight of that person who has explored mantra. O Parvati, deities (divine powers) are living in that water from which urine is made, then why is urine said to be contaminated? 166

SHIVA SAMHITA

1. Understanding Mudra

(4:13) When the sleeping goddess Kundalini is awakened through the grace of guru, then all the lotuses and the bonds are readily pierced through and through. 14

(4:14) Therefore, in order that the goddess, who is asleep in the mouth of the brahmarandhra (the innermost hollow of sushumna) be awakened, the mudras should be practised with the greatest care.   14

3. Mana Mudra: Head Mudras

(3:70) When the skillfull yogi, knowing the laws of the action of prana and apana, can drink the cold air through the contraction of the mouth in the form of a crow's bill, then he becomes entitled to liberation.   60

(3:74) When he drinks the air through the crow bill, both in the morning and in the evening twilight, contemplating that it goes to the mouth of the kundalini, consumption of the lungs is cured.   61

(3:75) When the wise yogi drinks the fluid day and night through the crow beak, his diseases are destroyed: he acquires certainly the powers of clairaudience and clairvoyance.   61

(5:22) Let him close the ears with his thumbs, the eyes with index fingers, the nostril with the middle fingers, and with the remaining four fingers let him press together the upper and lower lips. The yogi, by having thus firmly confined the air, sees his soul in the shape of light.   65

(5:23) When one sees, without obstruction, this light for even a moment, becoming free from sin, he reaches the highest end.   65

(5:24) The yogi, free from sin, and practising this (shanmukhi) continually, forgets his physical, subtle and causal bodies, and becomes one with that soul.   65

(5:25) He who practises this in secrecy, is absorbed in the Brahman, though he had been engaged in sinful works.   65

(5:26) This should be kept secret; it at once produces conviction; it gives nirvana to mankind. This is my most beloved yoga. From practising this (shanmukhi) gradually, the yogi begins to hear the mystic sounds.   66

(5:27) The first sound is like the hum of the honey-intoxicated bee, next that of a flute, then of a harp; after this, by the gradual practice of yoga, the destroyer of the darkness of the world, he hears the sounds of ringing bells; then sounds like the roar of thunder. When one fixes his full attention on this sound, being free from fear, he gets absorption, O my beloved! 66

(5:28) When the mind of the yogi is exceedingly engaged in this sound, he forgets all external things, and is absorbed in this sound. 67

(4:31) The wise yogi, sitting in vajrasana posture, in a place free from all disturbance, should firmly fix his gaze on the spot in the middle of the two eyebrows, and reversing the tongue backwards, fix it in the hollow under the epiglottis, placing it with great care on the mouth of the well of nectar. This mudra, described by me at the request of my devotees, is the khechari mudra. 92

(4:32) O my beloved! Know this to be the source of all success, always practising it let him drink the ambrosia daily. By this he obtains vigraha siddhi (power over the microcosm), even as a lion over the elephant of death. 93

(4:33) Whether pure or impure, in whatever condition one may be, if success be obtained in khechari, he becomes pure. 93

(4:34) One who practises it even for a moment crosses the great ocean of sins, and having enjoyed the pleasures of deva world, is born into a noble family. 93

(4:35) One who practises this khechari mudra calmly and without laziness counts as seconds the period of hundred Brahmas. 93

(4:36) One knows this khechari mudra according to the instructions of his guru, obtains the highest end, though immersed in great sins. 93

(4:37) O, ye adored of gods! This mudra, dear as life, should not be given to everybody; it should be kept concealed with great care. 93

(3:72) Pointing the tongue upwards, when the yogi can drink the nectar flowing from the moon (situated between the two eyebrows), within a month he certainly would conquer death. 94

321

(3:73) When having firmly closed the glottis by the proper yogic method, and contemplating on the goddess Kundalini, he drinks (the moon fluid of immortality), he becomes a sage or poet within six months. 108

5. Bandha Mudra: Lock Mudras

(4:16) My dearest, I shall now describe to you the maha mudra, from whose knowledge the ancient sages Kapila and others obtained success in yoga. 148

(4:18) In this way, even the most unfortunate yogi might obtain success. By this means all the vessels of the body are roused and stirred into activity; the life is increased and its decay is checked, and all sins are destroyed. All diseases are healed, and the gastric fire is increased. It gives faultless beauty to the body, and destroys decay and death. All fruits of desires and pleasures are obtained, and the senses are conquered. The yogi fixed in meditation acquires all the above-mentioned things, through practice. There should be no hesitation in doing so. 151

(4:23) Oh goddess of the three worlds! When the yogi, while performing maha bandha, causes the union of the prana and apana vayus and filling the viscera with air drives it slowly towards the buttocks, it is called maha vedha. 158

(3:24) The best of the yogis having, through the help of the vayu pierced with this perforator the knot which is in the path of sushumna, should then pierce the knot of Brahma. 158

(4:57) He who practises shakti chalana properly for two seconds, and with care, is very near to success. This mudra should be practised by the yogi in the proper posture. 164

6. Adhara Mudra: Perineal Mudras

(4:86) Know that the seminal fluid is the moon and the ovarian fluid is the sun. It is necessary to coalesce the two within one's own body. 190

(4:87) In fact I (Shiva) am the seminal fluid and the ovarian fluid is Shakti. When the two are united in the body of the yogi, he attains a divine body. 190

7. The Bandhas

(4:41) Pressing well the perineum with the heel, forcibly draw upwards the apana vayu slowly by practice. This is described as moola bandha – the destroyer of decay and death.   207

(4:49) The yogi who always practises it four times a day, purifies thereby his navel, through which the winds (pranas) are purified.   229

(4:50) By practising for six months, the yogi certainly conquers death; the gastric fire is kindled and there takes place an increase in the fluids of the body.   229

(4:21) Then (after mahamudra), having extended the (right) foot, place it on the (left) thigh; contract the perineum, and draw the apana vayu upwards and join it with the samana vayu; bend the prana vayu downwards, and then let the wise yogi bind them in trinity in the navel. I have told you now the maha bandha, which shows the way to emancipation. By this, all the fluids in the vessels of the body of the yogi are propelled towards the head. This should be practised with great care, alternately with both feet.   235

(4:27) The maha mudra and maha bandha become fruitless if they are not followed by maha vedha; therefore, the yogi should practise all these three successively with great care.   237

(4:22) Through this practice, the wind (prana) enters the middle channel of the sushumna, the body is invigorated by it, the bones are firmly knitted, the heart of the yogi becomes full (of cheerfulness). By this bandha, the great yogi accomplishes all his desires.   238

YOGA CHUDAMANI UPANISHAD

5. Bandha Mudras: Lock Mudras

(v. 65) The method taught for purification of the entire nadi structure governing the movement of the moon and the sun and absorption of the vital fluid is maha mudra.   152

(v. 70) The maha mudra, which was mentioned earlier, is the bestower of great powers for men. It should be kept secret, with care, and not taught to anyone.   153

(v. 107) Closing the nine gates properly and retaining the breath, intensify the concentration. Performing shakti chalini mudra correctly, take the divine element, kundalini, along with apana vayu and fire (samana vayu) to the (crown of the) head. By this method become absorbed in meditation on the Self. When steadiness and stillness are achieved, while remaining in that state, the company of great men is not needed.   160

7. The Bandhas
(v. 40) Sit in padmasana, crossing the legs with the hands pressed firmly on the knees. Press the chin firmly against the chest and meditate on That (Brahman). Again and again breathe in and out, and raise the apana force to the region of prana, filling it fully. In this way, with the help of Shakti the practitioner acquires infinite knowledge.   219

YOGA SUTRAS OF SAGE PATANJALI

1. Understanding Mudra
(1:24) God is a special soul untouched by afflictions, acts, their traces and their fruits.   37

Glossary

Adhara – basis, that which supports, foundation, substratum, receptacle; the sixteen specific bases or chakras in the body.

Adharma – disharmony; not fulfilling one's natural role in life; unrighteousness. See Dharma.

Adi – first, primary, original.

Adinath – literally, 'first lord'; primordial guru of all; cosmic consciousness; name of Lord Shiva given by the Nath sect of yogis; first guru of the Nath yogis.

Agni – fire; the god of fire.

Agni mandala – literally, 'zone of fire'; in the body relates to solar plexus and the digestive fire.

Agni tattwa – fire element; fire principle. See Tattwa.

Agnisar kriya – a breathing technique which strengthens the diaphragm and lower stomach region and awakens the digestive fire.

Ahamkara – faculty of ego, awareness of the existence of 'I'; one of the four parts of the antahkarana or inner instrument. See Antahkarana.

Ajna chakra – psychic/pranic centre situated at the medulla oblongata at the top of the spinal column in the midbrain; seat of intuition, higher knowledge; third eye.

Akasha – space.

Akasha tattwa – space element; ether principle. See Tattwa.

Amaroli – drinking of one's own urine in order to detoxify the body and develop immunity, stamina and vitality.

Amrita – the nectar of immortality which descends from bindu visarga.

Anahata chakra – psychic/pranic centre situated in the spine behind the sternum; associated physically with the cardiac plexus, heart and lungs, mentally with emotion, especially love, and spiritually with atma, the spirit.

Ananda – pure bliss; natural state of consciousness.

Anandamaya kosha – sheath or body of bliss; the innermost wrapper or sheath of the embodied spirit. See Kosha.

Anima siddhi – the power of wilfully making the body small like an atom; the power of making the body subtle. One of the eight major siddhis. See Siddhi.

Annamaya kosha – sheath or body of matter; the sphere of existence created by food, maintained by food and which ultimately becomes food, i.e. the body. See Kosha.

Antahkarana – literally, 'inner tool', experienced or manifest mind, consisting of: ahamkara, manas, buddhi and chitta.

Antar kumbhaka – internal breath retention; suspension of breath after a full inhalation.

Anubhooti – experience, perception, understanding.

Apana vayu – one of the pancha pranas or vayus, it is located between the navel and the perineum. It flows downward and controls elimination and reproduction.

Apara – ordinary; opposite of para; material dimension; worldly knowledge. See Para.

Apas – water.

Apas tattwa – water element, water principle. See Tattwa.

Arjuna – name of the third Pandava brother, who was the son of Lord Indra and Kunti. In the *Bhagavad Gita* he received a divine revelation from Sri Krishna.

Arohan – ascending; ascending energy flow in the subtle body; counterpart of awarohan.

Asana – a specific yoga posture; used in hatha yoga to channel prana, open the chakras and remove energy blocks; in raja yoga, a physical posture in which one is at ease and in harmony with oneself.

Atma roopi ishwara – God in the form of the soul or spirit.

Atma shakti – the power of the atma; spiritual energy.

Atma, atman – the self beyond mind and body; principle of life, highest reality, Supreme Consciousness, spirit, soul.

Aum – the universal cosmic mantra representing the four states of consciousness; the sound indicating the Supreme Reality or Brahman; conveys concepts of omniscience, omnipresence and omnipotence.

Avastha – state of consciousness or condition of the mind; states of mind in nada yoga practice according to *Hatha Yoga Pradipika*.

Awarohan – descending; descending energy flow in the subtle body; counterpart of arohan.

Bahir kumbhaka – external breath retention; suspension of breath after a full exhalation.

Bhagavad Gita – literally, 'divine song'; Sri Krishna's discourse to his disciple Arjuna delivered on the battlefield of Kurukshetra at the commencement of the great Mahabharata war; one of the source books of Hindu philosophy, containing the essence of the Upanishads and yoga.

Bhairava – the name of Lord Shiva in his fierce aspect; state of consciousness which preceds the ultimate experience of universal consciousness or Shiva.

Bhairavi – Bhairavi is Shiva's consort or Shakti, i.e. the power that manifests this particular aspect of existence. See Bhairava.

Bhakta – devotee.

Bhakti – intense inner devotion in which the intellect, emotions and self are channelled towards a relationship with the divine.

Bhakti yoga – branch of yoga in which emotional energy is channelled towards a divine relationship; a systematic path with nine stages which expand, strengthen, and purify the emotions.

Bhalarandhra – the forehead; the depression above the nose just above the eyebrow centre.

Bharat natyam – an Indian dance style.

Bhava, bhavana – feeling; condition; attitude; inclination or disposition of mind.

Bhoga – sensual enjoyment; external experience.

Bhogi – a person with gross mentality and materialistic tendencies; sensualist; an individual involved in karma for personal satisfaction and not for inner purification.

Bhopura – specific diagrammatic parts of a yantra; the symbolic 'walls' protecting the sides of the yantra.

Bhrumadhya – trigger point for ajna chakra located at the eyebrow centre.

Bhuh tattwa – earth element; also called prithvi tattwa.

Bija – seed; seed state; source, origin.

Bija mantra – seed sound; a basic mantra or syllable.

Bindu – point; seed, source, drop; point of potential energy and consciousness, used in kriya yoga; the basis from which emanated the first principle according to the tantra shastra; nucleus; psychic centre located in the brain; in tantra and hatha yoga it also represents a drop of semen.

Bindu chakra – Another name for bindu visarga. See Bindu visarga.

Bindu visarga – point at the top back of the head from where amrit, the nectar or elixir of life, is secreted; centre or source of individual creation from where psychic vibrations first emanate; also known as bindu chakra.

Brahma – god of the Hindu trinity who creates the universe; God as creator; manifest force of life and creation; ever-expanding, limitless consciousness; absolute reality.

Brahma granthi – psychic/muscular 'knot' of creation, situated in mooladhara chakra, symbolizing material and sensual attachment.

Brahma nadi – the most subtle pranic flow within sushumna nadi, the innermost layer of sushumna.

Brahmachari – one who practises brahmacharya; one who moves in consciousness of the true reality, Brahman; a person in the first quarter of life; one who preserves sexual energy; a celibate.

Brahmacharya – being absorbed in higher consciousness; sublimation of sexual energy for spiritual development; celibacy; conduct suitable for proceeding to the highest state of existence; one of the five yamas described by Sage Patanjali in the *Yoga Sutras* as a preliminary practice of yoga.

Brahmacharyasana – celibate's pose; an important pose for the conservation of sexual energy for spiritual purposes; also called vajroni mudra.

Brahmadvara – literally, 'the door or gate to Brahma', where kundalini enters sushumna nadi. According to the yogic viewpoint this is the door which exists between the experiences of the materialistic and spiritual worlds.

Brahmarandhra – crown of the head; the fontanelle; opening in the crown of the head through which the soul is said to escape on leaving the body.

Brahmin – the priestly caste; one whose consciousness is immersed in Brahman.

Buddhi – discerning, discriminating aspect of the mind; aspect of the mind closest to pure consciousness; one of the four parts of the antahkarana or inner instrument. See Antahkarana.

Chakra – circle, wheel or vortex; pranic/psychic centre; confluence point of energy flows (nadis) in the body; the seven major chakras for descent of divine energy or for human evolution are sahasrara, ajna, vishuddhi, anahata, manipura, swadhisthana and mooladhara.

Chandra – moon; representing the mental energy.

Chandra nadi – another name for ida nadi. See Ida nadi.

Chaturvarga – the four aims of human life, viz. material security (artha), fulfillment of desire (kama), righteousness (dharma) and spiritual liberation (moksha); also called purushartha.

Chetana – consciousness.

Chidakasha – the space of consciousness; the inner space visualized in meditation behind the closed eyes or in the region of ajna chakra.

Chinmaya – supreme intelligence; manifested consciousness; underlying consciousness behind the phenomenal world.

Chitta – individual consciousness, including the subconscious and unconscious layers of mind; thinking, concentration, attention, enquiry; storehouse of memory or samskaras; one of the four parts of the antahkarana or inner instrument. See Antahkarana.

Chitta shakti – the power of pure consciousness; mental force governing the subtle dimensions.

Chitta vritti – manifestations of the mind, disposition or state of the mind; inclination.

Dakini – the goddess of the skin, of the sense of touch who resides in mooladhara chakra.

Dehadhyasa – identification with the body.

Deva – being of light; divine being.

Devata – form of divine dignity or power; divine being representing the higher states of evolution.

Devi – female deity, goddess.

Dharana – practice of concentration or complete attention; sixth stage of ashtanga yoga described in Sage Patanjali's *Yoga Sutras* as holding or binding the mind to one point.

Dharma – the natural role one plays in life; ethical law; duty; the laws or fundamental support of life; righteousness.

Dhyana – spontaneous state of meditation; one-pointedness of mind through concentration on either a form, thought or sound; absorption in the object of meditation; seventh stage of Sage Patanjali's ashtanga yoga.

Dohan – milking; massage of the tongue in 'milking' movements.

Dosha – three humours of the body described in Ayurveda: mucus (kapha), bile (pitta) and wind (vata). Their imbalance prevents the flow of energy in sushumna nadi.

Drashta – witness, uninvolved observer, onlooker, seer; the consciousness which knows what is going on; the inner self.

Drishti – seeing, viewing, knowing.

Ekanta – solitary; aside, apart; absolute; invariable, perpetual.

Gandhari nadi – one of the seven lesser nadis flowing from the left eye to the left big toe. It is situated by the side of ida nadi and helps support it.

Garima siddhi – the power of making the body heavy at will. One of the eight major siddhis. See Siddhi.

Ghariya – a period of ninety minutes; the twenty-four hours of a day is divided into sixteen parts according to the yoga shastras.

Ghati – time measure equal to 24 minutes.

Gheranda Samhita – traditional text on hatha yoga by Sage Gheranda. It explains seven limbs (saptanga) of yoga: shatkarma, asana, mudra, pratyahara, pranayama, dhyana and samadhi.

Gheranda, Sage – author of *Gheranda Samhita*, a classical yoga text which describes seven limbs of yoga.

Go – the tongue; an organ of sense; indriya; cow.

Gorakhnath, Yogi – founder of the Nath sect; author of *Gorakhsha Samhita*.

Gorakhsha Samhita – ancient hatha yoga text, ascribed to Yogi Gorakhnath, founder of the Nath sect.

Granthi – psychic knot; the three granthis on the sushumna nadi which hinder the upward passage of kundalini, viz. Brahma granthi, Vishnu granthi and Rudra granthi. See Brahma granthi. See Rudra granthi. See Vishnu granthi.

Gupta nadi – a pranic channel running from the knees across the inside of the thighs into the perineum.

Guru – one who dispels the darkness caused by ignorance (avidya); teacher of the science of ultimate reality who by the light of his own atma can dispel darkness, ignorance and illusion from the mind and enlighten the consciousness of a devotee/disciple; preceptor.

Ha – seed mantra of solar energy, pranic force (pingala nadi); represents sun; first syllable of the word 'hatha'. See Tha.

Ham – mantra produced by the breath, unconsciously repeated on exhalation; representing individual consciousness; bija mantra of the space element and vishuddhi chakra. See So. See Soham.

Hamsa – mantra used in ajapa japa; correlate of the mantra Soham. See Soham.

Hastijihva nadi – one of the seven lesser nadis flowing from the right eye to the left big toe. Along with gandhari nadi it helps support ida nadi.

Hatha yoga – a system of yoga specifically using practices for bodily purification; yoga of attaining physical and mental purity and balancing the prana (energy) in ida and pingala nadis so that sushumna nadi opens, enabling the experiences of samadhi. See Ha. See Tha.

Hatha Yoga Pradipika – a major classical text on hatha yoga compiled by Yogi Swatmarama, usually translated as 'Light on Hatha Yoga'.

Hatharatnavali – a late medieval treatise on hatha yoga and tantra by Srinivasa Bhatta Mahayogindra.

Hoom – a bija mantra.

Hrid – interior of the body; the heart; core.

Iccha – wish, desire, will.

Iccha shakti – creative force or that desire which is the first manifestation of the greater mind.

Ida nadi – a major pranic channel running from the left side of mooladhara chakra to the left side of ajna chakra, governing the left side of the body and the right side of the brain. The ida energy flow criss-crosses the spine through the major chakras between mooladhara and ajna, conducting the passive aspect of prana manifesting as the mental force, lunar force or chitta shakti; also called chandra nadi as the lunar energy flows through it.

Indriya – sense organ; power of the senses; power.

Ishitva siddhi – the power to wilfully create and destroy. One of the eight major siddhis. See Siddhi.

Ishta devata – personal deity, one's favourite symbol of the Supreme.

Ishwara – higher reality; God; non-changing, indestructible principle or quality.

Jala tattwa – water element, water principle. See Tattwa.

Japa – a meditation practice involving repetition of a mantra.

Jiva – principle of life; individual or personal soul; living being.

332

Jivatma – individual or personal soul.

Jnana – knowledge, cognition, wisdom; higher knowledge derived from meditation or from inner experience.

Jnana yoga – yoga of knowledge and wisdom attained through spontaneous self-analysis and study of scriptures; leading a discriminative lifestyle, living with wisdom.

Jnanendriya – organ of sense perceptions and knowledge; five in number, viz. ears, eyes, nose, tongue and skin.

Jyoti – a small flame; light, brightness; fire.

Kabir Das – (b. 1440–d. 1518) a poet and mystic, his teachings blend Hinduism, Sufism and Bhakti.

Kaivalya – final liberation; highest state of samadhi; that state of consciousness which is beyond duality.

Kali Yuga – the present age, last of the four ages or cycles in the Day of Brahma and Maha Yuga, which began in 3,102 BC and has a duration of 432,000 years. During this cycle man is collectively at the height of technology, decadence, dishonesty and corruption of spiritual awareness; dark, evil, difficult and full of strife.

Kama – emotional, sensual fulfillment; love; lust; one of the four purusharthas. See Purushartha.

Kapha – mucus, phlegm, one of the three humours (doshas) described in Ayurveda; associated with the water element. See Dosha.

Karana sharira – causal body; also called anandamaya kosha.

Karma – action and result; law of cause and effect.

Karma bhoomi – land of action; the earthly plane.

Karma yoga – yogic path of action; union with the Supreme Consciousness through action; action without attachment to the fruits of action.

Karmakshetra – the field or sphere of action.

Karmendriya – motor organ; there are five physical organs of action, viz. vocal cords, hands, feet, genital organ and anus.

Kayakalpa – rejuvenation; intensive purificatory practice; transformation of the body.

Khe – literally 'in space'; from the word 'kham' meaning space, unlimited space; limitless existence; Brahman.

Klesha – pain, affliction, suffering; five afflictions or causes of suffering described in Sage Patanjali's *Yoga Sutras*, viz. avidya (ignorance), asmita (sense of 'I' identity), raga (attraction), dwesha (aversion), and abhinivesha (fear of death); in yoga the five kleshas are the sources of all suffering or troubles, with ignorance being considered the chief klesha.

Kosha – sheath or body; a dimension of experience and existence. The five koshas are: annamaya kosha, pranamaya kosha, manomaya kosha, vijnanamaya kosha, and anandamaya kosha.

Krishna, Sri – literally, 'black' or 'dark'; eighth incarnation of Vishnu; avatara who descended in the Dwapara Yuga. Sri Krishna is perhaps the most celebrated hero in Hindu mythology and seems to be an historical figure. To uphold dharma he orchestrated the Mahabharata war. His teachings to his friend and disciple Arjuna during that war are immortalized in the *Bhagavad Gita*.

Kriya – action; cleansing practice (shatkarma); practice of kriya yoga.

Kriya yoga – practices of kundalini yoga designed to speed the evolution of humanity.

Kshetram – field, ground; place of origin, womb; chakra trigger points located in the frontal psychic passage.

Kumbhaka – internal or external retention of the breath.

Kundalini – the evolutionary energy in a human being; spiritual energy; Devi described as the potential energy of a human being dormant in mooladhara chakra, which when awakened, awakens the chakras, resulting in progressive enlightenment.

Kundalini yoga – path of yoga which awakens the dormant spiritual force, kundalini. See Kundalini.

Laghima siddhi – the power of wilfully making the body light. One of the eight major siddhis. See Siddhi.

Lakshmi – wealth; good fortune, good luck; loveliness, grace; success, accomplishment; the goddess of fortune, prosperity and beauty, the consort of Vishnu.

Lalana chakra – minor chakra at the back of the throat above the palate where nectar (amrit) can be collected as it falls from bindu visarga, closely associated with vishuddhi chakra.

Lam – bija mantra of the earth element and of mooladhara chakra.

Laya – dissolution; union, fusion.

Laya yoga – literally, 'union by absorption'; yoga of conscious dissolution of individuality.

Loka – place, region; realm or plane of existence, dimension; the seven highest planes of consciousness or regions are called loka; seven divine regions said to be above sahasrara chakra.

Madya – wine; one of the panchamakara of tantra. See Panchamakara.

Maha bindu – great nucleus, source; the entire conscious creation; the point where consciousness and energy, Shiva and Shakti, meet at the universal level (for bindu is both macrocosmic and microcosmic). See Bindu.

Mahavakya – great saying or teaching; the four great statements of the Upanishads.

Mahesha – a name of Lord Shiva.

Maheshwara – great lord, sovereign; name of Shiva. See Ishwara.

Mahima siddhi – the power of wilfully making the body large. One of the eight major siddhis. See Siddhi.

Maithuna – physical union; the first basic instinct; copulation; fusion of male and female energies; one of the panchamakara of tantra. See Panchamakara.

Mala – garland; rosary used to aid mantra repetition.

Mamsa – flesh; meat; one of the panchamakara of tantra. See Panchamakara.

Mana – head.

Manas – finite mind, rational mind; the mind concerned with senses, thought and counter-thought; perception, intelligence; one of the four parts of the antahkarana or inner instrument. See Antahkarana.

Manas shakti – mental energy.

Mandala – visual image, form or symbol which one may visualize or concentrate on, externally or internally; may be two or three-dimensional; circular symbolic pictorial depiction of cosmic power and/or the human psyche.

Manipura chakra – literally, 'city of jewels'; psychic/pranic centre situated in the spine behind the navel; associated with the solar plexus and digestive organs and mentally with willpower; source of vitality and energy.

Manomaya kosha – mental sheath or body; mental sphere of life and awareness. See Kosha.

Manonmani – absence of individual mind.

Mantra – words of power; sound vibrations which liberate the mind when repeated.

Matsya – fish; one of the panchamakara of tantra. See Panchamakara.

Maya – means by which Brahman creates the phenomenal world; power of creation; illusive power; in Vedanta philosophy, the two powers of maya are: 1. the power of veiling, and 2. the power of projection; in Samkhya philosophy, another name for Prakriti.

Mayurasana – peacock pose; an advanced yogasana which exerts pressure on the abdominal region.

Mirabai – (born 1502) Indian poet saint devoted to Sri Krishna.

Moksha – liberation from the cycles of birth and death and the illusion of maya; one of the four purusharthas. See Purushartha.

Mooladhara chakra – the lowest psychic/pranic centre in the human body; situated in the perineal floor in men and the cervix in women; associated physically with the coccygeal plexus, excretory and reproductive organs, and mentally with the instinctive nature; spiritually it is the seat of kundalini.

Mouna – silence; measured speech.

Mudra – gesture; psychic, emotional, devotional, and aesthetic gestures; attitudes of energy intended to link individual pranic force with universal or cosmic force; grain, one of the panchamakara of tantra.

336

Mukti – release, liberation, final absolution of the consciousness from the chain of birth and death and from the illusion of maya.

Nada – sound; subtle sound or vibration created by the union of the Shiva and Shakti tattwas; the first manifestation of the unmanifest Absolute.

Nada yoga – the process of penetrating deeper and deeper into the nature of one's own reality by listening to subtle inner sounds.

Nadi – flow; a river or channel of energy; psychic current; subtle channel in the pranic body, conducting the flow of shakti; comparable to the meridians of acupuncture.

Nadi shodhana pranayama – nadi purification; a pranayama designed to purify and balance the two main energy flows of the body, ida and pingala nadis.

Narayana – epithet of Lord Vishnu, the god of the Hindu trinity who is the supporter of life.

Nasikagra – tip of the nose.

Nasikagra drishti – nosetip gazing; a practice to stimulate mooladhara chakra.

Natya – dance.

Nauli – abdominal massaging; one of the shatkarmas in which the rectus abdominis muscles are contracted and isolated vertically.

Nirbija – seedless, without any seed.

Nirvana – cessation of suffering; final liberation or emancipation in Buddhist thought.

Nitya – continual, perpetual, constant, uninterrupted, everlasting, eternal.

Niyama – observance of rules or rules of personal discipline to render the mind tranquil in preparation for meditation; the second step of the eight limbs (ashtanga yoga) of Sage Patanjali in the *Yoga Sutras*: shaucha (purity), santosha (contentment), tapas (austerity), swadhyaya (self-study) and Ishwara pranidhana (surrender to God).

Nyasa – a specific system of tantra; a practice of assigning the various parts of the body to different deities, usually accompanied with mantras and gestures or mudras.

Ojas – vitality, sublimated sexual energy, bodily strength, vigour, energy; virility, the generative faculty; kundalini shakti; splendour, light.

Om – See Aum.

Padmasana – lotus pose; classical meditative posture.

Pancha – five.

Pancha bhuta – the five elements (tattwas).

Pancha dharana – five kinds of concentration on the five elements.

Pancha kosha – the five koshas. See Kosha.

Pancha prana – five major divisions of the pranic energy located in the physical body, viz. apana, prana, samana, udana, vyana; also called vayu.

Pancha tattwa – the five elements, consisting of ether or space (akasha), gases or air (vayu), light or fire (agni), liquids or water (apas) and solids or earth (prithvi).

Panchamakara – five elements used in tantric sadhana, all of which begin with the letter 'M', viz. mudra (grain), mamsa (flesh), maithuna (physical union), matsya (fish) and madya (wine). The category of aspirant determines the symbolic interpretation.

Para – supreme dimension, the atma, soul or self. See Apara.

Paramatma – cosmic Soul or Consciousness; Supreme Self; the atma of the entire universe; God.

Paramshakti – supreme shakti or energy; kundalini.

Parvati – goddess and consort of Shiva, mother of Ganesha and Kartikeya.

Paschimottanasana – back stretching pose; a forward bending posture.

Patanjali, Sage – author of the *Yoga Sutras*; an ancient rishi who codified the system of raja yoga, including ashtanga yoga.

Pingala nadi – a major pranic channel in the body which conducts the dynamic pranic force manifesting as prana shakti from the right side of mooladhara chakra, criss-crossing the spine through the major chakras to the right side of ajna chakra; associated with the mundane realm of experience and externalized awareness; also called surya nadi as the solar energy flows through it.

Pitta – bile, one of the three humours (doshas) described in Ayurveda; associated with the fire element. See Dosha.

Pooraka – the first stage of pranayama; breathing in.

Prakamya siddhi – the power of unobstructed fulfilment of desire. One of the eight major siddhis. See Siddhi.

Prakash – light, brightness, shining, brilliance.

Prakriti – individual nature; nature; manifest and unmanifest nature composed of the three gunas; the active principle of manifest energy; counterpart of purusha in Samkhya philosophy. See Samkhya.

Prana – vital energy force sustaining life and creation, permeating the whole of creation and existing in both the macrocosmos and microcosmos.

Prana shakti – energy; dynamic solar force governing the dimension of matter; energy flow related to externalization of mind; the force of prana.

Prana vayu – pranic air current; also refers to a specific current, one of the pancha pranas or vayus, located in the thoracic region, from the throat to the diaphragm, responsible for processes of inspiration and absorption.

Prana vidya – knowledge and control of prana; a healing technique involving awareness and movement of prana.

Pranamaya kosha – energy sheath, or vital pranic body; the sheath covering the self which is composed of pranic vibration and the rhythm of pranic forces. See Kosha.

Pranayama – a series of techniques using the breath to control the flow of prana within the body.

Pranotthana – awakening of the pranas in the different nadis and chakras; a stage of awakening preparatory to kundalini awakening.

Prapti siddhi – the power of acquiring everything. One of the eight major siddhis. See Siddhi.

Prasad – favour, grace; blessed gift or object, something full of grace.

Pratyahara – restraining the sensory and motor organs; withdrawal and emancipation of the mind from the domination of the senses and sensual objects; training the senses to follow the mind within; fifth stage of ashtanga yoga described by Sage Patanjali in the *Yoga Sutras*.

Prithvi – earth.

Prithvi tattwa – earth element, earth principle. See Tattwa.

Puranas – eighteen ancient texts containing the earliest mythology of the tantric and vedic traditions.

Purusha – literally, 'the one who lives in the city (of the body)'; the soul; pure consciousness according to Samkhya philosophy, undefiled and unlimited by contact with prakriti or matter; can also refer to a man or a human being. See Samkhya.

Purushartha – human attainment; self-effort; the four basic needs or desires to be fulfilled in life, viz. artha (wealth), kama (desire), dharma (duty), moksha (liberation).

Raja yoga – the supreme yoga; union through control of the mental processes and concentration of the mind; the most authoritative text is Sage Patanjali's *Yoga Sutras* which contains ashtanga yoga, the eightfold path.

Rajas – one of the three gunas or attributes; dynamism; state of activity; creativity combined with full ego involvement; energy; vaginal secretions. See Guna.

Ram – bija mantra of the fire element and manipura chakra.

Ramana Maharshi – (b. 1879–d. 1950) a renowned jnana yogi and enlightened sage who taught mainly through silence; establisher of the path of self-enquiry.

Retas – sexual energy which may be sublimated or refined into ojas. See Ojas.

Rishi – seer; realized sage; one who contemplates or meditates on the Self.

Rudra – howling energy; deity of manipura chakra; name of Lord Shiva; signifies transformation through dissolution.

Rudra granthi – literally, 'knot of Rudra (Shiva)'; psychic knot within ajna chakra which symbolizes attachment to siddhis or higher mental attributes. As the psychic block is overcome, the sense of personal identity ceases to block one's identification with the cosmic consciousness. See Granthi.

Sadhaka – one who practises sadhana; a spiritual aspirant.

Sadhana – spiritual practice or discipline performed regularly.

Sahaja – spontaneous, natural; true.

Sahasrara chakra – 'thousand-petalled lotus'; abode of Shiva or superconsciousness; highest chakra or psychic centre, it symbolizes the threshold between the psychic and spiritual realms and is located at the crown of the head.

Samadhi – the culmination of meditation, state of oneness of the mind with the object of concentration and the universal consciousness; self-realization; the eighth stage of raja yoga.

Samana vayu – one of the five pancha pranas or vayus, it is located between the navel and the diaphragm; it flows from side to side and controls the digestion.

Samkhya – one of the six systems of Indian philosophy. Attributed to Sage Kapila, Samkhya is a spiritual science based on the division of all existence into the two eternal principles of purusha and prakriti, and the twenty-three elements of creation; the philosophical basis of the yoga system.

Samsara – illusory world; the course or circuit of worldly life; unending cycle of birth and death.

Samskara – mental impression stored in the subtle body as an archetype; the impressions which condition one's nature, causing one to react or respond in a certain way.

Sannyasa – dedication; complete renunciation of the world, its possessions and attachments; abandonment of the phenomenal world.

Sannyasi, sannyasin – one who has taken sannyasa initiation, surrendering everything to the guru and the spiritual journey.

341

Sarvangasana – shoulder stand pose; an inverted posture.

Satguru – the guru who directs the disciple towards the truth (sat); the dispeller of darkness and ignorance (avidya); inner guru.

Sati – virtuous or good woman (or wife); female ascetic; a name of the goddess Durga; Sati, the wife of Shiva, immolated herself and was then reborn as Parvati.

Sattwa – one of the three gunas, or attributes of nature; state of luminosity, harmony, equilibrium and purity. See Guna.

Shabda – sound; perceptible sound; object of the sense of hearing and property of space; word.

Shakti – primal energy; manifest consciousness; power, ability, capacity, strength, energy; counterpart of Shiva; the moving power of nature and consciousness; in Hindu mythology Shakti is often symbolized as a divine woman.

Shambhu – name for Shiva.

Shankhaprakshalana – literally, 'cleaning the conch'; a cleansing technique (shatkarma) of hatha yoga that uses saline water to clean the stomach (which is shaped like a conch) and the small and large intestines.

Shanti – peace, tranquillity; absence of passion, complete indifference to all worldly enjoyment.

Shashankasana – the hare pose; a forward bending asana performed from vajrasana.

Shastra – an authoritative treatise on any subject, particularly science and religion; sacred book.

Shatkarma – the six hatha yoga techniques of purification: neti, dhauti, basti, nauli, kapalbhati and trataka.

Sheetali pranayama – the cooling breath; a tranquiltizing pranayama.

Sheetkari pranayama – the hissing breath; a tranquiltizing pranayama.

Shiva – state of pure consciousness, individual and cosmic, original source of yoga. Lord of yogis; auspicious, benevolent one; name of the god of the Hindu trinity who is entrusted with the work of destruction; destroyer of the ego and duality.

Shiva Samhita – Sanskrit text enumerating the concepts and principles essential to the practice of yoga; classical text on hatha yoga.

Shivambhu – auspicious (or beneficial) water; another name for amaroli.

Shoonya – void, state of transcendental consciousness; space behind the eyebrow centre.

Shuddha – pure in nature.

Shukra – semen; essence of anything; the planet Venus.

Siddha – an adept or perfected person; one who has developed his/her psychic and pranic capacity to the point of mastery.

Siddha yoni asana – classical meditation posture, the male equivalent is siddhasana.

Siddhasana – accomplished pose; classical cross-legged meditation posture.

Siddhi – perfection; enhanced pranic and psychic capacity; paranormal or supernormal accomplishment; control of mind and prana; eight supernatural powers obtained by yogis as a result of long practice.

Sirshasana – headstand pose.

Sloka – verse.

So – mantra produced by the breath, unconsciously repeated on inhalation; representing Cosmic Consciousness. See Ham. See Soham.

Soham – mantra used in ajapa japa, said to be the unconscious repetitive prayer produced by the breath itself.

Soma chakra – a minor chakra situated in the head above manas chakra in the mid-cerebrum.

Sthoola sharira – gross, physical body; annamaya kosha.

Sukshma – subtle; relating to the world of the psyche.

Surya – sun; vital pranic energy governing the world of matter.

Sushumna – central energy flow (nadi) in the spine; it conducts the kundalini or spiritual force from mooladhara chakra to sahasrara chakra; the main energy flow related to transcendental awareness; situated in the spinal cord of the human body, it opens when balance is achieved between ida and pingala nadis.

Swadhisthana chakra – literally, 'one's own abode'; second psychic/pranic centre; located in the coccyx; associated with the sacral plexus and governing the urogenital system; the storehouse of subconscious impressions.

Swara – breathing cycle; flow of the breath in the nostrils.

Swara yoga – science of the breathing cycle; the system of yoga using understanding and management of the breathing cycle as a means to attain self-realization.

Swatmarama, Yogi – literally, 'one who revels within oneself'; the author of *Hatha Yoga Pradipika*, a classical text book on hatha yoga.

Tamas – one of the three gunas or attributes of nature; inertia, stability; ignorance, darkness; unwillingness to change. See Guna.

Tantra – most ancient universal science and culture which deals with the transition of human nature from the present level of evolution and understanding to a transcendental level of knowledge, experience and awareness; a particular path of sadhana including mantra, yantra and other esoteric practices. ·

Tapas – austerity; undergoing hardship for the purpose of purification; pain of three types: *adhyatmika*, spiritual, *adhidevika*, natural or environmental, and *adhibhautika*, physical; one of the niyamas described by Sage Patanjali in the *Yoga Sutras* as a preliminary practice of yoga. See Niyama.

Tapasya – practice of austerity.

Tattwa – 'that-ness'; true essential nature; an element, a primary substance; the five elements (space, air, fire, water and earth); another name for mahabhoota.

Tattwa shuddhi – 'purification of elements'; the tantric science of inner purification.

Tha – seed mantra of lunar energy, psychic or mental force (ida nadi); represents moon; second syllable of the word 'hatha'. See Ha.

Trataka – one of the shatkarmas; a technique of gazing steadfastly upon an object such as a candle flame, black dot or yantra with unblinking eyes.

Udana vayu – one of the five pancha pranas or vayus, it is located in the extremities of the body: arms, legs and head; it flows with a spiralling motion and rises up the throat entering the head; it controls the sensory and motor organs.

Ujjayi pranayama – a subtle pranayama often used during meditation; the psychic breath.

Unmani – mindless; beyond the mind.

Upanishads – the philosophical portion of the Vedas, traditionally one hundred and eight in number, containing intimate dialogues and discussions between guru and disciple on the nature of the Absolute and the path leading towards it; literally, 'to sit near and listen' (to the spiritual teacher); regarded as the source of Vedanta, Yoga and Samkhya philosophies.

Urdhvaretas – one who has accomplished sublimation of sexual energy.

Utthanpadasana – stretched leg pose; a forward bending asana in sitting position.

Vahni – fire.

Vajra – literally, 'thunderbolt'.

Vajra nadi – the nadi starting on the left side of the anus governing the sexual organs and processes, the digestive system, and related to the sciatic nerve.

Vajrasana – thunderbolt pose; a kneeling meditative posture.

Vam – bija mantra of the water element and swadhisthana chakra.

Varuna – god of water and the oceans.

Vashitva siddhi – the power of gaining control over everything. One of the eight major siddhis. See Siddhi.

Vata – wind, gas; one of the three humours (doshas) described in Ayurveda; associated with the air element. See Dosha.

Vayu – wind, air; life breath or vital air; prana.

Vedanta – one of the six principle systems of Indian philosophy; literally, 'the last part of the Vedas'; the school of Hindu thought based primarily on the Upanishads; the doctrine of non-dualism (Advaita).

Vedantin – practitioner of Vedanta, a philosophy stating one non-dual eternal principle underlying and causing all creation.

Vedas – ancient texts revealed to the sages and saints of India, explaining and regulating every aspect of life from the Supreme Reality to worldly affairs; four in number: Rig, Yajur, Sama, Atharva, which are further divided into the Samhita, Brahmana, Aranyaka and Upanishads; the oldest books in the library of mankind, parts of them revealed to sages and seers before 5,000 BC.

Veerya – semen; strength; courage; energy.

Vidya – knowledge or science, particularly knowledge of spiritual truth and non-mundane reality.

Vidyut – lightning; a thunderbolt; white light.

Vijnanamaya kosha – astral or psychic (higher mental) sheath or body; one of the sheaths of the soul, consisting of the principle of intellect or buddhi, the subtler level of our own existence with its vision, intuition, wisdom and power of understanding; the covering of the self which is made of knowledge. See Kosha.

Vishnu – vedic deity; the second deity of the Hindu trinity (Brahma, Vishnu, Shiva), entrusted with the preservation of the universe, a duty which obliges him to appear in several incarnations; Supreme Consciousness.

Vishnu granthi – psychic block or knot particularly related to manipura, anahata and vishuddhi chakras, symbolizing the bondage of personal and emotional attachment. See Granthi.

Vishuddhi chakra – literally, 'centre of purification', the psychic/pranic centre located at the level of the throat pit or the thyroid gland; it is the psychic centre particularly connected with purification and communication.

Vritti – a modification arising in the mind related to a thought pattern; a particular state or condition.

Vyana vayu – one of the pancha pranas or vayus; the reserve of pranic energy pervading the entire body.

Yama – one-eighth part of a day, a period of three hours.

Yama – self-restraints or rules of conduct which render the mind tranquil; first stage of the eight limbs of yoga (ashtanga yoga) of Sage Patanjali's *Yoga Sutras*: ahimsa (non-violence), satya (truth), asteya (honesty), brahmacharya (continence) and aparigraha (abstention from greed).

Yantra – a geometric symbol of cosmic power designed to unleash the hidden potential energy within consciousness; used in meditation and concentration practices.

Yoga – union; the root is yuj, meaning 'to join', 'to yoke'; a system of practice leading to a state of union between the individual and universal awareness; practices, philosophy and lifestyle to achieve peace, power and spiritual wisdom as well as perfect health, a sound mind and a balanced personality; one of the six main systems of Indian philosophy.

Yoga Chudamani Upanishad – a yogic text elucidating a unique combination of kundalini yoga and vedantic upasana.

Yoga nidra – psychic sleep; practice in which the body sleeps while the mind remains aware as its movements are guided and quietened by instructions, inducing deep relaxation of body, mind and emotions.

Yoga Shastras – the yoga system of philosophy and practice where the chief aim is to teach the means for the human soul to unite completely with the Supreme Spirit; elaborate rules for the proper practice of concentration of mind.

Yoga Sutras – ancient authoritative text on raja yoga by Sage Patanjali.

Yogadanda – is a u-shaped wooden prop that is placesd under the armpit, regulating the breath by its pressure; 'danda' means stick or symbol of authority or discipline, also giving the literal meaning, 'power of yoga'.

Yogamaya – the power of divine illusion; shakti, the primordial power, has two roles to play, to unite and to separate.

Yoganga – limbs or aspects of yoga.

Yogavit – literally, 'knower of yoga', which is equated to knowledge of Brahman in *Gheranda Samhita*; yoga specialist.

Yogi – an adept of yoga; follower of the yoga system of philosophy and practice.

Yogini – a female adept of yoga; female follower of the yoga system of philosophy and practice.

Yoni – womb; source.

General Index

Adhara, see chakra
Adi mudra 44–45
Agnisara kriya 230
Ajna chakra, see chakra
Akashi mudra 88–90
Amaroli mudra 165–170, 199
Amrita 102–108, 111–113,
    115, 134–135, 139–140,
    218–219, 226–227
Anahata chakra, see chakra
Anandamaya kosha, see kosha
Annamaya kosha, see kosha
Apana vayu, see pancha prana
Archetype, see samskara
Asana, brahmacharyasana
    170–173; padadhirasana
    124–125; sarvangasana 132–
    133; siddhasana 240–241;
    sirshasana 140; vipareeta
    karani asana 131
Ashwini mudra 173–176, 210
Atma, see soul
Attachment 252–253, 258
Attitude 8–9, 10–11, 12–13,
    41, 143
Awareness 32, 80, 111, 141–
    142, 187, 236; development

76, 182; effect of bandha
    240, 254; effect of mudra 54,
    76, 79, 151

Bandha 203–239; classification
    203–204; definition 203;
    effect 205, 206, 237–238,
    240–260; origin 9; practice
    236–237, 238; purpose 5–6,
    204, 239
Bhairava mudra 47
Bhairavi mudra 47
Bhava, see attitude
Bhoochari mudra 86–88, 90
Bhrumadhya drishti, see
    shambhavi mudra
Bhujangini mudra 63–64
Bindu 120–121
Bindu visarga, see chakra
Bliss 72, 106
Blockages, see granthi
Body language 12–13
Brahmacharya 178–179, 186,
    190–194, 213
Brahma mudra 45
Brain 30, 119, 226; effect
    of bandha 54, 212–213,

349

Notes

---- Notes ----